GW00537496

o

The Charter of the A. .

General Information. Banner of the Army Cadet . .. . . :t
  Prayer. Enrollment Ceremony Personal Details. Personal
  Records of Achievements Shooting Records. Whos' who in the
  County. D of E Record. Expectations of your Commanding
  Officer. Staff Appointments 1-12

Annual Camp. Preparation. Do's and Dont's. Kit Check list.
  Medical Certificate. Safety and Security. Medical
  Certificates and Insurance cover. .... 12 -19

The **Cadet and The Community**. A responsible citizen.
  Know your community .... 19 -20

The **Cadet NCO**. Duties and Responsibilities. Delegation.
  Qualities required. Discipline. Opportunities for
  promotion. Promotion Cadres. Your Cap Badge. 21-32

Drill. Paying Compliments (Saluting). Drill and Dress.
  Care of Uniform. Appearance and Dress. Badges of Rank.
  Words of Command. Dressing, Marching and Wheeling 32-44

History of the Army Cadet Force. The early days.
  The two World Wars. The changes made 45-51

The Direction of the ACF. Role of MOD and ACFA. The Cadet
  Journal and Gazette. The Cadet Supply Department. County
  Cadet Committee. County Staff 52-60

Fieldcraft. The place of a Section in the Battalion. Individual
  Skills, Judging Distance. Range Cards. Personal
  Camouflage and Concealment. Movement. Target
  Recognition. Fire Control Orders. Night Vision. Duties
  of a Sentry. Section Battle Drills. Section and
  Platoon Field Signals. Section Formations.
  Choosing a Route. Pacing. Aids to keeping direction.
  Selecting Lines of Advance. Searching ground................... 61-95

  Patrols. Types of Patrol. Sequence of Action to Mount, Carry
  out and Debrief a Patrol. Rehearsals. Patrol Reports.

  Ambushes. Types and Principles. Orders and Preparation.
  Safety with Blank ammunition 96-112

i

CONTENTS

Skill at Arms. The Rules of Safety and Safety Precautions.
   L 98 Cadet GP Rifle. Introduction and Safety Precautions.
   The Iron Sight. The sling and how to fit and use it.
   The Rifle stripped into groups. Care and Cleaning.
   The Cleaning Tool Kit. Ammunition. How the weapon
   works. Correct Aim Picture. GP Rifle Training Tests
   The LMG. How the gun works. Safety Precautions.
   Loading and Unloading. Making Safe. Immediate
   Action. LMG Training Tests .... 113 -144
The Duke of Edinburgh's Award Scheme.
   The challenge. The Award Scheme and how it works
   with APC. Sport and Physical Fitness Tests for APC
   and D of E, Conditions and Scoring .... 145 -163
Expedition Training. The Country Code. The Discipline of
   how to Walk. Personal Health and Hygiene. Kit
   and Equipment. Choosing a Camp Site. Construction of
   Latrines. Cooking and Fires. Types of food. Menu Planning
   and Preparation and use of Compo Rations. Insurance Cover.
   Safety, Planning and Preparation of Exercises.
   Prevention of Accidents. Communications.
   The Wind Chill Factor and Hypothermia .... 164 - 204
Map and Compass. Introduction. The Grid System.
   The Silva Compass. Bearings and Types of Bearings.
   Relief. Understanding and Interpreting Contours.
   Scales and Measuring Distance. Finding North.
   Route Cards. 24 hour Clock System.
   Orienteering. How organised. Check Points. Equipment
   Keeping Direction. Choosing a Route. Aiming Off......... 205 - 246
First Aid. How to use a Telephone First Aid.
   The Aims of First Aid. The Casualty Code. Clearing an
   obstructed airway. Ventilation — Kiss of Life.
   Stopping Bleeding. Recovery Position. Types of Fracture
   and treatment. Treatment of Burns and Scalds. Shock.
   Head injuries. Extremes of temperature .... 247 - 262
The Cadet and the Facts of Life. Education for life. Self
   improvement and development. The challenge. Decision
   making. Your role in life. Health and Hygiene. Personal
   Disciplines... 263 - 277

CONTENTS

Method of Instruction.
Qualities of an Instructor. Preparation & Planning.
Questioning technique. The Lesson Plan. Stages and Key
Points.Training Aids .... 278 - 284
Competitive Shooting Skills.
Improving your Skills. Types of Competitive Shooting.
Personal Qualities. Going on the Range. Marksmanship
Principles. Correct position. Correct Aim Picture.
Control of Breathing.Trigger contro!. Use of a Sling.
Targets. Shooting Badges .... 285 - 315
Shooting Competitions.
How organised. Backing given. Air Rifle and .22 Rifle
Postal Competitions for ACF and CCF and conditions.
Full bore Rifle Competitions, conditions for
firing and entry, ACF and CCF .... 316 - 332
Knots and their Uses. Information and illustrations .... 333 - 336
Signals Training. Introduction. Security. Codes. Phonetic
Alphabet. Voice procedure. Pro words. Disciplines.
Organisation of a Radio net .... 337 - 349
Opportunities for the 2Star plus Cadet. Chart showing courses
and opportunities open to cadets. Details of MOD Courses,
visits and attachments at home and abroad................... 350 - 363
The World of Work. A second career. Job changes. Cost of
experience. Opportunities or Qualifications. Writing a Job
Application letter. Building your C.V. Going for an interview.
The interview. Question you may be asked. Right attitude at
work. Welbeck College .... 364 - 383
Bands in the ACF. Band Units. Drum and Bugle Bands.
Recognised Music Qualifications and APC grades. Drum and
Pipe Bands. D of E Award. Other Skills........................... 384 - 388
APC Syllabus and your Training Records. Detailed syllabus
and personal Training Record for every subject................ 389 - 404
Abbreviations. Alphabetical list of abbreviation in
common use in the ACF/CCF.. 404 - 406
Names, Addresses and Telephone Numbers Forward Dates,
pages to record your own information ....407 - 413
Inside back cover. Key to the Badges of Acheivement as
illustrated on outside of back cover.

iii

THE BANNER OF THE ARMY CADET FORCE

The Banner of the ACF was first presented on 9th Feb. 1960 at the Tower of London, by his Royal Highness the Duke of Edinburgh as Colonel in Chief, on the Occasion of the Centenary. A new banner was presented by His Royal Highness the Duke of Edinburgh at the Chapel of the Royal Hospital, Chelsea on 27th March 1982. The original Banner was laid up in St. Peter's Church, Frimley, Surrey in July 1982.

THE CADET PRAYER

O God our heavenly father, who haste brought us together as members of the Army Cadet Force; help us to do our duty at all times, and be loyal to each other. May all that is good and true prosper among us; strengthen us to defend the right; and bless our work that it may be acceptable to thee.

1

INTRODUCTION

Since the Cadet Pocket Book was first produced many thousands of cadets have used it to improve their knowledge and skills.

Although there is no substitute for good instruction given by an experienced instructor, your Pock Book is designed for you to be able to refer to it at anytime, preferably when you are not on parade and read up on the subject(s) you are currently being taught and for revision.

Your time and that of your instructors when you **are** "on parade", is very limited for them to teach you a full lesson on a topic and cover the whole syllabus. The Pocket Book is designed to point you in the right direction to "do it yourself", safely, correctly and efficiently.

Many instructors find that it is an invaluable aid when revising or planning a lesson.

With its help, you will attain a high standard in the Army Proficiency Certificate (APC) subjects and also carry out the aims as set out in the Charter of the Army Cadet Force, thus making you a good cadet and a better citizen.

Some of its content does not relate directly to helping with your APC, but it does relate to you as a person and the way you hopefully develop as a future British citizen.

It serves as a record of your training progress, promotions, achievements and activities you have taken part in during your cadet career.

It is of particular value when you are asked for information by a potential employer or on being interviewed to join one of the Armed Services.

Keep it up to date, ensure correct information and dates are entered, and those items that are required to be initialled by your Officer or Instructors ARE in fact, done so.

Take care of it, it will become a valuable document to you — it is YOUR own personal property. Keep it clean and dry — enjoy using it.

THE ENROLMENT CEREMONY

When you first join the ACF as a Recruit, you will undergo your initial training. Provided you attend regularly it will be about six to eight weeks before you are officially ENROLLED and allowed to wear your Cap Badge of the Regiment or Corps to which you unit is affiliated.

The Enrolment Ceremony is very simple and is normally kept personal to you and your two friends in the unit who are your 'sponsors'.

Your OC will have invited your Parents or Guardians to be present and hopefully will also have the unit Padre to help him officiate in the ceremony.

This is in no way an event where all and sundry attend, it is a 'milestone' in your cadet career, and serves as a reminder for the other cadets in your unit who will be present, of their commitments to their unit and the Army Cadet Force.

THE CADET PROMISE

I cadet .... (name in full)

Promise to honour God, my Queen and my Country and to do my best to serve them loyally and honourably at all times through the

....
(Cadet unit or detachment)

of the .... to which I now belong.
(Regiment or Corps

Date 		Signature of Cadet ....

GENERAL INFORMATION

PERSONAL DETAILS

Surname .... Other Names ....

Home Address
....
.... Post Code ....

Date of Birt   /   /   Nat Insurance No..

Blood Group.................. Home Telephone No ....

Next of Kin Relationship... Tel No.....................

Address..Post Code ....

Religious Denomination ....

Relevant Medical Information, Allergies, etc

....

School Attending/Employer

....

Date Joined............... Date passed Recruit test ....

Enrolled on ....   at ....

Sponsors:-

1 .... 2 ....

Signed.. Officer i/c

Unit .... Date ....

GENERAL INFORMATION

PROMOTIONS

RANK	DATE PROMOTED	OFFICERS INITIALS
Cadet Lance Corporal		
Cadet Corporal		
Cadet Sergeant		
Cadet Staff Sergeant		
Cadet Company Sgt Major		
Cadet Regimental Sgt Major		
Under Officer		

TRAINING ACHIEVEMENTS

QUALIFICATION	DATE	OFFICERS SIGNATURE
PASSED RECRUIT TEST		
PASSED APC 1 STAR		
PASSED APC 2 STAR		
PASSED APC 3 STAR		
PASSED APC 4 STAR		
APPOINTED MASTER CADET		

ENSURE ALL ENTRIES ARE SIGNED BY YOUR OFFICER

GENERAL INFORMATION

SHOOTING RECORDS

Date	Weapon Fired	Typeof Practices Fired Type of Range	HPS	Score or Group Size	Comments

GENERAL INFORMATION

ANNUAL CAMPS ATTENDED

Dates	Location

COURSES, ATTACHMENTS and VISITS

Dates	Location and Unit Name	Type

"WHO' S WHO" IN YOUR COUNTY ACF

The next two pages are for you to record the names and ranks of all the County Staff that you will come into contact with during your cadet career.
It is advisable to write this information in **PENCIL**, as appointments change quite frequently.

COUNTY ACF HEADQUARTERS STAFF APPOINTMENTS

Appointment	Name	Rank
County Cadet Commandant		
Cadet Executive Officer		
County Cadet Quartermaster		
County Training Officer		
County Shooting Officer		
County D of E Award Officer		
County Medical Officer		
County Padre (CofE)		
County Padre (RC)		
County Padre (other denominations)		
County Publicity Officer		
County R S M		

GENERAL INFORMATION

STAFF APPOINTMENTS
AREA/SQUADRON/COMPANY or BATTERY

Appointment	Name	Rank
Officer Commanding		
Staff Officer		
Sergeant Major		
Quartermaster		
Training Officer		

DETACHMENT/PLATOON/TROOP or UNIT

Appointment	Name	Rank
Officer Commanding		
Second in Command		
Sgt Major Instructor		
Sergeant Instructor(s)		
ADULT HELPERS		

GENERAL INFORMATION

DUKE OF EDINBURGH' S AWARD

AWARD	DATE AWARDED	OFFICERS NAME
BRONZE		
SILVER		
GOLD		

GOLD Award Certificate presented by:-

....

at ....on........................

RESPONSIBILITIES
The Expectations of your Commanding Officer

The following notes are some of the expectations of
your Platoon, Troop or Detachment commander, You
must remember at all times that like you, s/he is a
volunteer, their hobby - again like yours - is the Army
Cadet Force. They can only run a good unit if you do
your share, working together as a team, bearing in mind
that you and s/he will also have other interests and
commitments to work, school, and family etc.

S/HE WILL EXPECT YOU TO :-

Attend parades at least once a week or let them know if
you are not able to attend.
Be on time - five minutes before parade - not five
minutes after.

GENERAL INFORMATION

Be smartly turned out both in uniform and in your normal clothes.

Read and comply with notices and orders put up on the notice board.

Obey orders - if they seem unfair, obey them and complain after.

Have good manners and behave as would be expected of a cadet.

Treat other peoples property with respect, prevent damage and vandalism.

Have a soldierly bearing, and wear your uniform correctly at all times.

Keep fit, play and work hard, take part in all sports and games.

Work in the unit as you should do at home — be prepared to help with the "chores" without having to be asked.

Clean up behind you, put things away - be tidy, don't rely on others.

Never to be afraid of doing more than you have been asked to do.

FULL MEMBER

You must be a **"FULL MEMBER"** of the unit — whenever events, parades, weekend exercises are planned at the unit or the time of the year gets round to Annual Camp — remember that a lot of people from your Cadet Commandant to your own officers and instructors will have put a lot of time into planning your programme, especially Annual Camp.

It has all been organised for your benefit, which means that if your officers and instructors are to rely upon you as a FULL MEMBER of the unit, you will be expected to:-

1. Take an active part in the life of the unit and make the progress required not only in training but as a person.

2. With the time you have available for cadets, put the maximum effort into becoming efficient and backing your friends in the unit and your Officers and Instructors.
3. Help others who may be less able than you - especially those who find difficulties in learning, handling weapons or equipment.
4. Look after new recruits, to ensure that they are brought into the 'life of the unit' as soon as possible.
5. When your unit is "open to recruit", bring in new members who you consider it would be good for them and that they would make a good cadet.
6. Be ALERT, be SAFETY and SECURITY CONSCIOUS AT ALL TIMES

ANNUAL CAMP

For many years the Army Cadet Force and the Combined Cadet Force have both enjoyed the training camps provided by the Ministry of Defence.

In the future we may not be so lucky as the changes that are taking place within the services could mean that we have less opportunities to use these camps, therefore we must make the best possible use of what we have, while we can.

Annual Camp has always been the highlight of the cadets year, a time when all the training you have received during the year should be put into practice in "the field", by taking part in exercises and expeditions.

Many counties - depending upon the distance and location of the camp - have "open days", when parents and friends visit the camp.

The day is often planned as a sports day, with demonstrations and displays, many of which are organised and carried out by the cadets themselves.

Some events are set up to involve the visitors, very often obstacle courses or similar create a lot of fun and make it a really entertaining day.

GENERAL INFORMATION

One of the great opportunities Annual Camp offers you is the chance to be in a very different part of the country, perhaps for the first time in your life.

It is important that you learn about the county you are in for the camp period, find out what the area is famous for, what is made there, what is different from home, do all you can to meet new people and make more friends. This is another very good reason why it is important that you should always make a special effort to get to Annual Camp.

ANNUAL CAMP "DO's" and "DON' TS"

The information set out below as a list of "do's" and "don'ts" are to help make your camp enjoyable, by keeping you out of trouble and for you to get the most out of it.

Remember that while you are under the supervision of your Officers and Instructors, they are responsible for your SAFETY and WELFARE.

This applies to ANY training that you are carrying out as part of a programme ARRANGED BY THEM, no matter if it's in your cadet hut, weekend training or Annual Camp. Therefore rules, instructions and orders that are given by them are for your own and other cadets good.

See to it that you as a cadet obey them, and if you are an NCO, make sure that you set the example by complying with them and seeing that they are properly carried out.

BEFORE CAMP - PREPARATION

1. Save up for camp - be ready to pay your camp fees when asked for them.
2. Get to know where and when you are going as early as possible.
3. Get to know the programme, camp orders and what you are to be doing.
4. Practice some of the training that you will be

13

carrying out at camp — those subjects that you are not very good at.

5. Get your OC to find a map of the camp and surrounding area - build up a picture in your mind of what it will be like.

6. Do a project on the places of interest, special features of the countryside, the people, industries or other interesting information.

7. Do you have any friends or relations in the area - if so arrange to visit them.

8. Check your uniform fits you correctly, if not get it changed early enough to give the Quarter Master a chance to help you.

9. Check all your kit for camp - make a list of all your needs and get it organised well before hand, your OC will give you a check list for camp.

10. Do your own packing- don't leave it to others - don't start packing your kit the night before you are going.

11. Have your MEDICAL CERTIFICATE (see sample certificate over page) correctly filled in AND SIGNED by your Parent/Guardian, and in your pocket when leaving home for camp.

NOTE: Camp Fees.
Remember your Camp Fees are a contribution towards the cost of your rations.
The exact Daily Ration amount varies from time to time, your officers/instructors will tell you of any changes.

> **IF YOU ARE TAKING PART IN A "CADET" ACTIVITY AND HAVE AN ACCIDENT OR ARE INVOLVED IN ONE, ARE YOU INSURED?** SEE PAGE 17

GENERAL INFORMATION

IMPORTANT MEDICAL NOTICE
IF YOU HAVE BEEN IN HOSPITAL OR HAD AN
ILLNESS WHICH HAS KEPT YOU IN BED FOR ANY
LENGTH OF TIME, AND ARE ATTENDING CAMP OR
DOING TRAINING REQUIRING STRENUOUS ACTIVITY,
YOU MUST FIRST ASK YOUR DOCTORS ADVICE IF YOU
ARE FIT ENOUGH TO ATTEND.

IT IS BETTER TO TELL YOUR INSTRUCTORS THAT
YOU ARE NOT YET FIT, THAN TO TRY AND BE A "HERO",
LATER COLLAPSING ON AN EXERCISE, PUTTING
EVERYONE IN A 'FLAP', WHEN IN FACT IT WAS ALL
YOUR OWN FAULT.

MEDICAL CERTIFICATE

(To be signed by your Parent/Guardian)
CADET's FULL NAME

....
Detachment/Unit .... Name of County ACF...........
CONSENT BY PARENT/GUARDIAN:

I wish my Son/Daughter/Ward to be considered for
acceptance on ACF Camp/Course to be held at
.... and if accepted, to participate in any
of the activities listed below.
I understand that acceptance for training will be subject
to the complete discretion of the Cadet Commandant
ACF, his medical staff and instructors, before and during
the training period.
I certify that to the best of my knowledge my son/
daughter/ward is not suffering from an infectious disease
and has not been in contact with any case of infectious
disease during the previous three weeks.

 Date .... Signed...............................
                                      Parent/Guardian/Ward

GENERAL INFORMATION

FITNESS and PHYSICAL ABILITY CONDITIONS

The Ministry of Defence cannot entertain certain risks and these must be eliminated by regulations.

For example:—

a. Epileptics are not allowed to undertake such activities as, Rock Climbing, Swimming, Shooting, Canoeing, Orienteering, expeditions in wild country etc.

b. Asthmatics, whether or not they are receiving any form of therapy are not allowed to undertake activities involving strenuous exertion.

c. Diabetics dependent on Insulin treatment may not undertake activities involving irregular meals or long periods of exertion.

d. Heart cases are of such a variable nature that they must be judged individually by a cadet's medical practitioner.

Should any doubts exist on whether a Cadet is fit to undertake all the activities listed below a doctor should be consulted before a certificate is signed.

EXAMPLES OF PHYSICAL & SPORTING ACTIVITIES

Rock Climbing, Canoeing, Hang Gliding, Hill Walking on Expeditions, Life Saving, Parachuting, Parascending, Sailing, Dingy, Offshore and Windsurfing.

Skiing: Cross Country and Downhill, Water Skiing, Caving, Sub-aqua Diving.

Athletics, Boxing, Circuit Training, Cricket, Cross Country Running, Cycling, Football, Rugby, Hockey, Judo, Orienteering, Swimming.

16

GENERAL INFORMATION

> ## IMPORTANT NOTICE - INSURANCE
> **The Ministry of Defence and the Army Cadet Force Association have Insurance Policies for Cadets who may have an accident.**
> **BUT, THIS INSURANCE IS ONLY VALID IF YOU ARE TAKING PART IN AN ACTIVITY THAT IS PLANNED AND ORGANISED AS PART OF YOUR CADET TRAINING.**
> **Therefore if any of you were to decide to go off WITHOUT AUTHORITY on an expedition or exercise and as a result someone was injured they would NOT be covered by insurance.**
> ## YOU HAVE BEEN WARNED.

ON YOUR WAY TO CAMP
Do Not :—

When travelling by coach or train:-

Make unnecessary noise to the annoyance of other travellers

Leave your kit unattended, or in a place dangerous to other travellers.

Cause problems for rail/coach staff or those who are in charge of you.

Leave any litter or cause damage.

Go wandering off without permission.

WHEN AT CAMP
Do the following :—

1. Read standing orders, paying special attention to Security Procedures, Fire and Safety instructions.
2. Read every day, daily routine orders and comply with them.
3. Put your spare cash in the camp bank or other means of safe keeping as arranged by your county staff at camp.

4. Pay special attention to your personal hygiene and use the toilet facilities regularly.
5. Clean your kit daily, wash out dirty socks and underclothes properly, try to take home as little washing as you can.
6. Pull your weight - work and play hard at all times.
7. Carry out all duties and "chores" cheerfully and properly.
8. Write or phone home to let them know you have arrived, always keep in contact while you are away.
9. Help others - especially those who are very young, being away from home AND at camp for the first time.
10. Be polite to the people you meet in the area and especially the civilian staff in the camp and those who help run the canteens etc.
11. Observe the 'Out of Bounds' rules and signs in Camp.
12. Be safety conscious at all times, report any suspicious persons or events.

WHEN AT CAMP
Do NOT:-
1. Make work for others by dropping litter, not taking your dirty plates back to the washing up area, leave kit lying about.
2. Leave the toilets or wash basins in a dirty state - leave them as YOU would wish to find them.
3. Without telling anyone - wander off on your own or with others.
4. Be a nuisance to local people by being noisy or 'ragging about' in the streets or other public places.
5. Hitch-Hike in uniform - it is not approved of.
6. Get unduly wet, when you could have sheltered from the rain.

7. Stay out of camp later than permitted, without first having asked for permission.
8. Touch or pick up strange objects on a training area, report anything you find..
9. Leave valuable items of personal kit lying about - lock them up safely.
10. Get involved with local 'trouble makers' who will try to create problems bringing dis-credit on the Cadet Force, just don't get involved.

THE CADET AND THE COMMUNITY

A part of the Charter of the ACF reads:-
"to inspire young people to achieve success in life with a spirit of service to the Queen, their country and their local community, and to develop in them the qualities required of a good citizen"

As a person - an individual - a cadet, YOU ARE A CITIZEN - a native of this country, of your own city, town or village, a member of your family - a part of the community you live in.

The support you give, the part you play, the care and affection you have - not only for your own family, but for the people in your community will be the measure of you as a citizen. If you are a FULL MEMBER of your unit - you will be starting on the right track.

During your training - depending on how your officers and instructors plan it - you should be taking part in various projects and activities, both within your unit and the community outside.

KNOW WHO's WHO IN YOUR COMMUNITY

This will bring you and your unit into close contact with the community in which you live.

You will meet new people in a variety of situations,

some may be employers, others local councillors, professional people like doctors, solicitors or accountants.

It will all present opportunities for them to get to know you, your unit and the Cadet Force and of course for you to get to know them. What impression you make on them will be important, were you helpful, did you go out of your way to help, did you have good manners, will they ask you again, what will be their lasting impression of you - good/bad ?.

Make no mistake about it, being involved in the community can very often be difficult and demanding of you, but it can also be great fun and at the same time give you a great deal of satisfaction.

Hopefully your Unit is 'on the ball' and many of you are already taking part the Duke of Edinburgh's Award Scheme, as these activities and projects are all a part of your development and will go towards your own DofE Award.

It is hoped, that as a result of you being a cadet, that you will become a good citizen - you will have fulfilled that part of the Charter of the Army Cadet Force, and at the same time proved to your Commanding Officer that you are worthy of the qualifications awarded to you at the various stages of your cadet career.

THE CADET NCO
Duties and Responsibilities.

Initially as a Junior Cadet NCO you must learn how to instruct the basic APC subjects and also how to take command of a squad.

With other NCO's in the Unit you are responsible to your Detachment Commander to assist with the organisation and smooth running of the detachment at the level of your rank.

GENERAL INFORMATION

THE CADET SERGEANT

As a Cadet Sergeant you would have the authority of a senior cadet NCO in your unit.
Don't forget :-

WITH AUTHORITY GOES - RESPONSIBILITY

As the Senior Cadet NCO in your unit you have the heaviest responsibilities which are yours at all times, both on and off parade, even when engaged in all other activities where cadets are involved or it is known that you represent the Army Cadet Force.

You will be directly responsible to your detachment commander and at the same time be responsible to your OC for the Cadets in your unit.

To become an NCO not only must you have a good knowledge of all the military subjects, but you must be able to put it over correctly to others, holding their interest and earning their respect.

Every cadet has the opportunity to earn promotion. The skills and ability you require can only be developed by training and practice through the cadet ranks during your time in the Cadet Force.

DELEGATION OF RESPONSIBILITY.

A word of caution here. For you to be an effective Cadet NCO - no matter what rank you hold, will require a great amount of understanding and skill on the part of your Officers and Adult Instructors.

It is very difficult to understand, but it does mean that those adults in your unit will have to have had the training and experience for them to be prepared to share some of their authority in 'running the unit'.

This is not as bad as it sounds, what it means is that they must be seen to give you the backing or authority to carry out tasks within the unit, to leave you alone to no doubt make mistakes, but at the same time to start on the ladder of promotion.

Once this is done — it's up to you to prove they made the right decision in promoting you. Only if you have the right qualities and the ability to develop and use them will you be successful.

SOME OF THE ESSENTIAL QUALITIES ARE:-

Loyalty and pride in the Regiment or Corps to which you are badged, your County, and Detachment.

Enthusiasm in all that you do and your cadets imitate you.

Help and encourage those who you are responsible for.

A good Sense of humour — especially when things go wrong.

Knowledge of your subject - giving others confidence in your ability.

Initiative to always have your cadets doing something interesting/active.

Instructional ability — always having well prepared and planned activities.

Disciplinary powers — ability to control Junior NCO's, who with the cadets perform tasks correctly and to the standards set by you.

Physical fitness - as a leader to set the example from the front, making allowances for those not as old or fit as you.

Appearance - you must maintain the highest standard of personal turnout.

Ensure that you and others maintain the Cadet Force image in 'the eye of the public — as others see the ACF — such as:-

Good Manners, be an influence on and insist that others have good behaviour and manners in the

Detachment, public places, especially on public transport, in shopping precincts etc.

Be helpful, efficient, alert, well turned out, both on and off duty.

Have patience with those that are 'slow' at learning.

Encourage cadets to "get on", to take part in all activities in the Unit.

NOT LACKING IN "MORAL FIBRE" ("GUT"s) to bring before your OC any cadet or NCO who is in breach of established good conduct and discipline.

DEVELOPING YOUR ABILITY AS AN NCO

No matter how well you know your subject or how good you are an as instructor you cannot 'make the cadet learn' - like everyone in the ACF it is their hobby, if they enjoy it - then they will come to the lessons you have prepared. If they don't, they will show it with their feet by staying away from the Detachment.

If they have fun they will tell their friends about it, come back for more bringing them along, as a result of this it will help to build a thriving unit. BUT, this will only be achieved through your ability to get the cadet to want to do things for you.

You have to develop the right relationships to form the foundations upon which to build GOOD RELATIONS.

It is worth remembering that the "Foundations for Good Relations" are:-

1. **Let your cadets know in advance of things that effect them; what's on, date, time and place and the reason why it is being done.**
2. **If someone does well - give them credit for it , when it is due - at the time, NOT afterwards.**
3. **NEVER criticise or check other NCO's in front of cadets.**
4. **Always take a cadet "out of ear shot" of others if you are to reprimand them.**

5. **Recognise the ability of other Cadets and NCO's, giving them every opportunity to show and use their talents.**

DISCIPLINE

Times have changed, in the past the image of the Army was that of loud voices, issuing orders with every other word a swear word.

It could be said, it might have been the only language that the soldier in those days understood and re-acted to. Today the majority of you have learned English and understand most of what is said.

If someone uses foul language just remember that, perhaps the person using it has not had the benefit of being taught how to express themselves correctly.

THERE IS NO NEED TO USE FOUL LANGUAGE
UNDER ANY CIRCUMSTANCES.

THE CONSEQUENCES OF BAD LANGUAGE

If, as an NCO you are stupid enough, and resort to swearing, immediately you will loose the respect of the majority of your cadets, and respect is what you have to earn as an NCO before any cadet will listen to you.

You will get far more co-operation out of your squad on the square or on the sports field by have a good sense of humour, but be warned though, not at the expense of the tallest, shortest, fattest, ugliest individual in the squad, that is a form of bullying.

BULLYING

Most of us have been subjected to bullying at one time or another. It is a duty of every individual to immediately report any form of bullying that comes to their notice. You will often find that the issuing of "threats" or "promises" in one form or another is a common method of bullying.

The constant "picking" on an individual makes them very

unhappy, they **are** being bullied, they feel threatened
and leave, taking with them all those bad feelings about
the Cadet Force.

We cannot afford to have BULLYING in the Cadet Force
by anyone, of any rank, as a result of which YOU have a
duty to bring it to the notice of more senior ranks, don't
take no for an answer, don't stop until the bully is
stopped - *ABOVE ALL - DON'T TAKE ACTION YOURSELF
OR WITH OTHERS.*

FIRST PROMOTION

When you first get your Lance Corporal stripes, it is a
milestone in your cadet career. You MAY think you have
arrived, and as a result are inclined to throw your weight
about, the first to know about it are your mates who
yesterday were quite happy to have a laugh with you,
but today - you are a Lance Jack and they seem to be
less friendly.

This could mean that they respect your promotion, now
you have to get their confidence to prove that you are
worthy of it.

So now would be a good time to consider some of the
actions and failings of bad cadet NCO's.

Be sure you **DO NOT** follow their example.

1. Intimidate individuals by shouting at them, especially
   when standing close up to them.
2. Making personal contact (touch) an individual when
   addressing them.
3. Use foul language or offensive remarks to an
   individual, or make threats of what might become of
   them.
4. Make an example of an individual, such as punishing
   them without due cause or reason.
5. Using first names when "On Parade". Difficult, but
   when "ON PARADE" be "ON PARADE", when "OFF

PARADE", then be "OFF PARADE".

6. Borrowing money or ask favours of cadets.
7. Keep picking on an individual in front of others. If they are persistently disruptive, then let to your OC discipline them.
8. Not sharing duties or "chores" fairly, not having a 'duty roster' displayed.
9. Being late with orders/information in time for all to respond.
10. Asking cadets to clean, press etc, personal kit or equipment.
11. Not read Daily Orders, un-informed of programme, duties and events.
12. Fails to check untidy cadets and or their rooms.
13. Is always late for parades and duties.
14. Puts off dealing with complaints and problems immediately reported to them.
15. Does not give any encouragement or praise for good work.
16. Passes on responsibilities to others, lacks personal discipline.
17. Fails to report, serious breaches of conduct and discipline, drugs, smoking, theft, cadet out of bounds, security etc.
18. Sets a bad example by untidy appearance in their own clothes.
19. Mannerisms or bad habits, always saying "OK" or "RIGHT" after a sentence, pulling your ear or scratching your nose, etc.

You will think of many other points to add to the list of **"DON'TS"**, so long as you are **NOT** guilty of them, you may - hopefully, with experience - become a **GOOD NCO**.

IT TAKES A LONG TIME TO BUILD UP A GOOD REPUTATION, BUT ONLY SECONDS TO LOSE IT.

GENERAL INFORMATION

THE ARMY EXAMPLE.

The Army sets the example that we should follow in the
Cadet Force. If you are to become an NCO, then
discipline - SELF DISCIPLINE — is your guide.
Your self-respect, self control, sense of purpose and pride
in your ability to do properly what ever you do, will
ensure that you become reliable and efficient.
Discipline is the pride that we should have in ourselves
and "our team" and the fear that by not carrying out
orders and instructions to the best of our ability - we will
be letting down our own high standards and also our
friends.
Surely discipline is something to be proud of.

OPPORTUNITY for PROMOTION

Now that you have read the previous paragraphs in this
section, you will now realise that APC qualifications in
themselves are not qualifications in self discipline, pride,
respect etc, although it will have helped you to become
disciplined in the learning of those subjects
You will have an opportunity to be trained on a Junior
Cadet Instructors Cadre in the Methods of Instruction,
and later attend the Senior NCO's course at Frimley and
several other courses, but these alone will not make you
a good NCO.
With practice you may become a very good instructor,
with experience and practice you will develop all the
qualities and skills which will go towards making up your
character as a person, it is something that you will have
to develop.
Only you will know how well you are performing by the
way that others respond and the results you are able to
achieve.
Watch and listen to all those that you come in contact
with who are considered to be good NCO's, are they
GOOD NCO's and GOOD INSTRUCTORS, or are they

JUST good instructors.

You must learn how to judge the difference, to help you gain experience making sure you are a good NCO as well as being a good instructor.

PROMOTION

It is recognised that promotion must be related to your qualifications, as well as your ability, plus the recommendation of your Commanding Officer and Instructors, they will have been watching your development during your time in the unit.

They will be asking themselves "is this really the sort of cadet we want to be one of our NCO's", like so many things, you will find out — it's down to you.

Promotion is never automatic.

You will always have to achieve the standards as set out below and more importantly be recommended for consideration as a candidate for promotion by your officers and instructors.

To Lance Corporal not before passing your 1 STAR.

To Corporal not before passing your 2 STAR.

To Sergeant not before passing your 3 STAR.

To Master Cadet, having completed the Master Cadet Course, and subsequently been recommended by your County Cadet Commandant.

To Under Officer not before you have passed your 4 STAR and also been recommended by your County Cadet Commandant.

Changes to this rule will only be permissible in very exceptional circumstances and with the approval of your County Cadet Commandant. ACF.

PROMOTION CADRES

Most County Cadet Forces take the question of promoting their cadets very seriously, and so they should, as it is a very important "milestone" in your life, especially your first promotion.

They have a system of promotion courses the same as the Army system, these courses are called NCO's Cadres.

This is usually organised over a weekend or perhaps at Annual Camp, when potential NCO's are brought together and given the opportunity of showing how they have developed, not only in their APC skills, but to see how they behave, if they have any manners, the example they set and if they can gain the respect of those working with them.

This usually follows the form of; planning and taking lessons, command exercises, lecturettes, initiative tests, games and other activities.

Those cadets who take part always say it's great fun and a good method for their instructors to find out their strengths and weaknesses, also to see how you behave under different conditions, before making their final recommendations as to your suitability as an NCO.

If you have a chance to go on an NCO's CADRE - jump at it !

THE FUTURE OFFICERS and INSTRUCTORS

Many Cadets having reached the age of eighteen, apply to stay on the Army Cadet Force as adult instructors.

For more information see the Section in the Pocket Book "Opportunities for the 2 Star Plus Cadet".

DISCIPLINE.

In our "minds eye" we picture a soldier as a well disciplined, smartly dressed individual, in the Queens uniform.

An important part of your training involves teaching you to be a smartly "turned out", a disciplined and well organised individual.

All soldiers have to obey orders instantly, orders in

battle can mean life or death to them.

In a voluntary youth organisation it would seem to be a difficult task to instill discipline.

However, it is not really a problem since, after all, you are a volunteer like everyone else who is serving with you, who all rely on a much more important and special type of discipline - SELF Discipline.

YOUR BADGE

At your Enrolment Ceremony when you joined the ACF, you will have been given a cap badge of the Regiment or Corps to which your cadet unit/detachment is affiliated (badged).

This has a special meaning. The badge you wear carries with it all the history and traditions of that Regiment or Corps.

Within your community there will be many people who had the same cap badge during their service,

It is most likely that you will be taking part in a parade at which there will be members of a Regimental Association who wear the same cap badge as yours.

Some cadet units have close liaison with their local ex-service associations, whose members take part in the units activities.

Make sure that your bearing and turnout when wearing it, is a credit to the Regiment or Corps to whom you are badged, as it is a privilege, not to be taken for granted, that you are allowed to wear it.

**WHO IS THE SECRETARY OF YOUR
LOCAL REGIMENTAL OR CORPS ASSOCIATION ?**

QUESTIONS

1. When and who by was the first Banner presented to the Army Cadet Force.
2. Say the Cadet Prayer.
3. Say the Cadet Promise.
4. What do you understand by being a 'FULL MEMBER' of your unit.
5. When must you have a Medical Certificate.
6. When you get to camp, what must you do about your folks at home.
7. What type of Discipline do we have in the ACF.
8. How should you wear your uniform and when.
9. What must you read every day at camp.
10. Can you Hitch Hike in uniform, if not why not.
11. To be promoted to Corporal you have to be a ... Star Cadet.
12. As an NCO, what goes with 'AUTHORITY'.
13. What do you understand about behaviour in public.
14. How should you treat other peoples property.
15. When are you NOT insured for accident injuries.
16. You MUST be SAFETY and .... conscious at ALL TIMES.
17. As an instructor what is a "mannerism".
18. If an NCO uses bad language, what does he lose.
19. What is meant by the Foundations of Good Relations.
20. At what "time" should you always be "On Parade".
21. What is a Promotion Cadre.
22. What should you know about the area where your next Annual Camp is being held.
23. If given an order that seems unfair, what do you do about it.
24. What is the history of your cap badge.

BE "ON TIME" — FIVE MINUTES EARLY — NOT FIVE MINUTES LATE

FOOT DRILL

The traditional way of instilling discipline in an army has always been through the use of drill. Another way is through the use of a uniform.

Both methods require you to pay attention to detail, in the first case so that you can march correctly as a member of a squad who all respond to the words of command as a team and in the second so that you will develop a smart appearance, both as an individual and a member of a team. There is a lot more to drill than you might think, it is a team effort more precise that the most highly trained football team, the amount of concentration you all need to have, and the individual effort and self discipline would be hard to find in any other situation.

If you are fortunate enough to have a good drill instructor, then you will find that taking part in a drill lesson can be great fun, especially if your instructor has a good turn of Army humour — drill periods will be something to look forward to.

Once you have perfected this better than most others in your unit and taken part in parades in public, marching

 through the town with the band playing, on a Cadet Sunday Parade, or a Remembrance Sunday, and felt fully in control with the swing of your arms and the roll of your shoulders, you will feel the pride in your unit and yourself that takes some beating, you will enjoy it - every minute of it.

FOOT DRILL

COMPLIMENTS
Saluting - Origin and Information

The salute with the hand, the present arms and the salute with the sword were methods by which the person paying a compliment could show the person to whom the compliment was paid that no offence was meant.

They were all gestures symbolic of loyalty and trust.

A salute is the normal greeting between comrades in arms. That a salute is properly and smartly given when you meet an officer is a basic matter of discipline.

That the salute is properly and smartly given is a matter of training.

Failure by an officer to return a salute shows a lack of courtesy on their part.

THE QUEENS COMMISSION

All compliments derive their origin from the Sovereign, to whom the highest compliment, the Royal Salute, is paid.

All officers in the Army Cadet Force are holders of the Queens Commission, and when compliments are paid by saluting it is in recognition of the Sovereign's Commission held in trust by that officer.

The actual Commission an officer receives is in fact a document on parchment paper signed and sealed by Her Majesty The Queen.

Ask one of your officer to bring theirs along for you to see, it is a very special and interesting document.

When Compliments are paid:-
NATIONAL ANTHEM

When on parade, stand to attention, **only** officers and warrant officers salute, NCO's will **if** i/c a party.

When **not** on parade, but in **uni form**, all ranks **will** salute.

PAYING COMPLIMENTS

When not on parade, and in **plain clothes**, all ranks will stand to attention. If a hat is worn, it will be removed.
STANDARDS GUIDONS AND COLOURS.
As a squad on the march you will give an 'Eyes Left' or 'Right'. As an individual will halt, face passing Standards, Guidons or Colours and salute or if passing will salute to left or right
ARMY CADET FORCE BANNER.
The Banner, presented by HRH The Duke of Edinburgh, is dedicated, but not consecrated and does not rank as a Colour, Standard or Guidon.
It will be accorded the respect of a Colour except that :-
1. When marched on parade arms will be shouldered.
2. Will not be saluted by individuals or parties of cadets passing.
3. When Banner passes, individual or parties stand to attention.
4. When taken over, individual taking it will salute first.
5. When on parade (except church parade) an armed escort.

**THE REPUTATION OF THE
ARMY CADET FORCE
IN THE COMMUNITY
IS JUDGED BY THE
BEHAVIOUR AND MANNERS
OF THE CADETS
IN THE LOCAL DETACHMENT**

PAYING COMPLIMENTS
Saluting to the front — Common Faults

a. The body and head not remaining erect.

b. Allowing the right elbow to come forward.

c. Hand not straight, not in correct position, wrist not straight.

d. Allowing the left arm to creep forward.

e. Left fist not clenched with thumb to front, and in line with seam of trousers. Arm not tight into side.

As an aid to good saluting, remember your right hand — with the palm of your hand flat, thumb on top, travels the "longest way up and the shortest way down" when saluting correctly.

PUTTEES

Puttees are made of a long strip of material, to secure a NEAT connection between the bottom of your trousers and the top of your boots - see illustration opposite. Wrapped round three three times with the end finishing in line with the seam of trousers. To achieve this go anti-clockwise round your

round your LEFT leg and clockwise round your RIGHT.
Tape bound round puttee several times with the end
looped and tucked into puttee.

Unless otherwise directed by Regimental or Corps
custom, puttees will be worn as illustrated.

You will find that if you wash your puttees and iron them
when slightly damp, they fit properly as you wind them
round your ankles - making sure of course, that they are
dry before wearing them.

THE BRASSARD

The brassard is a separate
detachable sleeve shaped to
the con tours of the upper
arm from the point of the
shoulder to just above the
elbow.

It is secured at two points, at
the point of the shoulder and
at the lower end of the upper
arm.

It is difficult to keep clean, it
can be dry cleaned, but has
to be treated with care. The
ironing/pressing of the
Brassard can be done in

several ways according to the instructions that a County
may give.

Brassard - Badges of Achievement.

The simplest method is to lay it out flat and carefully iron
it with a WARM IRON, not to scorch it.

It is worn in Jersey and Shirt Sleeve Orders only and the

following badges and insignia may be sewn on to it. Embroidered ACF shoulder titles County insignia or tartan patch Badges of rank, and chevrons in white tape. Not more than 4 embroidered proficiency/Skill at Arms badges taking precedence from the top right, where the APC(ACF) star will be sewn, to top left to bottom right to bottom left.

CLOTHING

You are fortunate to have your uniform issued to you free of charge. It must be appreciated that this costs a great deal of money to provide all cadets with uniforms and to carry stocks for exchanges. It follows that it must be treated with respect and taken care of.

If you are to be a credit to yourself and the ACF you must keep it clean, pressed and in good repair at all times. Ask your detatchment officer/instructor for instructions on the accepted methods of cleaning.

It is understood that young people grow quite rapidly at times, your Quartermaster will have a system for exchanging uniforms, again, your officer/instructor will give you information.

REMEMBER - uniform is much easier to iron if you hang it up properly on a clothes hanger after use, rather than in a heap on the floor.

HINTS FOR PRESSING UNIFORM

Do not let the hot iron come into direct contact with the material.. It makes it shiny or worse still, may burn it. You will then have to pay for a replacement.

Use a damp not wet, non-fluffy cloth, (an old tea towel is ideal), place this on your trousers/skirt then place paper over this.

Do not use newspaper as the print comes off onto the cloth. If you have a steam iron, still use a cloth, but this time a dry one.

Always look for and follow the instructions on the clothing labels for the correct heat for your iron.

YOUR UNIFORM WILL NOT BE WORN WITHOUT PERMISSION OTHER THAN ON CADET DUTIES.

EXTRA KIT

Most cadets find that there are items of kit not issued, but are most useful to have. The most difficult question is that of Webbing Equipment. The old 1938 Pattern is the only webbing on issue at the time this edition of the Pocket Book is being written.

Many cadets buy themselves sets of the "58 Webbing. The Cadet Supply Department stock it and although it is expensive, it is in new condition, complete with British Army style water bottle.

There are several other items of kit that are not issued and you will need to save up and buy them.

They fall into two types of kit:-

1. Essential to have.   **2. Desirable to have.**

ESSENTIAL - A pair of regulation black boots. Your own Silva or Suunto Compass (mils) Compass and a Pathfinder Protractor/Romer.

DESIRABLE - A Rucsac - not too large for your age/size. A Sleeping Bag liner - good for personal hygiene. A Survival blanket. An Army Cadet Force tie and Lapel Badge.

APPEARANCE and DRESS

CARE and CLEANING of BOOTS

There are different ideas about how clean your boots should be.

It is most likely that you will only have one pair of boots and they have to be worn for all your cadet activities. It is very difficult to wear them on an expedition one day and then have them fit for a "drill competition" the next!! Most Units have the common sense approach, they plan their activities so as their cadets can have time to smarten their boots for some special parade.

What is important is to make sure that they fit you comfortably and are kept in good repair, the uppers clean and well polished.

The laces must be straight across the eyelet holes, not crossing over them - see diagram of boot/puttees.

Should you get your boots wet, do not dry them in front of a fire or over heat. Leather is a natural material and so must dry naturally. It helps if you stuff newspaper into them to absorb the wet/damp, replacing it after a couple of hours with dry paper.

Always have a spare pair of leather laces, with you - the Cadet Supply Department have them. Only wear thick woollen socks with boots

If shoes are worn in uniform, they must be clean/polished, laces tied neatly, and the shoes in good repair.

APPEARANCE and DRESS

Jersey Order

Head-dress - Clean and free from sweat and hair grease.

Beret band square on head.

Badge clean and correctly positioned.

Fullness pulled down correctly.

Bow at back neatly tied with ends sewn down and central.

Hair - Not protruding over the collar nor hiding the ears.

Sideburns not below the bottom of ears.

Face and Neck - Clean with face shaved when necessary.

Shirt: collar - Neatly pressed and outside jersey.

Brassard - Worn on right arm and neatly pressed.

Jersey Pullover - Clean and well maintained. Lightweight/Barrack Trousers - Neatly pressed with bottoms just resting on uppers, of boots/shoes or, if puttees or anklets are worn, tidily overlapping them. Pockets - contents not making bulges. Hands - Clean with no stains. Nails clean and trimmed.

RANKS AND BADGES OF RANK

2nd Lt	Lt	Capt	Maj	Lt Col	Col	Brig
◊	◊◊	◊◊◊	♔	♔◊	♔◊◊	♔◊

L/Cpl	Cpl	Sgt	S/Sgt	WO 2	WO 1 (RSM)
∨	∨∨	⋁⋁⋁	♔⋁⋁⋁	♔	(crest)

40

FOOT DRILL

INTRODUCTORY WORDS OF COMMAND
Words of command on the march in Quick Time.
HALT - Given as the LEFT foot is on the ground.
ABOUT TURN - Given as the LEFT foot passes the RIGHT.
SALUTING ON THE MARCH - Given as the LEFT heel
strikes the ground.
SALUTING TO THE FRONT - Given as the RIGHT foot
passes the LEFT.
MARK TIME - Given over a LEFT pace.
HALT and FORWARD - (when MARKING TIME) -
"SQUAD HALT" given when LEFT
knee is at it's highest point.
RIGHT TURN or (INCLINE) - Given as the RIGHT foot
passes the LEFT.
LEFT TURN or (INCLINE) - Given as the LEFT foot
passes the RIGHT.

INTRODUCTORY WORDS OF COMMAND
Used for Squad Drill.

Once you start to take part in drill as a squad, you should
be given words of command that give advanced warning
of what the next word of command is to be.

Many insttructors taking Drill do not use this facility, as a
result of which you will see a squad turning in different
directions, all at the same time!.

Before moving a squad in any direction, the instructor
indicates as to what direction he intends to move them, by
using a form of words of command, before giving the
actual command to execute the order.

As a member of the squad, it does give you time to work
out exactly the direction you are next to move.

Refer to the diagram on the next page; and turn the page

WORDS OF COMMAND

INTRODUCTORY WORDS OF COMMAND

round - anti-clockwise, so as the ARROW under the word ADVANCING is pointing away from you, you are now standing in the FRONT RANK of a squad doing drill on the square. The words of command you should be given are as set out in the diagram.

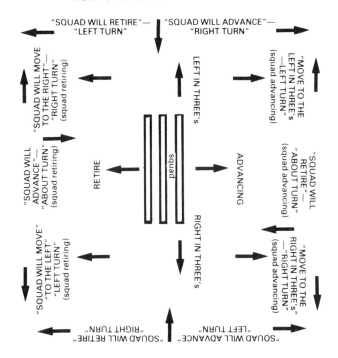

"MOVE TO THE RIGHT IN THREE's ABOUT TURN"

"SQUAD WILL RETIRE"— "LEFT TURN"

"SQUAD WILL ADVANCE"— "RIGHT TURN"

LEFT IN THREE's

"MOVE TO THE LEFT IN THREE's" —"LEFT TURN" (squad advancing)

"SQUAD WILL MOVE TO THE RIGHT" —"RIGHT TURN" (squad retiring)

RETIRE

squad

ADVANCING

"SQUAD WILL ADVANCE"— "ABOUT TURN" (squad retiring)

"SQUAD WILL RETIRE" —"ABOUT TURN" (squad advancing)

"SQUAD WILL MOVE "TO THE LEFT" "LEFT TURN" (squad retiring)

RIGHT IN THREE's

"MOVE TO THE RIGHT IN THREE's" —"RIGHT TURN" (squad advancing)

"SQUAD WILL ADVANCE" "LEFT TURN" "SQUAD WILL RETIRE" "RIGHT TURN"

"MOVE TO THE LEFT IN THREE's ABOUT TURN"

42

MARCHING AND DRESSING OFF

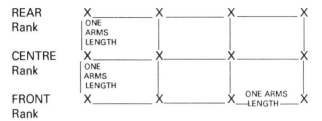

REAR Rank

CENTRE Rank

FRONT Rank

ONE ARMS LENGTH

ONE ARMS LENGTH

ONE ARMS LENGTH

DIAGRAM OF A SQUAD CORRECTLY DRESSED AND COVERED OFF
FROM LEFT TO RIGHT, AND FROM FRONT RANK - TO REAR.

CHANGING DIRECTION - WHEELING ON THE MARCH

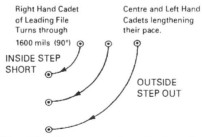

Right Hand Cadet
of Leading File
Turns through
1600 mils (90°)

Centre and Left Hand
Cadets lengthening
their pace.

INSIDE STEP
SHORT

OUTSIDE
STEP OUT

The term "Step Short" means reduce the length of your
pace, "Step out" means slightly lengthen your pace.
By doing this while Wheeling you keep your Dressing in
each file as it changes direction.
A common fault when giving the "Left or Right Wheel" is
for the command to be given sharply, when in fact it should
be drawn out - "WHEE-EEL", allowing the files to slowly
change direction, keeping their dressing in three's.

QUESTIONS

1. What is Saluting in recognition of.
2. Who salutes when the National Anthem is played.
3. When is an armed escort NOT given to the ACF Banner.
4. What would you be doing correctly "the longest way up and shortest down".
5. What are "wrapped round three times"
6. How many Proficiency Badge are allowed on a Brassard.
7. How do you dry out your leather boots.
8. How many "pips" does a Brigadier wear on each shoulder.
9. The pocket of your uniform must not be what...
10. How should your Beret band be on your forehead.
11. On what foot is the HALT given.
12. Marking Time, when is the HALT given.
13. Given the preliminary word of command; "squad will retire", is the squad "advancing" or "retiring".
14. When wheeling in a squad who 'steps short'.
15. What do you understand by an "INTRODUCTORY" word of command.
16. What sort of socks should you wear with boots.
17. When do you "Step Short" and "Step Out"
18. At Close Order what is the distance between ranks.
19. Marking Time, the HALT is given when the knee is ...
20. What is the essential kit you have to buy as a cadet.

HISTORY OF THE ARMY CADET FORCE

THE EARLIEST DAYS

The Cadet Force can trace its beginnings to 1859, at the time of the threat of invasion by the French. Few units of the British Army were at home, most of them were serving in India after the Indian Mutiny. Due to threat of invasion the Volunteers were formed. History was repeated again in 1940 when there was the threat of invasion from the German Army.

1860
VICTORIA RIFLES
CADET CORPS
GREEN UNIFORM
& PILLBOX HATS

THE VOLUNTEERS

The formation of the Volunteers - ancestors of the Territorial Army - saw the start of the cadets.
In 1860 at least eight schools had formed units. Volunteer units formed Cadet Companies. One of these, the Queen's Westministers, paraded their cadets when Queen Victoria carried out a review of the Volunteers in 1860.
The cadet movement continued, as at that time it was seen as great value to boys, bearing in mind the terrible conditions that so many of them lived in.

OCTAVIA HILL - SOCIAL WORKER

One of the most respected social workers at that time was Miss Octavia Hill. She realised that cadet training was of great benefit to these boys, and as a result formed the Southwark Cadet Company to introduce boys of the area to the virtues of order, cleanliness, team work and self-reliance.

HISTORY OF THE ACF

At the start of the Boer War, about fifty schools had Cadet Corps (the forerunners of the Combined Cadet Force). Many 'open units' (forebears of the present Army Cadet Force) had started in the large cities.

AFTER THE BOER WAR

In 1908, the Volunteers were converted to the Territorial Army, Public Schools and Universities were asked to provide units of the Officers Training Corps, Cadet Corps were formed in schools and 'open units' for those who had left school. The title Cadet Force was introduced and the administration was taken over by the Territorial Army Associations.

THE FIRST WORLD WAR

In 1914, the first World War, there was a big expansion of the Cadet Force, the War Office took over the administration, and continued until 1923 when control and administration reverted to the Territorial Army Associations. In that year 1923, the government ceased to

1918
PIPE BAND BEARDMORE
CADET CORPS

recognise the Cadet Force, taking away all financial support. This was a very difficult period for everyone, but the voluntary spirit that had been it's greatest strength in the early days, once again came to the surface. Everything that was required had to be paid for by individuals, and even the wearing of Regimental badges and buttons was forbidden, it certainly was a difficult and unhappy time

BRITISH NATIONAL CADET ASSOCIATION (BNCA)

Trying to keep the Cadet Force alive and at the same time to get back government support, brought about the formation of the BNCA (British National Cadet Association).

By 1932 the BNCA had gained recognition and achieved some measure of success, and was allowed - under the guidance of the Territorial Army Associations - to run the Cadet Force.

THE SECOND WORLD WAR

Shortly after the start of the Second World War (1939-45) saw a massive expansion of all the Cadet Forces, not only the Army Cadet and the Sea Cadets, but included the formation of the Air Training Corps.

By 1942 the War Office - known today as the Ministry of Defence - took over the administration of the ACF once again, giving it support beyond the members wildest dreams.

Uniforms were provided - free, they had rifles issued, although they were from the Boer War period!, camps were set

1942
BERKSHIRE
ARMY CADET
IN BATTLEDRESS

up and assistance given to help run them and train the Cadets.

The War Certificate 'A' Parts 1 and 2 were then the Proficiency Tests for training, with the red star worn on the arm of uniforms similar to your APC blue Stars of today.

At one period there were more than 140,000 Army Cadets serving, though not without problems to find officers and instructors to run the cadet detachments throughout the country.

Most fit and able bodied men were already in the forces or committed members of the Home Guard or other Emergency Services.

Working hours for the civilian population were extended to help the 'war effort', few people had spare time to be involved with Cadets or for that matter any other activities.

HISTORY OF THE ACF

ARMY CADET FORCE ASSOCIATION (ACFA)

At the end of the war in 1945, the BNCA changed its name to the ACFA (ARMY CADET FORCE ASSOCIATION) who today are responsible for the guidance of the Army Cadet Force and through many committees act as advisors to the Ministry of Defence and other Government bodies on all matters connected with the ACF.

THE AMERY REPORT

In 1957 a special Government report (the Amery Report) was published on the future of the ACF in the immediate post war years. Many changes were made, in 1959 the Cadet Training Centre, Frimley Park was founded.

The Army Cadet Force Association was one of the youth organisations who were given substantial grants from the late King George VI Memorial Trust Fund, and as a result of this the Cadet Officers and Instructors Courses that were run at Frimley Park were called the KGVI Leadership Courses.

Training in the Cadet Force took on a new direction, the 'war was over', and National Service was about to be stopped.

It then became more important to develop the cadet as a person, more responsible for their actions, guiding and developing them through their training to become good citizens.

ADVENTUROUS TRAINING INTRODUCED

With the emphasis on this change of direction, Adventurous Training was introduced as a specific subject in the cadet syllabus.

Special grants were made available to County Territorial Army Associations to set up County Adventure Training Centres. Many Counties took advantage of this and set up Adventure Training Centres for cadets in their counties, where hopefully many of you still have the opportunity to go for your weekend training.

THE DUKE OF EDINBURGH'S AWARD SCHEME

It was by happy coincidence that the Duke of Edinburgh Award was started soon after Adventure Training was introduced into the ACF.

As a result of this the ACF became involved in the Award Scheme right from the start.

It was not appreciated at the time but, with the ending of National Service, the Cadet Forces in general soon began to realise, that many Officers and Senior Ranks who joined the Cadet Forces at the end of their two years National Service, were not going to be available and to the future would have to train and recruit many ex-cadets as their future officers and instructors.

Since then many hundreds of officers and instructors have been recruited from the "ranks of cadets". They have been senior cadets, who have shown that they are the "right material" during their cadet career and have been offered the opportunity to be considered as future officers or instructors.

ACF ONE HUNDRETH ANNIVERSARY

The year 1960 was the centenary of the ACF and was marked by the presentation of a Banner to the Force by H.R.H. The Duke of Edinburgh.

Another highlight of the year was a review of the ACF and CCF in the grounds of Buckingham Palace by Her Majesty the Queen and H.R.H The Duke of Edinburgh.

In the period from 1960 to the mid 80's the ACF had moved with the times, seeing the enrolment of girls into some counties, firstly as a pilot scheme and now accepted as a normal part of our cadet movement, making an increasing contribution to the aims of the Cadet Force.

NEW UNIFORMS

New and improved accommodation, better uniforms, both as working dress and barrack dress have been provided for you.

The Regular Army continues to provide Cadet Training Teams to assist with the training of senior cadets, also your officers and instructors.

NEW RIFLES INTRODUCED

1986 was a special 'milestone' in our history with the introduction of a new rifle, the L98. A1. Cadet GP Rifle, made specially for the Cadet Forces, many of you will have now become well trained in its use.

1980-90
NORTHERN IRELAND
ARMY CADET FORCE
ROYAL IRISH RANGER
CADET IN BARRACK DRESS

Also introduced at this time was the new Cadet Target Rifle, L81A1, this was essentially to encourage target shooting in the Cadet Forces.

The "well-being" of the Cadet Force to a great extent, depends upon you as a Cadet, the standards you attain and the support you give it throughout your own career.

TO THE FUTURE

At the present time we are all living in a rapidly changing world, no doubt it will affect the cadet force and us as individuals.

We trust that history will not repeat itself and the cadet forces again go through difficult times to survive the changes.

At this particular time, you are one of those who is expected to do your best to give all the support required to ensure the future of the Army Cadet Force.

Many of us who were once cadets owe the Force a debt for

many reasons, we are sure, that you too, will not be any different from those who have gone before you.

You are a member of an organisation with a long history and many traditions to be upheld. Be sure that you keep up those traditions, and high standards, no matter what career path you take.

Many Cadets naturally join the Regular Army or Territorial Army. Some stay on as Instructors or Officers in the Force.

Many ex-cadets rejoin the ACF after their Army or TA service, passing on to you — the next generation — their wisdom and knowledge, be sure you are worthy of it.

QUESTIONS

1. What is the earliest known date of the Cadet movement.
2. Who was Octavia Hill.
3. When was the title Cadet Force introduced.
4. When did the Government of the day withdraw support for the Cadet movement.
5. Who ran the Cadets when the finance was withdrawn.
6. How was the Army Cadet Force Association formed.
7. What was War Certificate "A".
8. What was the Amery Report.
9. When was the Cadet Training Centre, Frimley Park founded.
10. When was the 100th Anniversary of the Cadet Force.
11. What year was the Cadet GP rifle and the Target Rifle introduced.
12. Who were the ancestors of the TA.
13. Why was the name the "KGVI" given to courses started at Frimley Park.
14. As a result of what, caused the change in the syllabus to include Adventure Training as a subject.

CONTROL AND DIRECTION OF THE A.C.F

INTRODUCTION

This section explains how the Army Cadet Force is controlled, organised and supported. It is important for you to have an understanding of this to realise how much is done for you, by whom it is done and the need to for you to make an effort to show how much it is appreciated.

The Charter of the ACF combines two mutually supporting themes - firstly as a youth organisation, designed to help you develop as an individual and a citizen, and secondly for you to identify with and understand the Army, as the ACF is modelled on some of the methods used by the Army.

As a national youth organisation the ACF is represented by the Army Cadet Force Association (ACFA).

The ACF is not a part of the Armed Services.

THE ROLE OF ACFA

The ACFA has three main roles, they are as follows:-

1. To direct activities outside military training in which the ACF is involved in as a Youth Service. National Sporting events. Duke of Edinburgh's Award. National Shooting Competitions. Commonwealth Cadet Forces.

2. To advise the Ministry of Defence on all matters of policy. This is a very important role on your behalf.

3. To maintain the spirit of the Army Cadet Force throughout the UK, to act very much in the same way as a Regimental Headquarters does.

ACTIVITIES OF THE ACFA

As mentioned in the History of the ACF, the ACFA was formed from the BNCA — the volunteers — who "kept the flag flying" when the government of the day was giving them a difficult time.

As far as the "members" of the ACFA are concerned it is in many respects similar to a Regimental Association, keeping them informed of all that is going on.

It is a source of information, that is of course, if you keep in touch by joining the Association and paying your annual subscription.

All officers and Instructors in the ACF are expected to be members of ACFA, although anyone can join by writing to the Membership Secretary, ACFA, Duke of Yorks HQ, Kings Road, Chelsea, London, SW3 4RR.

THE CADET JOURNAL and GAZETTE

As a member of ACFA you will be sent the official magazine of the Army Cadet Force, the CADET JOURNAL and GAZETTE. This always has interesting articles on cadet activities from at home and abroad, ask your officers or instructors to show you their copy.

At the end of every year ACFA produces an Annual Report setting out the different activities in which they have been involved and a report on the general "state" of the ACF throughout the UK.

Also listed are the various committees and the members who serve on them, illustrating the close liaison with the Ministry of Defence to give advice and guidance on the future role and policy for the continued success of the Army Cadet Force.

ASK YOUR OFFICERS OR INSTRUCTORS TO LET YOU READ THEIR COPY OF THE CADET JOURNAL & GAZETTE

MINISTRY OF DEFENCE & TAVRA

CADET SUPPLY DEPARTMENT

The Cadet Supply Department which is sponsored by ACFA and run by their own staff, is like a 'Military Aladdins Cave', it is **YOUR Cadet Shop** and relies on your support whenever you can.

It has a great selection of kit on display and the staff are always very helpful.

Should you go to London at any time it is one of the places you must find some time to visit.

The Supply Department have an excellent catalogue, each year one of them is sent via your County HQ to your Cadet Detachment

Ask your officers or instructors to show it to you.

SUPPLY DEPARTMENT CATALOGUE

If you would like a personal copy, send a Postal Order for not less than 50p to the Cadet Supply Department, Duke of Yorks Barracks, Kings Road, Chelsea, London SW3 4RR. Many of you spend your money on "items of kit" from the Military Shops in your local area.

You will be surprised how much cheaper it is to buy from the Cadet Supply Department, even if you have to pay the postage, so get your own catalogue.

This is not only good sense, but by supporting the Supply Department you will be helping the funds of ACFA, who will then be better able to support national sporting events and other activities on your behalf.

THE MINISTRY OF DEFENCE (MOD)

The MOD provides the military organisation, equipment and facilities for training and the finance via Territorial Army and Volunteer Reserve Associations (TAVRA) to run the Army Cadet Force.

THE COUNTY CADET COMMITTEE

The MOD direction comes through a department called the **Director Reserve Forces and Cadets (DRFC)**, the training syllabus is provided and standards set for the Army Proficiency Certificate (APC).

This control is then passed down through the Headquarters of **United Kingdom Land Forces (UKLF)** to the TAVRA's within Counties in the UK.

Perhaps the most important facility provided by MOD is the Cadet Training Centre, Frimley Park, Nr Camberley, Surrey. The majority of officers and Adult Instructors will have attended courses at Frimley during their cadet careers. As a senior cadet NCO you could also have an opportunity to be a student at Frimley Park.

THE TERRITORIAL ARMY & VOLUNTEER RESERVE ASSOCIATION (TAVRA)

The TAVRA's on behalf of the MOD look after most of the Organisation and Administration of the ARMY CADET FORCE within their Counties.

We are dependent on their help and the history of the Army Cadet Force shows that we were in the same position way back in the 19th century, when the cadets were a part of the Volunteer Battalions of the day, who were the ancestors of the present day Territorial Army. The TAVRA's have a full time staff at their own County Headquarters. This usually comprises the Secretary who is a retired senior officer from the services, his deputy — also a retired officer, plus a small Administrative Office staff.

Their work as far as the ACF is concerned is to look after the property provided for us, from the provision of new premises and the maintenance of existing cadet huts. This in no way means that we should not help to look after our property, as the money available for this is very carefully controlled through a system of grants.

They keep a "watching brief" on how the administration is carried out by the County ACF Headquarters, checking the different accounts where Public Money is being spent, the control of Rations, cleaning and maintenance of uniform held in stock, general expenses and many other activities, so, you can see that they have a very important role to play in the smooth running of the ACF in their County.

THE COUNTY CADET COMMITTEE

To assist the TAVRA in 'cadet matters' there is a special **County Cadet Committee**. The committee members are usually people who have special interest and experience of the Cadet Forces in general within the County.

As an example, the members of the committee could be the following:-

The Secretary of TAVRA, the present County Cadet Commandant, ex-Cadet Commandants of the County, Commanding Officers of TA units who have cadet badged to them, the County Cadet Medical Officer, serving ACF Area/Battalion/commanders, representative of the County Youth Service, the County Padre. Others may be co-opted for special purposes.

TAVRA STAFF AT COUNTY HQ

In addition TAVRA's employ the full-time staff you will find at your own County Cadet Headquarters.

The Cadet Executive Officer (CEO) is the senior member of the staff and is accountable for the efficient and proper running of the Administration within the County for the Cadet Commandant. This is a very important job and requires a great deal of experience in controlling and accounting for clothing, equipment, weapons, ammunition and on the financial side the Cadets Welfare Funds, Pay and Allowances, Rations, also Officers Mess and the Sergeants and Warrant Officers Mess Accounts.

The CEO is assisted by a small staff who take on the jobs of County **Quartermaster** and **Administrative Assistants** who visit Detachments carrying out routine checks of equipment and security. In most County Headquarters there is also a **Clerical Officer** who is responsible for the efficient operation of the office, dealing with the requests for courses, orders and general office routine.

THE COUNTY CADET COMMANDANT

Like you the Commandant is a volunteer, and may be an officer who has had many years experience in the Cadet Force or is a retired senior officer from the Army or TA. They are appointed by the MOD on the recommendation of the County Cadet Committee and normally serve for a three year term of office.

As the Chief Executive officer they are responsible for all matters relating to the ACF in the County

As the leader, they will be involved in the initial selection of potential officers or instructors, and later their training and the results they are producing with their cadets.

The Cadet Commandants time is more directed at building an efficient and enthusiastic team of the right people, who put into practice the policies agreed by the County Cadet Committee.

COUNTY (ACF) STAFF
THE DEPUTY COUNTY CADET COMMANDANT

Like the Commandant they are appointed by the MOD on the recommendation of the County Cadet Committee. S/he will 'stand in' on occasions when the Commandant is not available.

Very often they take on special responsibilities for the Commandant, such as; Discipline of the officers and instructors or planning Special Projects such as fund raising on a large scale, and setting up audit boards. Organising 'special event' days at Annual Camp and many more.

THE COUNTY TRAINING OFFICER

This job is normally taken on by a senior officer who has had a great deal of experience in training cadets at all levels.

They will be in close contact with the Cadet Commandant, keeping them informed of the standards of training being carried out in the detachments.

They will pay special attention to new detachments, help new or inexperienced officers and instructors. They are often responsible for arrranging adult training, Cadet NCO's Promotion Cadres, and monitoring the APC testing of cadets within the County.

They play a large part in drawing up the Annual Camp plans under the guidance of the Cadet Commandant and work in liaison with the CADET TRAINING TEAM (CTT).

DUKE OF EDINBURGH'S AWARD OFFICER

S/he is appointed by the Cadet Commandant as the County DofE Officer. His/her role is to give assistance to

HELP FROM THE REGULAR ARMY

Areas and Detachments who have cadets already enrolled in the scheme or helping those who wish to do so.

THE CADET TRAINING TEAM (CTT)

The CTT is part of the direct MOD support for the ACF.
The Cadet Training Team may be seen by you at your
Detachment to give special demonstrations or help run
an exercise for your Detachment Commander.
Their main job is to assist in the training of Officers and
Instructors.
This is mostly carried out at Annual Camp, when a group
of officers and instructors undergo a weeks training as a
part of their initial training course.
Many members of the CCT's are ex-cadets and have a
good understanding of what you require to know.

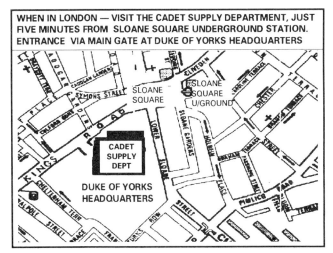

WHEN IN LONDON — VISIT THE CADET SUPPLY DEPARTMENT, JUST
FIVE MINUTES FROM SLOANE SQUARE UNDERGROUND STATION.
ENTRANCE VIA MAIN GATE AT DUKE OF YORKS HEADQUARTERS

CONTROL AND DIRECTION OF THE ACF

QUESTIONS

1. What are the TWO supporting themes of the ACF.
2. What are the THREE roles of ACFA.
3. How can you become a member of ACFA.
4. How can you get a Cadet Journal and Gazette.
5. Who sponsors the Cadet Supply Department.
6. How can you get Supply Department Catalogue.
7. What does MOD stand for.
8. What does DRFC stand for.
9. What does UKLF stand for.
10. What does TAVRA stand for.
11. What does TAVRA do for the ACF in the County.
12. What is the County Cadet Committee.
13. Name THREE people who might be on the County Cadet Committee.
14. Who is the CEO in your County.
15. What is the CEO responsible for in the County.
16. Who appoints the County Cadet Commandant.
17. How long is the Commandants normal "Term of Service".
18. What is your County Commandants rank and name.
19. What do you know about Frimley Park.
20. Who is your County DofE Officer.
21. What is the Cadet Training Team.
22. Who is responsible for training in your County.
23. Visiting the Cadet Supply dept, which London Underground station would you get out at.
24. What is the address of the Cadet Supply Department.

FIELDCRAFT

INTRODUCTION

Fieldcraft is the one subject that always gets you and your "mates" to turn out in strength, especially if it says on the programme that it is a "Patrol" or "Section" exercise, and if it's a "night exercise" so much the better. We are not suggesting that all cadets still like playing "cowboys and Indians", but may be Fieldcraft could be described as "organised" cowboys and Indians!.

If you live in a city/town are you are at some disadvantage to see Fieldcraft in action, however, if you are able to get into the countryside or live in or near it, you will be aware that the wild life "get a living" off the land by being experts in the use of their skills of; stealth, patience,speed and fitness, stamina, planning and cunning and being natural experts at camouflage and concealment.

NATURAL SKILLS

Fieldcraft is their prime skill in catching their food and in many ways to be good at Fieldcraft you could do no better than to study wildlife at every opportunity. Observe how a cat stalks its quarry, how the Sparrow Hawk, hovers patiently, observing the right moment to drop in on the Field Mouse, the Fox who uses the hedgrows to move from one field to another, see how well a Rabbit is camouflage against the ground, all of these examples are types of Individual Fieldcraft skills exercised for the purpose of either "defence" or "attack". In your case, being trained in Fieldcraft brings together and practices all the skills you learn in your APC subjects not only as a individual but as a member of a team/section.

As cadets you should normally work only at SECTION LEVEL, and for you to understand where a section "fits into" the organisation of an Infantry Battalion, we set out the diagram below and the following information.

THE OUTLINE ORGANISATION OF A BATTALION

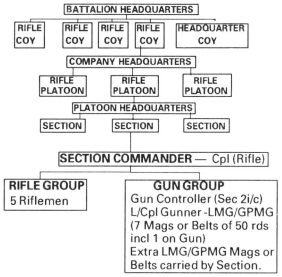

SECTION ORGANISATION

The normal fighting strength of a Section in the Regular Army (650 strength Battalion) is two NCO's and six men, but it can operate with one NCO and five men.

The Rifle and the machine gun are the main weapons of the Section. The Riflemen can be divided into smaller groups to provide better "fire and movement" capability. The machine gun provides support for the movement of the Section especially in the assault.

FIELDCRAFT

With the introduction of the Light Support Weapon (LSW) into the Army , a new organisation with 2 LSW's and 6 Rifles has been adopted. The section is divided into two FIRE TEAMS, however, for the purposes of cadet training it will be more usual to operate as a Gun Group and a Rifle Group.

INDIVIDUAL FIELDCRAFT

Once you have an understanding of the need to imitate those skills that wild life practice to survive in the field, then you will be on the way to attaining an acceptable standard of Individual Fieldcraft.

Even when you are mentally and physically fit, you will need a lot of practice and patience, to develop the natural ability to react in defence of your survival, both as an individual and as a member of a group.

Be good at fieldcraft and survive - you seldom get a second chance.

METHODS OF JUDGING DISTANCE

WHY JUDGE DISTANCE; if you can judge distance you will know the approximate area in which to look when given an order. If your sights are not correctly adjusted, your shots will probably miss the target.

USE A UNIT OF MEASURE

100 metres is a good unit, The Range is marked out at 100 metre intervals.

A Full Size Football pitch is about 100 metres long.

DO NOT USE THE UNIT OF MEASURE METHOD OVER 400 METRES IF YOU CAN'T SEE ALL THE GROUND BETWEEN YOU AND THE TARGET.

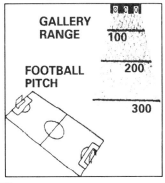

FIELDCRAFT

JUDGING DISTANCE

When you know what 100 metres looks like, practice fitting your Unit of Measure between you and your target.

AIDS TO JUDGING DISTANCE

APPEARANCE METHOD
By noting what a person looks like at a set distance, you can then use the Appearance Method

Common objects may also be used for this method.

FIELDCRAFT

Things seem closer

Further away

REMEMBER

Things seem closer .. In bright light, if they are bigger
than their surroundings, if there is dead ground between
you and them, if they are higher up than you.

Further away ... With sun in your eyes, in bad light. When
smaller than surroundings. Looking across a valley, down
a street or along a path in a wood, if you are lying down.

AIDS TO JUDGING DISTANCE

KEY RANGES

If the range to one object is known, estimate the distance
from it to the target.

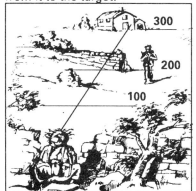

BRACKETING

Calculate mid-
distance between
nearest possible and
furthest possible
distance of target.
Nearest - 100
Farthest - 300.
Mid-distance - 200.

HALVING

Estimate the distance
halfway to the target
then double it:
100 x 2 = 200

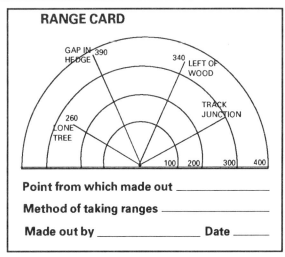

RANGE CARD

GAP IN HEDGE 390

340 LEFT OF WOOD

TRACK JUNCTION

260 LONE TREE

100 200 300 400

Point from which made out _____

Method of taking ranges _____

Made out by _____ **Date** _____

THE SMALL ARMS RANGE CARD

Range Cards are to be prepared whenever a position is occupied for more than 30 minutes or more.
Section and Platoon Commanders are responsible for ensuring the Range Card is made out accurately.
A Range Card must be made out for every position and should be passed on to the next occupant who must check its accuracy.
A printed Range Card is available on the 24 hour Ration Pack boxes, these should be retained and used when required.
By practicing at making out Range Cards you will apply all the skills of Judging Distance and as a result improve your accuracy better than most.

FIELDCRAFT

PERSONAL CAMOUFLAGE AND CONCEALMENT

**The enemy is looking for you so- don't make it easy.
Merge with your surroundings**

| TOO MUCH | JUST RIGHT | TOO LITTLE |

LOSE YOUR SHAPE
Make sure nothing
shines.
Blend in with your
surroundings - if
they vary, so must
you.

AVOID SKYLINES

**Stand back from
windows - merge into
the shadows - don't
lean out you will be
seen.**

Don't use isolated cover - it stands out.

SOMETHING IS SEEN BECAUSE ITS:-

Shape
Shadow ————— IS FAMILIAR OR STANDS OUT
Silhouette

Surface
Spacing —— IS DIFFERENT FROM ITS SURROUNDINGS
Movement

SEEING IS .... Noticing details.

EASY TO SEE   **DIFFICULT TO FIND**

SHAPE...... Disguise your shape - including equipment and weapons.

FIELDCRAFT

SHADOW .... Keep in the shadows

SILHOUETTE .... Don't skyline

SURFACE..... Don't differ from your surroundings.

FIELDCRAFT

SPACING... Keep spread out - but not equally spaced.

MOVEMENT .... Move carefully - slowly when concealed - sudden movement will attract attention.

Look through cover - if possible - not round it . You MUST SEE without being SEEN.

FIELDCRAFT

TARGET RECOGNITION

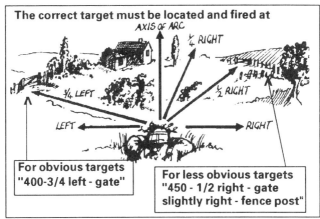

The correct target must be located and fired at

For obvious targets
"400-3/4 left - gate"

For less obvious targets
"450 - 1/2 right - gate
slightly right - fence post"

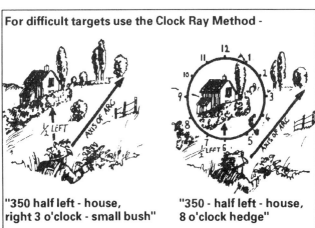

For difficult targets use the Clock Ray Method -

"350 half left - house,
right 3 o'clock - small bush"

"350 - half left - house,
8 o'clock hedge"

FIRE CONTROL ORDERS.

When the Section comes under fire the Section
Commander will give the order 'TAKE COVER'.
The drills for this are covered later, however there will
come a time when the Section Commander will need to
take control of the fire power of the Section to
concentrate it on the enemy, this is achieved using a
Fire Control Order.
You must learn how to do this instinctively so that you
can:

- a. Re-act to the Fire Control Order correctly.
- b. Give an order yourself if no one else can see the
     target.

To give a correct Fire Control Order you have to follow
tha set sequence, it will help you if you remember it by
the "Key Word" **GRIT**, as follows:-

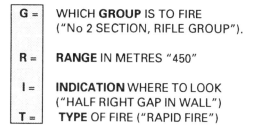

G =	WHICH **GROUP** IS TO FIRE ("No 2 SECTION, RIFLE GROUP").
R =	**RANGE** IN METRES "450"
I =	**INDICATION** WHERE TO LOOK ("HALF RIGHT GAP IN WALL")
T =	**TYPE** OF FIRE ("RAPID FIRE")

When giving this type or order remember it is an order
therefore to give it: -

C =	**Clearly**
L =	**Loudly**
A =	**As an order**
P =	**With Pauses**

FIELDCRAFT

TYPES OF FIRE CONTROL ORDER

The details of the Fire Control Order you get depends on the Type of Target to be engaged.

> **BRIEF Orders -**
> *"Sights down quarter right rapid fire".*
> **FULL Orders -** *"Gun group- 450 left-house doorway- bursts-fire".*
>
> **DELAYED Orders.**
> *"No 2 Section-300-quarter right-small wood - when enemy appears - rapid -fire".*
>
> **INDIVIDUAL Orders**
> *"No 1 Section 300 - slightly left - small bushes - enemy in that area - watch and shoot".*

MOVEMENT IN THE FIELD

When close to the enemy you do not want your movements to be seen-therefore use cover. Remember to - Use the hedges and walls for cover.

Leopard Crawl

Crawl on the inside of your knees and your elbows. Useful for moving behind very low cover. Move by using alternate elbows and knees, rolling your body a little as you bend your knees.

Keep your heels, head and body down, you must observe at all times.

Over page is the Leopard Crawl with a rifle.

LEOPARD CRAWL

Leopard Crawl — with a rifle.

Hold your Rifle with the right hand on the Pistol Grip and the left hand on the Hand Guard.

The Monkey Run

This is a normal "hands and knees" crawl. Useful to move behind cover about two feet high.

You can move quite fast, but it does make a noise.

Moving slower and to prevent twigs cracking as you move, put your knees on the spot where your hands have been.

Keep your "rear end" and head down, but continue to observe.

Witha rifle hold it at the point of balance, make sure that no dirt gets into the muzzle.

The Walk

The Rifle is held in the ALERT position, ready for instant action. You must adopt a positive and alert attitude, observing in all directions.

Don't walk on the flat sole of your boots, use the edge so as to walk quietly. It helps to keep your balance if you slightly bend your knees as you move.

FIELDCRAFT

The Roll
The quickest way of getting off a skyline or crest of a hill.
Protect your Rifle, hold closely into your side. Keep feet together and your body straight.

MOVEMENT AT NIGHT
Always move quietly.
Movements used during daylight are not suitable at night- they have to be adapted.

The Ghost Walk
Lift legs high, sweeping them slowly outwards. Feel gently with toes for safe place for each foot, put weight down gently. Keep knees bent. Use the left hand to feel the air in front of you from head height down to the ground checking for obstructions, trip wires, booby traps or alarms etc

The Cat Walk
Crawl on hands and knees. Search ground ahead for twigs, move knee to where hand has searched.

The Kitten Crawl
It is quiet-but slow. It is very tiring.
Lie on your front, search ahead for twigs, move them to one side.
Lift your body on your forearms and toes, press forward and lower yourself on to the ground.

NIGHT NOISES

At night you hear more than you see. Stop and listen. Keep close to the ground, turn your head slowly and use a cupped hand behind the ear.. Freeze if you hear a noise.

MOVING AT NIGHT - REMEMBER

Keep quiet .... have no loose equipment. Move carefully ... use the ghost walk, cat walk or kitten crawl.
Clear your route ... dry vegetation will make a noise.
Use available cover ... flares, thermal imaging and night observation devices will turn night into day.
Keep to the low ground ... you split your party at night at your peril.

LISTENING AT NIGHT

If the enemy is about - keep an ear close to the ground.
The closer you are to the ground, the more chance you have of seeing the enemy on 'skyline'.

NIGHT VISION

We can see in the dark - but REMEMBER our eyes take
30 minutes to get used to the dark.
We see less than in daylight. We see shapes - not detail.
We see skylines and silhouettes. We may see movement.

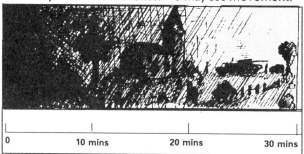

| 0 | 10 mins | 20 mins | 30 mins |

YOUR EYESIGHT

Your eyes have two sets of cells, one set for daylight
(CONES) in the centre of your eyes, the other set for
darkness (RODS), which are around the CONES.
The night cells work when the day cells are affected by
falling darkness.
With constant practice night observation can be
improved. If you have a cold, headache or are tired it can
reduce your night vision.
You will find that there is a limit to the time you can
concentrate effectively on any given point or your vision
becomes blurred.
Most Army unit use Thermal Imaging (night sights) that
"turn darkness into daylight" in as much that they pick
out an object giving out heat (body heat), The SUSAT
sights on the SA80 Rifle (an optical sight) has
advantages similar to that of binoculars for night
observation.

FIELDCRAFT

BRIGHT LIGHT RUINS YOUR NIGHT VISION

If caught in the light of
flares take cover at once in
open ground.

If in a wood - FREEZE. If
you see a flare, quickly
close one eye to protect
your night vision, use the
other eye to look about
you taking advantage of
the light, but do not move
suddenly as this will give
you away.

DUTIES OF A SENTRY

A sentry is the eyes and ears of the unit.
If the job is done well, the unit will be safe and secure.
When you are a Sentry make sure:-

That you know and
understand your orders.
That you know what to do
if your post is approached
by a person or vehicle.
That you ask questions if
you do not understand
anything.
What ground to watch.
Direction of the enemy.
Signal for defensive fire.

Names of prominent landmarks.
Where neighbouring posts are.
About patrols that maybe in the area, or coming through your post.

SENTRIES AT NIGHT IN THE FIELD

At night sentries work in pairs.
Sentries must know:-

What to do if anyone approaches their post.
What ground to watch.
The Password.

Sentries close to the enemy must know :-
Direction of the enemy.
Name of land marks.
Where neighbouring posts are.
Signal for defensive fire.
About patrols that may come in or out through their post or near them.

HOW TO CHALLENGE.

When you see movements which you think may not be your own troops - alert your Section Commander.

Say **'HALT' HANDS UP.**
'Advance one and be recognised'.
"Halt".
Give the challenge half of the password - quietly, so that only the first man can hear it.

ACTION - Allow friendly troops through, **know how many and count them through - one at a time.**
Section opens fire at enemy troops.

NOTE Be aware of a common trick which is for the enemy to approach a sentry, listen and learn the first half of a PASS WORD then fade away.

An inexperienced sentry may allow this to happen. The same enemy then approaches another sentry and challenges them before they can challenge them.

Again the inexperienced sentry might then give the reply then allow the enemy into the position.

So be careful and never allow anyone into your position unless you can positively identify them, when in doubt call for help.

USE YOUR SENSES.

What are your senses, how can they help in Fieldcraft?
On a patrol or on duty as a sentry you will use your **EYES** and **EARS**, and your **TOUCH** when feeling your way through woods or difficult cover.

Your sense of **TASTE** may not be used, but your sense of **SMELL** — depending upon the SMELL — may remind you of taste. SMELL — Body smell or the smell of cooking, or anything else that drifts on the air and can give yours and the enemies presence away.

SECTION BATTLE DRILLS

These notes are for a Section organised with the **GUN GROUP** and **ONE RIFLE GROUP**.

DRILL No 1. BATTLE PREPARATION.

a. Personal camouflage.
b. Check weapons.
c. Check ammo.

Section Commanders Orders

a. Ground ref points.
b. Situation Enemy forces. Friendly forces. Pl formation and Task.
c. Mission - the section mission.
d. Execution Section formations Flank for GUN. Route.
e. Service support - Info passed down from Pl Commanders orders.
f. Command & Signals; any info passed down from Pl Commander.

REFERENCE POINTS & ANTICIPATORY ORDERS.

In the 'Advance to Contact' the Section Commander will look out for :-

1. New reference points for fire orders.
2. Place where the Section can take cover if it comes under effective fire.

DRILL No 2 - REACTION TO EFFECTIVE FIRE.

The drill to be adopted is: On the order of the section commander -

"TAKE COVER", DASH - DOWN - CRAWL - OBSERVE - SIGHTS - FIRE.

DRILLS No 3 - LOCATION OF THE ENEMY

Location of the enemy is usually difficult, failure means casualties and section not be able to move and may lose the initiative as result. Three stages in this drill:

a. Observation - look in area from which thump came from.

b. Fire - fire order to couple of riflemen to fire at likely target.

c. Movement - Section commander orders rifleman to move while remainder of section observe.

DRILL No 4 WINNING THE FIRE FIGHT

As soon as the Section Commander knows the enemies position a fire order must be given to bring sufficient weight of fire on the enemy to neutralize them. (See Fire Control Orders)

DRILL No 5 - THE ATTACK BATTLE ORDERS

Will always be one of the following depending on the number of stages in the attack. They will be as brief as possible.

Orders for a **one stage attack,** that is when the rifle group goes straight into the assault.

Orders for a **two stage attack,** that if when the GUN group must move to another position before the rifle group assaults.

Orders for a **three stage attack** in which the rifle group moves, followed by the GUN group and finally the rifle group assaults.

The Advance

a. The section Commander will lead the rifle group in the assault.

b. All movement in the open by either group must be covered by the other group.

c. When rifle group gets into fire position after a bound, the GUN group must move forward to a new position automatically.

d. The section 2i/c who is the gun controller, watches the Section Commander, listens for orders and watches rifle group to give them covering fire at critical moments.

FIELDCRAFT

The Assault and Fighting through the Objective

The assault goes on as fast as possible.
Riflemen fire from the shoulder or thew "on guard"
position.
GUN group fires as long as possible during the assault,
then switches it's fire across the objective in front of rifle
group.

DRILL No 6 REORGANISATION

When objective cleared of enemy the Section
Commander must regain close control over men and
position, ready to beat off counter attack.
Reorganisation must beswift and efficient, if not all that
was gained will be lost.
The Section Commander will:
1 Allot fire tasks to each member of section.
2. Post sentries.
3. Check on casualties and ammunition.
4. Arrange re-distribution of ammo.
5. Supervise re-digging of shell scrapes.
6. Send prisoners and captured kit to rear.
7. Report to Pl Cmrd for orders.

SECTION AND PLATOON FIELD SIGNALS

Field Signal are a silent means of communication
between members of the section and platoon.
They should be used whenever possible and be
constantly practiced, even when going about normal
duties it is as well to use them, so as they become
second nature to everyone.
Very often there is a need to attract the attention of those
who are to receive the signal, especially if the Section
Commander wants to tell several members of his section
at the same time.

Watch and Listen

This does not absolve you as a member of the section from watching out for signals, as there may be times when an audible signal is not practical for obvious reasons.

There are four recognised methods of attracting attention, they are:-

1. A **SINGLE** whistle blast - during fire contact only.
2. Snapping forefinger and thumb.
3. Knocking butt of weapon with knuckles.
4. Silent whistle.

Whistle BLASTS are often used to indicate situations, they are as follows:-

1. **SHORT BLASTS - ALARM** - air attack, NBC attack, etc.
2. **LONG BLASTS** indicate "STAND DOWN".

FIELD SIGNALS

On the following pages are set out the normal Field Signals used by the Infantry. We have not put the name of description of the signal with it, but have numbered them and listed the description etc — you will learn them better this way.

Key and Description of Field Signals

1. READY TO MOVE. Move hands as if cranking handle.
2. DEPLOY. Arm extended below shoulder level, waved slowly from side to side, hand open. If deployment to either flank is wanted, commander points to flank, after completing signal.
3. ADVANCE or FOLLOW ME. Arm swung from rear to front below shoulder.
4. HALT or REST. Arm raised until the hand is level with shoulder. Indicate length of halt by number of fingers. Point to 'rest area'.
5. GO BACK or TURN ABOUT. Hand circled at hip height.
6. CLOSE or JOIN ME. Hand placed on top of head, elbow

square to the right or left, according to which hand is used. Point to RV area.

7. DOUBLE. Clenched hand moved up and down between thigh and shoulder.

8. SLOW DOWN (APC). Arm extended to the side below shoulder, palm downwards, moved slowly up and down, wrist loose.

9. LIE DOWN or DISMOUNT (APC). Two or three slight movements with the open hand towards the ground (palm downwards).

10. AS YOU WERE or SWITCH OFF (APC). Forearm extended downwards, hand open, waved across body parallel to ground.

11. ENEMY SEEN or SUSPECTED. Thumb pointed towards ground from clenched fist.

12. NO ENEMY IN SIGHT or ALL CLEAR. Thumb pointed upwards from clenched fist.

13. GUN GROUP. Clenched fist raised to shoulder height.

14. SCOUT GROUP. Clenched fist with forefinger upright.

15. RIFLE GROUP. 'Victory' sign - fist and second finger extended and open in 'V' remainder of fist clenched.

16. LIGHT MORTAR. Weapon held vertical. Imitate loading mortar rounds.

17. LAW/MAW. Weapon placed on shoulder and held like a LAW/MAW.

18. SECTION CMDR. Two opened fingers held against arm to indicate Corporal's Stripes.

19. PLATOON CMDR. Two opened fingers held on shoulder to indicate a Lieutenant's stars.

20. GIVE COVERING FIRE. Weapon brought into aim.

21. OBSTACLES. CROSSING. TRACK JUNCTION. Arms crossed. For water obstacle make waves.

22. HOUSE or HUT. Hands folded in inverted 'V'; to indicate shape of roof.

23. RECONNAISSANCE. Hand held to eye, as though using eye glass.
24. ATTACK. A chopping movement with edge of hand in direction attack is required.
25. MOVE UP. Fingers spread, arms swung slowly in direction movement is required.
26. FORM AMBUSH. Hand placed over face, followed by pointing to place of ambush.
27. FREEZE AND LISTEN. Hand cupped to ear.
28. 'O' GROUP. Fingers together, moved in conjunction with thumb to indicate person talking.
29 RIGHT or LEFT FLANKING. A curved sweeping movement of the arm in direction concerned.
30. FIRE & MANOEUVRE. One hand used in a rolling forward action in front of the body.
31. SPACE OUT. Palm of hands held against weapon and moved away several times.
32. ARROW HEAD. Both arms forced backwards or forwards at an angle of 800 mils, depending whether arrow is backward or forward.
33. SINGLE FILE. One arm fully extended above head.
34. STAGGERED FILE. Both arms fully extended above head.
35. SPEARHEAD. As for arrowhead plus indicating Gun Group to move in at rear.
36. DIAMOND. Arms raised above the head with arms slightly bent so that hands touch to form diamond shape.
37. EXTENDED LINE. Arms raised to the side level with the ground, indicate which side group is to go.

THE ONLY WAY TO LEARN FIELD SIGNALS IS TO PRACTICE AN USE THEM ON EVERY POSSIBLE OCCASION

FIELDCRAFT

SECTION FORMATIONS

As a member of a Rifle Section you move as a part of the Section. How you move depends upon six factors

1. The type of ground you are moving across.
2. How far you can see.
3. The likely direction from which the enemy may fire on you.
4. How your Section Commander can best control the Section.
5. The need for the Section to produce the maximum fire with minimum delay.
6. Who controls the Air Space.

FORMATIONS

Section Formations are used to meet the above factors and are mostly decided upon by the Section Commander, who will change the formations as the Section moves over different types of ground during its advance.
Some of the formations are described as follows:-

Single File

This is good for moving along hedges or ditches or along the edge of woods.

FIELDCRAFT

SINGLE FILE

Good for control by the Section Commander especially at night.
Bad formation to produce fire to the front. Vunerable from frontal fire, especially down a ditch or sunken road/stream.
Not good for observation or passing information to the members of the section.

FILE

A good formation for control and night movement.
Can be used going down a track or either side of a hedge.
Disadvantage — it makes a good target for the enemy.

ARROWHEAD

Best for moving across open country, produces effective fire against frontal attack. Easy to control, has good all round observation. Bad for exposing good target to enemy fire.

FIELDCRAFT

DIAMOND

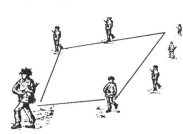

Formation used only when crossing open country at night. Easy to control, has all round observation and protection, each person can see the next, the Section Commander can be at the front or in the middle.

EXTENDED LINE

Formation used for the "final assault", difficult to control, needs good "field discipline" by members of Section to watch/listen.

REMEMBER

When moving in a Section Formation:-
1. Watch your Section Commander for hand signals.
2. Keep in contact with members of the Section on each side of you — but not too close.
3. Keep quiet and listen for commands and anticipatory orders.
4. Keep in correct position for formation.
5. Be observant.
6. Be ready to change to a new Section Formation.

FIELDCRAFT

CHOOSING A ROUTE.

If you have to advance across country, check that you
know where to make for. Then decide on the best route.
REMEMBER
Routes must be planned ahead.
You must move in bounds or stages from one
observation point to another.
You must check your direction - are you keeping on
course.
Always use a compass
Must not be seen but should be able to see the enemy.
If you have to take a chance choose a route which offers
the risks early in your approach rather than later on,
since you will have less chance of being seen.
The best route will - have places to observe the enemy -
without being seen yourself.
Don't go blindly towards the enemy.
Give good fire positions.
You must be able to fire if necessary. Give cover from
enemy fire. Let you move without being seen. Not to
have impassable obstacles such as marsh land or open
ground or ravines.

PACING

Pacing is necessary because you must always know how exactly far you have gone when counting a number of your own 'paces'.

You should know your 'Pacing Scale', over different types of ground conditions, IE tarmac roads or tracks, grasslands, woodlands etc.

To find your PACING SCALE, put two markers out 100m apart. Walk the distance between them as you would on a patrol, counting the paces as you go.

If it has taken you 120 paces to cover the 100m, then that is your PACING SCALE.

It follows, to use this scale if you were on a patrol and had to go a distance of 300m, you would have to count out 360 paces.

Under some conditions you can use a specific length of string, tying knots at every 120 paces. Having used the length of string, un-tie the knots and repeat the process on the next 'leg' of your route.

It is always advisable to have a CHECK PACER, remembering to check that your PACING SCALE is the same by day and night.

NAVIGATION

This is the art of moving from one place to another and consists of three important stages that MUST be carried out if you are to be successful, they are as follows:-
1. **PLANNING.**
2. **KEEPING DIRECTION.**
3. **GOOD PACING.**

PLANNING -You must plan your route in advance, using maps, air photos, sketches and information from previous patrols or recces.

KEEPING DIRECTION - Always take several compasses and as many 'pacers'. Always get someone else to check your navigation, at both the planning stage and while you are executing the movement.

It is often hard to keep direction, especially at night, in fog or in close country.

When it is necessary to make a detour to avoid an obstacle or seek cover, it is easy for leaders to miss the correct lines of advance.

AIDS TO KEEPING DIRECTION.

Some of the aids to keeping direction are:-

a. The compass, map and air photographs.

b. A rough sketch copied from a map or air photograph.

 c. Keeping two prominent objects in view.

d. Using a series of easily recognisable landmarks, each visible from the previous one.

e. The stars and also the sun and moon if their natural movement in the sky is understood.

f. Memorizing the route from a map or air photograph. Helpful details are the direction of streams, distances between recognisable features coupled with pacing, and the course of contours.

g. Trees in exposed country tend to grow away from the direction of the prevailing wind. Moss may grow on the leeward side of tree trunks.

h. Remembering the back view, patrols and others who may have to find their way back should look behind them from time to time and pick up landmarks to remember for the return journey.

j. Leaving directions marks on the outward journey, these may be pegs, small heaps of stones.

k. If the route is being walked by day by those who are to guide along it by night, they must take note of skylines and objects or features which they will be able to recognize in the dark.

HAVE YOU CHECKED YOUR INDIVIDUAL COMPASS ERROR ?

FIELDCRAFT

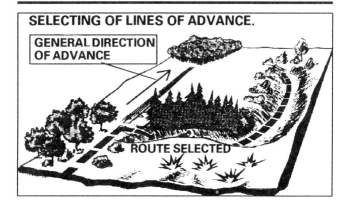

SELECTING OF LINES OF ADVANCE.

GENERAL DIRECTION OF ADVANCE

ROUTE SELECTED

Remember the keyword - **'G R O U N D'**

G Ground from the map. Open/close country, Rolling/flat.

R Ridges, water courses and watersheds (highest) mark on map or talc.

O Observation good view points.

U Undergrowth - study woods, scrub, trees, villages.

N Non Passable obstacles, such as rivers, ravines, marsh land.

D Defilade covered lines of advance and areas which offer cover can now be selected.

OBSERVATION — SEARCHING GROUND

The skill of searching ground is based upon learning to "scan" an area using an accepted system.

It will test your concentration and exercise your knowledge of "why things are seen" and the principles of Camouflage and Concealment.

In the diagram we have - for the purpose of illustrating to you — drawn lines across the landscape.

FIELDCRAFT

In practice you would choose prominent features, landmarks, roads etc., and draw your imaginary lines across the landscape through these reference points.

Scanning.

The landscape is divided into **FOREGROUND, MIDDLE DISTANCE** and **DISTANCE**. You can further divide this by indicating a centre line (again based on reference points), calling left of the line **"LEFT OF ARC"**, and right of the line **"RIGHT OF ARC"** as shown in the illustration.

Having divided the landscape, the correct method is to scan each area horizontally (left to right or right to left). View the area in short overlapping movements in a very precise manner, especially any features that are at an angle from your position.

Searching

While scanning you may see something move or that requires further investigation. There may be an area where you may come under observation from, it would be as well to check that out early.

Weather conditions can give you a clue when searching, frost on bushes, foot marks will show up clearly, if the weather is hot camouflaged positions can be given away when leaves or grass dry off changing colour.

Search across hedges and rows of trees , NOT along them. At all times consider WHY THINGS ARE SEEN.

PATROLS

There are three reasons for patrolling:

1. To obtain up-to-date and accurate information.
2. To dominate the ground between a commanders own unit and that of the enemy.
3. To destroy and disrupt enemy forces.

Successful patrolling calls for a high standard of individual training, good team work, initiative and determination on the part of the patrol leader. Patrolling enables the defence to be conducted in an aggressive manner.

The foundation of successful patrolling is through preparation.

TYPES OF PATROL.

Reconnaissance Patrols

Patrols of minimum strength for task, usually 1 NCO and 3 men, who gain information by observation and operate by stealth.

They avoid combat except for self-protection or to take advantage of unusual opportunities.

The roles in which a reconnaissance patrol may be employed include:-

1. Collecting topographical information on features, tracks and state of ground.
2. Obtaining details of minefields and the extent of enemy positions.
3. Locating enemy machine gun and defensive fire (DF) areas, where fire is immediately directed on call in case of emergency.
4. Investigating noises made by the enemy, enemy habits and patrol routes.
5. Checking our wire and/or minefields at first or last light.
6. Acting as listening posts, to give early warning of enemy approach and with the ability to call down fire.

FIELDCRAFT

Standing Patrols

Minimum strength 1 NCO and 3 men, to gain information of enemy movement, to prevent or disrupt enemy infiltration.

They move into position quietly - try to remain hidden - gain information until required to withdraw or if discovered fight their way out.

Their main tasks are to:-

1. Watch and listen on likely enemy approaches.
2. Watch over dead ground in front of and between friendly areas.
3. Watch over mine fields and obstacles, for which they should have good communications, so that they can inform the main body.

Fighting Patrols

These are patrols organised for a particular task with sufficient strength and back-up to achieve the mission. The strength can vary according to the task to be performed and the expected combat level:

1. Denying enemy patrols freedom of action in No Man's Land.
2. Driving in enemy protective patrols.
3. Interfering with enemy working parties.
4. Distracting enemy attention from other activities.
5. Carrying out raids.
6. Capturing prisoners for identification purposes.
7. Tank hunting.
8. Laying ambushes.
9. Protecting reconnaissance and working parties of other arms.
10. Escorting stretcher parties.

SEQUENCE OF ACTION TO MOUNT CARRY OUT AND DEBRIEF A PATROL.

The success of a patrol depends on good planning beforehand as well as good action during the actual patrol. Compliance with the following by the Patrol Commander ensures that nothing is forgotten.

PATROL COMMANDER

Issues a warning order to include brief outline of patrol task, members of patrol including second-in-command, time and place for briefing and any special administrative arrangements including weapons and equipment. Normally dress and equipment should be as light as possible but must include water and emergency rations in case the patrol is cut off and has to lie up for a period before returning to base. Studies Air Photos, Maps, previous Patrol Reports and sketches. Selects observation posts for his recce.

RECCE

Carries out recce from OP's during which they look for:

a. Routes to and from objective (to be different).
b. Landmarks.
c. OP's.
d. Dead ground and covered approaches.
e. Obstacles.
f. Likely places for ambush - by us or by enemy.
g. Enemy positions, likely positions and DF areas.

CONSIDERS LIGHT and weather conditions, moon, etc.

Makes his Appreciation and Plan, keeping them as simple as possible.

DRAWS A FIELD SKETCH showing distances (in paces), bearings and timings of bounds.

PREPARES MODEL of the area for briefing the patrol.

PREPARES HIS ORDERS. MEETS PATROL AT RV.

BRIEFS THE PATROL

By showing members the ground from an OP (individually if necessary) and points out minefield lanes and gaps in wire etc.,

Gives out his orders:

With the aid of a cloth or sand model of ground, under the following headings:-

1. GROUND.

Describes, incl. landmarks, obstacles, and "going". Use OP's, maps, air photos, models, etc.

2. SITUATION

a. Enemy Forces. FEBA, ptl activity, routine, sentries, DF, FPF, minefields, wire, trip flares, fixed lines.

b. Friendly Forces. Own positions, other ptls, fire support available, minefields, wire, trip flares, fixed lines. DF, FPF, stand by ptl.

3. MISSION.

To Recce, Fighting - definite task.

4. EXECUTION Phase 1. General Outline.

a. Number of phases - route, action on objective, return.

b. Who taking part - appointments and position in the platoon.

c. Prep Moves - Drop Off Point. Time leaving rehearsal/base area. Method of move. Loading Plan. Route to and ref of DOP. Arcs of obsn/fire. Order of March (OOM).

d.Action if Ambushed. Action at DOP. Time out. Confirmation or orders/detail.

Phase 2. Route Out, to final RV (FRV).

Fmn. Obs drills/action on mines/trip wires/booby traps.

Actions on: PW. Cas. If separated from ptl. If lost.

Confirm FRV ref.

FROM/TO	Bearing	Distance	Fmn	Ground	RV
(1) Leg 1					
(2) Leg 2					
(3) Leg 3					

Phase 3. Action in final RV.

On arrival:

(1) Occupation. Move in. Secure. Fmns, position of grps, sig for FRV.

(2) Recce Group - Composition, Tasks. Route. OOM, fmns, arcs. Action on ambush, sig to open fire. Action if FRV gp loc by en.

(3) Remainder - Composition, Tasks, Arcs, Actions - on en pre-seen or ambush, sig to open fire, if recce gp loc by en, on return of recce gp or if fails to return. Confirmation or orders/info.

Phase 4. Action on Objective

(1) Cover/Fire Gp. Composition, Fmn, posn, routes, tasks, arcs, action if en act first, duration on SP's, Sigs for opening fire. Action if separated from group.

(2) Recce/Assist/Snatch. Composition, fmn, task, posn, routes, action on recce/asslt/snatch, sigs for sp fire. Action if surprised, sig net, wire, illumination.

Phase 5. Withdrawal and action in final RV.

Sig to wdr. OOM sequence of gp wdr, arcs, fmns. Action and posns in FRV -pack kit etc. Head check and sig to move out. Actions: if in contact, PW's, if gp fails to return, if FRV gp has moved, if surprised in FRV. Pass on info sketches etc. Confirmation of orders/info.

Phase 6. Route Back

Route. Fmns. RV's. Obs. Actions; en pre-seen, ambush, sig to open fire, cas, if lost, if separated. Action on arr at pick up point (PUP). Time in. Confirm orders/info.

Co-ordinating Instructions

Timings. Meals, rest, rehearsals (day/ni), weapons test, inspections, time in/out constraints. Debrief. Action on halts, lights. Fireplan. Rehearsals loc and details. Deception and security.

Summary of execution.

1) Summary of Timings - Rehearsals, prep of eqpt, inspection, rest, meals test wpns, night rehearsals, final check time out, time in. RV's and refs.
(2) Action on white Lts
(3) Action on Halts - for obsn/protection.
(4) Action to take on Meeting En if:-
   Pre-seen or Ambushed
   On the Route Out .... On the Route In ....
(5) Action on Cas
   On Route Out........ On obj......... On the Route In........
(6) Action on crossing Obs
(7) Action with PW
(8) Rehearsals
(9) Lost procedure
(10) Action on Mines
(11) Distr on Ni Vis Aids

5. SERVICE SUPPORT

Ammo. Feeding. Dress and Eqpt. Special Eqpt - Toggle ropes, wire cutters, IWS/Suit, radio spares, etc. Wpns type and distribution. Rats, meals before during and after, water. Med, Fd dressings, stretcher, med pack, morphine, casevac method. PW handing on/after capture. Tpt to DOP/from PUP. Confirm orders/info.

6. COMMAND AND SIGNAL

Chain of command 1i/c, 2i/c and 3i/c and conditions for taking over cmd. Location of ptl comd. Sigs, radio, radio checks, other sigs. Password. Use of Radio and restrictions. De-briefing location, who doing. Patrol report. Special instrs on reporting Info.

**TIME SPENT IN RECONNAISSANCE
IS SELDOM WASTED**

FIELDCRAFT

Rehearsals

Carries out daylight or night rehearsals which must include:

a. **Moving out** and returning through own FEBAS. Patrol Commander goes forward to contact the sentry. Normal challenging procedure follows.

b. **Formations** and drill for changing formations. One or more of the three formations = single file, file or diamond - is adopted during a patrol depending on ground and visibility.

c. **Use of Scouts.** Move by bounds ahead and are followed by the Command Group (Patrol Commander, Radio Operator and his protector).

d. **Movement.** Every member is allotted his specific task, movement must be silent, frequent halts to observe and listen, when approaching the enemy position and also at night. When halted sink down to the ground level, avoiding a jerky movement, and make use of the skyline. Make use of the previously prepared signal to move - a silent "touch" signal - to ensure that no-one is left behind.

e. **Action on objective.** Nearby RV. This is an RV to which the patrol goes after completing the task, it must be easy to find and indicated to all members of the patrol during the approach to the objective.

f. **Firm Base.** If a patrol has to move a long way it may leave a party between its own and the enemy position, this forms a "firm base" from which remainder of patrol carries out main task and to return afterwards. On arriving near the objective, the Patrol Commander will:-

(1) Search the area, especially the RV or Firm Base for unexpected enemy.

(2) Make a brief Recce, Appreciation and Plan, brief the patrol members concerned

g. **Action on Lights.** If time allows get away - otherwise, freeze, close one eye to preserve night vision. If a trip flare move from area quickly as possible, get down and observe.

h. Encounter drill.

Action will depend on the task and circumstances. It may be desirable to avoid action and move away as quickly as possible. If this is impossible an immediate assault is the alternative.

If ambushed, scatter and move individually to previously arranged RV.

j. Crossing Obstacles

(1) On encountering an obstacle, Commander goes forward to recce it, decides whether to cross or go round.

(2) Requirements of obstacle crossing drill are:-

(a) Silent movement.

(b) Posting a man to guide others over.

(c) At all times at least one man ready to fire his weapon or throw a grenade if the patrol is surprised.

k. Casualty Evacuation

(1) All casualties must be brought back.

(2) Improvise a stretcher.

(3) If on the way out, the patrol may have to pick up the casualty on its return or summon help.

Prisoners

(1) If a fighting patrol takes a prisoner they must be brought back alive whether or not this was the task of the patrol. - prisoners are valuable sources of information.

(2) If a prisoner cannot be taken with the patrol, they may be put under guard and collected later either by the sane patrol or by another one detailed or summoned by radio for this purpose.

Carries out Final Inspection

a. Dress and equipment light as possible, but include emergency rations and water.

b. Dress and equipment to be properly fitted and silent. Jumping up and down will show whether it is satisfactory.

c. No documents will be taken which can afford useful information to the enemy if captured.

LEADS PATROL OUT THROUGH FEBA.

a. **Navigation**. Previous study of air photos and maps etc. use of landmarks. By compass bearing and counting paces -especially at night. "Legs" to be measured to the nearest 50 paces from map. If the patrol becomes dispersed, RV at the end of the previous leg. Avoid prominent cover, e.g. edges of woods, tracks, hedges, defiles - likely places for enemy ambushes or standing patrols.

b. **Fire Support**. Pre arranged or called for by radio -

(1) To distract enemy.

(2) For support on objective.

(3) To help the patrol extricate itself in emergency.

DE-BRIEFED ON RETURN.

Verbal report followed by a written report.

On the next page is shown the layout of a Patrol Report. This is produced as guidelines for you to use when preparing a report, and includes many of the factors that should be taken into consideration.

This serves as a reminder of the vast amount of valuable information and activities that a Patrol Commander is expected to deal with.

This is a standard format use as a Patrol Report and you would be well advised to study it in readiness for when you have to do a report.

FIELDCRAFT

PATROL REPORT

Date _____ **Destination of Patrol**_____

Aim _____

Maps_____

Size and composition of Patrol_____

Task _____

Time of Departure _____**Time of Return** _____

Routes Out and Back _____

Terrain - (Description of the terrain - dry, swampy, jungle, thickly wooded, high brush, rocky, deepness of ravines, rivers/streams/canals, width/ depth, condition of bridges as to type, size and strength, effect on armour and wheeled vehicles.)

Enemy - (Strength, disposition, condition of defences, equipment, weapons, attitude, morale, exact location, movements and any shift in dispositions. Time activity was observed, co-ordinates where activity occurred.

Conditions of Patrol -including disposition of any casualties)

Conclusions and Recommendations - (including to what extent the mission was accomplished and recommendations as to patrol equipment and tactics)

Date _____ **Time** _____hrs

Signature _____of Patrol Commander

ADDITIONAL REMARKS BY INTERROGATOR

Date_____ **Time** _____hrs _____**Signature.**

FIELDCRAFT

AMBUSHES

INTRODUCTION
Ambushes are usually carried out as a part of patrolling activity. It requires close team work, skill, intelligence, fitness, cunning and discipline.

An ambush is a surprise attack, by a force lying in wait, upon a moving or temporarily halted enemy. It is usually a brief encounter, conducted at comparatively close quarters. When well prepared and executed it can cause heavy causalities and serious loss of morale amongst the enemy; however poor planning, preparation and execution may result in failure, and serious losses to the ambush party.

TYPES OF AMBUSH
a. **DELIBERATE** - with time to plan in advance.
b. **IMMEDIATE** - In response to 'hot' information, to 'contact' the enemy, with no time for recce.

AMBUSH SITES
The best places for an ambush site include:-
a. Known enemy routes.
b. Known admin/supply/water points, food or ammo dumps, approaches to villages.
c. Where the terrain changes - edge of woods or forest, where a valley has steep sides. Where a river crossing is shallow etc.
d. Approaches to own bases or positions, also on route out of your own positions - if enemy follows you back.

PRINCIPLES OF AMBUSH
a. Good intelligence to ensure contact and success.
b. Thorough planning and preparation, planned Recce, ambush well rehearsed.

106

c. Security - careful Recce - not to betray ambush site. Be prepared for an attack on yourselves.

d. Concealment - good track discipline, no signs of your whereabouts, good camouflage and concealment.

e. Good control and communications - all know the plan in detail, signals, plan for springing ambush. Must be kept simple, and thoroughly rehearsed.

f. Discipline -ambush only successful if everyone alert, no noise, restricted movement, fast re-action to signals, weapons always ready to fire.

g. Safety - all weapons in "made safe" state while on the move. No firing at individuals - even when minimum distance of 50 metres between muzzle and the enemy.

THE DELIBERATE AMBUSH

The ambush parties are sub-divided into smaller groups, each with their own leaders. Normally the groups are as follows:-

a. **THE AMBUSH GROUP** - covers the chosen place for the ambush and springs the ambush. Group contains Ambush Commander and the GUN Group(s)). Four men to ambush a section. A Section and Platoon HQ to ambush a Platoon.

b. **CUT-OFF/STOP GROUPS** - serve to give warning of enemy approach, cut off their lines of retreat or help to take care of a counter attack from a flank. For a section ambush the group would consist of two men. A platoon ambush would be a section strength.

PLANNING - prior to occupying an ambush position the following sequence of planning events must be carried out:-

Recce. Issue preliminary orders in the base camp.

Preparation and rehearsals in the base camp.

Move to the ambush area.

Final Recce by Amb Cmdr and Cut Off Grp Cmdr's.
Amb Cmdr issues final orders if required.
Occupy ambush position.

RECCE - Amb Cmdr should - if possible - carry out recce of amb site before giving orders. He may be limited to air photographs, maps, patrol reports or sketches made. Must try to put himself in enemy position/point of view, he must select/confirm:-

a. Ambush area, positions of the Ambush Group and cut off Groups, detailed siting of GUN GROUP(s), booby traps, trip flares etc.

b. Check positions for each group for: concealment, approach routes, good fields of view and fire and of the enemy approach route.

c. The withdrawal routes for all groups.

d. The final RV, and routes to and from it.

ORDERS, PREPARATION, REHEARSALS and MOVE OUT.

ORDERS - Like all Patrols the information given and the quality of the orders must be very thorough and detailed, using a model of the area and leaving sufficient time for preparation and rehearsals.

The orders for an ambush follow the same sequence and detail as Patrol Orders, but need to have extra details under the 'EXECUTION' phase, as follow:-

ACTION ON ARRIVAL AT FINAL RV/FIRM BASE

Entry order of march. Positions and arcs of fire - describe these, also cover in rehearsals. Sentries if necessary. Action if surprised. Action if recce party does not return within.... minutes. Confirmation of orders, timing, refs, RV's etc.

ACTION IN AMBUSH AREA

Order of march. Method of entry. Positions. Laying of communication cord. Arcs to be covered.
Sig for 'Ambush Set'. Time ambush to be set by ..... hrs.

FIELDCRAFT

ACTION ON APPROACH OF ENEMY -
Warning signal from Cut Off Groups. Signal to stop.
Search party if required.
WITHDRAWL TO RV/FIRM BASE - Signal for withdrawl.
Order of march. Action at final RV/Firm Base - reorg,
check numbers, weapons, re-distribute ammo, prepare to
move out.
Thorough preparation is essential for success and
should include the following:-
Cleaning and testing of all weapons. Testing and
checking special equipment, ropes, night viewing aids,
boats or rafts, safety and medics. Radios and spare
batteries. Camouflage of clothing and equipment.
REHEARSAL - If for a night ambush, then rehearsals
should be held in the daytime and also at night.
They must:—
Show where each group and those who are within them
are in relation to each other.
Test signals/communications.
Cover alerting, and springing of the ambush.
Practice withdrawal to Firm Base/Final RV.
MOVE TO AMBUSH AREA - Ambush party move to the
Final RV/Firm Base and take up defensive position and
wait for the Amb Cmdr and the Cut Off Grp Cmdrs to do
their final recce.
FINAL ORDERS Only need for confirmation or last minute
changes that need to be made as a result of the final
recce. This could be more likely and important by night
than day and could include:-
a. Description of the ambush area, enemy approaches
   and counter attack routes.
b. Individual tasks if they vary from rehearsals.
OCCUPATION SEQUENCE
Having completed his recce and returned from any Final
Orders briefing, Ambush Cmdr will remain on the

position, sending Cut Off Group Cmdrs back for remainder of party. If a platoon operation, sentries would be taken forward, posted and remain in position throughout the move to the ambush area.

Cut Off Group followed by Killing Group move into position, Ambush Cmdr places himself in central position for control and near to GUN GROUP.

SETTING UP AMBUSH - Once all groups in position, Cut Off Group start laying communications cord/cable to Ambush Cmdr. Set up trip flares, booby traps etc are set.

AMBUSH SET - When Ambush Cmdr receives signal from all groups that everyone in position, gives the 'Ambush Set' signal. After this signal no one leaves their position, Care to make no movement or noise. Get into a comfortable position for the time you are waiting for the ambush to be sprung.

SPRINGING THE AMBUSH - On sighting the enemy, Cut Off Group alerts Ambush Cmdr of their approach and direction using communication cord, alerts remainder of the force. All prepare for ambush, carefully moving into aim . Ambush Cmdr waits until as many of enemy are in ambush area. Gives signal for springing ambush. This signal usually a burst of fire from the GUN GROUP, a shot from commanders weapon or setting off a trip flare. **It is NEVER the commander shouting 'FIRE'.**

AFTER SPRINGING AMBUSH THE FIRE FIGHT - short and sharp. Cmdr gives 'STOP' or 'CEASE FIRE'. pause while all check for: movement of enemy survivors. Enemy counter attack. Enemy moving back to collect casualties, thinking ambush has withdrawn.

WITHDRAWAL - On receiving withdrawal signal, all groups withdraw to Final RV, in order as rehearsed. Minimum time spent there, check all present, check no enemy follow up, re-call sentries and move off by return route.

WARNING
SAFETY - FIRING BLANK AMMUNITION
With all field training when blank
ammunition is in use, *NEVER* aim directly
at any of your "buddies",
DO NOT AIM AT ALL IF THEY ARE LESS
THAN 50 METRES AWAY FROM YOU.
DO NOT FIRE BLINDLY IN THE DARK
-YOU HAVE BEEN WARNED -
THINK BEFORE YOU SHOOT.

QUESTIONS

1. To be good at Fieldcraft you need to have what.
2. For what reason do you use: Unit of Measure. Key Ranges. Bracketing.
3. Who makes out a RANGE Card, what for and when.
4. When carrying out Personal Cam what do you have to remember.
5. What is "Isolated cover", would you use it.
6. Why are things seen, what must you remember about "smell".
7. What is important about Shape, Shadow, Silhouette.
8. How do you indicate a DIFFICULT target.
9. What is the "Key Word" for fire control orders and what does it mean, and how do you give an order.
10. How many types of Fire Control Orders are there and what are they.
11. Give a method of moving at night.
12. How long does it take for your eyes to get used to the dark.

13. When a FLARE 'goes up', what do you do.
14. When do sentries work in pairs.
15. Name the Duties of a Sentry.
16. What is the correct CHALLENGE a sentry should give, when and how should it be given.
17. A Section has 8 members, how few members can it operate with.
18. What is the main role of the Gun Group within the Section.
19. How many Sections are there in a Platoon.
20. What helps you to listen at night.
21. What is the "drill" if you come under effective fire.
22. A Sentry close to the enemy must know — What.
23. Wat is the sequence and headings used by a Section Commander giving his orders
24. Give the three important points to consider when "choosing a route".
25. How do you work out your own PACING SCALE.
26. Give six methods used to help you Keep your Direction when on a Patrol.
27. Give the meaning of the Key Word : G R O U N D and explain its use.
28. How do you split up an area you are going to SCAN and SEARCH.
29. Name two types of Patrols and the role that they play.
30. In daylight, you must not fire a blank at anyone less than, how many yards away, and at night what is the rule.

FIELDCRAFT IS GREAT, YOU USE THE COMBINED SKILLS OF MAP READING, WEAPON TRAINING AND, FIELDCRAFT, PLUS, YOU HAVE TO BE FIT.
OBSERVE THE SAFETY RULES —
THEN *YOU* WON'T HAVE TO USE *YOUR*
FIRST AID SKILLS.

SKILL AT ARMS

SAFETY RULES FOR HANDLING WEAPONS OF ANY TYPE AT ALL TIMES

1. Whenever you pick up a weapon or have a weapon handed to you ALWAYS carry out the SAFETY PRECAUTIONS, whether it is your own or someone elses, ALWAYS examine it to ensure that it is NOT loaded.

2. NEVER point a weapon at anyone - even in fun.

3. ALWAYS handle a weapon so that it points in a SAFE direction, so that there is no danger if a round is accidentally fired.

4. NEVER rest the muzzel of a loaded weapon, or a weapon 'made safe' against your body. Similarily, do not hold a weapon with your hand or hands placed over the muzzle.

5. Weapons will NEVER be carried in VEHICLES either loaded or in a "made safe" state.

6. YOU will NOT fire any weapon until such time as you have been fully trained, exercised and tested to be capable of safely handling the weapon.

7. When handing over a weapon to someone else, SHOW/PROVE to them first that it is in a SAFE and in an UNLOADED STATE.

8. When anyone hands a weapon to you - NO MATTER WHO THEY ARE - INSIST THAT THEY SHOW/PROVE IT TO YOU.

"IT IS BETTER TO BE SAFE, THAN SORRY"

INTRODUCTION

The L98. A1 CADET GP RIFLE - to give its full name - is the first rifle ever to be designed specifically for the Cadet Forces in the UK. It's appearance is almost identical with the Regular Army's SA80 Rifle.

The SA80 is has a flash eliminator, which the Cadet Rifle does not have, and of course when the SA80 is fitted with the SUSAT SIGHT, it looks very different from the CADET GP RIFLE

GENERAL DESCRIPTION OF THE 5.56mm CADET GENERAL PURPOSE RIFLE.

The GP Rifle is a magazine fed, bolt operated, single shot weapon, which has been modelled on the British Army SA80 Rifle.

It **MUST** be fired from the RIGHT shoulder.

The magazine holds 30 rounds. The rifle is easy to learn and use, good to handle and fire, and is very accurate. The "kick" or recoil is light, making it ideal for all trained cadets to handle and shoot with.

THE COMPONENT PARTS OF THE WEAPON

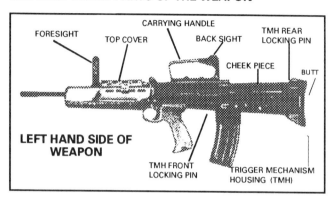

FORESIGHT · TOP COVER · CARRYING HANDLE · BACK SIGHT · TMH REAR LOCKING PIN · CHEEK PIECE · BUTT

LEFT HAND SIDE OF WEAPON

TMH FRONT LOCKING PIN · TRIGGER MECHANISM HOUSING (TMH)

SAFETY PRECAUTIONS.

As with all SKILL at ARMS training the first thing you must learn are the -

NORMAL SAFETY PRECAUTIONS. (NSP)

They will always be carried out at the beginning and end of every lesson, practice or range period, and immediately on returning from a patrol or exercise or duty, and when handing the weapon over to anyone.

To carry out the **SAFETY PRECAUTIONS** with the L98. A1 CADET GP RIFLE the **LOW PORT POSITION** is adopted as shown in the illustration over page.

**NO MATTER HOW WELL YOU HAVE DONE
YOU WILL FAIL ANY WEAPON TRAINING
TEST IF YOU MAKE A MISTAKE ON SAFETY.
MAKE SAFETY — YOUR GOOD HABIT**

THE LOW PORT POSITION

1.Hold by PISTOL GRIP, forefinger outside the TRIGGER GUARD. Point MUZZLE upwards and rest the butt on waist belt or right pouch.Tilt weapon to the right

THIS IS THE POSITION ADOPTED TO CARRY OUT THE FULL ROUTINE OF SAFETY PRECAUTIONS

2. Make sure that theSAFETY CATCH is at SAFE. (S).

3. Cock the RIFLE by gripping the COCKING HANDLE with thumb and forefinger of right hand, now pull AND HOLD IT FULLY TO THE REAR.

4. Pass your LEFT hand under the BUTT, depress HOLDING OPEN CATCH with fingers of LEFT hand, easing COCKING HANDLE forward until catch stops its forward movement.

When done place LEFT hand underneath HAND GUARD, and return RIGHT hand to hold RIFLE by PISTOL GRIP.

NOTE: When LEFT hand is applying HOLDING OPEN CATCH the RIFLE is being held with BUTT against your Waist Belt by pulling back on COCKING HANDLE with the fingers of RIGHT hand, with thumb of RIGHT hand hooked round rear of CARRYING HANDLE.

5. For the rifle to be inspected, push it away from your body, horizontal to the ground and tilting to the left, so as the breech can be inspected.

After it has been inspected adopt the LOW PORT POSITION.

6. On the command "EASE SPRINGS":-

SKILL AT ARMS

(a) Operate the BOLT RELEASE CATCH with your left hand, letting the working part go forward.
(b) Put SAFETY CATCH to FIRE (F) with RIGHT forefinger
(c) Operate the TRIGGER.
(d) Put the SAFETY CATCH to (S) using left thumb.
(e) Close the DUST COVER with RIGHT hand, folding up and back in its slot.
(f) Put RIRLE in FRONT SLUNG position or if SLING not fitted, Ground arms, rifle laid on its left side - COCKING HANDLE uppermost.
(g) Unfasten pouches and remove MAGAZINES and contents for inspection.
When the inspection has been completed, you put the magazines back in your pouches, FASTEN YOUR POUCHES, pick up your rifle and adopt LOW PORT position.

> **THESE SAFETY PRECAUTIONS MUST BE CARRIED OUT BY EVERYONE IN THE SQUAD TAKING PART IN THE TRAINING OR WHEN WEAPONS ARE BEING HANDLED — THIS INCLUDES *ALL* INSTRUCTORS.**

COMPONENT PARTS OF THE WEAPON

RIGHT HAND SIDE OF WEAPON
BACKSIGHT
COCKING HANDLE
EJECTION OPENING
DUST COVER
SAFETY CATCH
HAND GUARD
HOLDING OPEN CATCH
TRIGGER GUARD
PISTOL GRIP

FITTING THE SLING

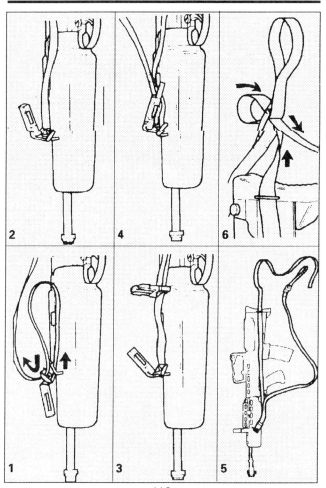

THE RIFLE SLING - see diagrams on previous page.

The SLING is made of two lengths of webbing type material, which link together with a special quick release BUCKLE CLIP.

The first longer piece has, at one end, a female part of the clip and a flat plastic loop attached, the other end of the strap is clear.

The second shorter piece has the male part of the clip at one end, and the quick release buckle and loop at the other.

Fitting the Sling - see illustrations

1. Take the longer strap and lay it flat along the weapon, with the FEMALE CLIP end towards the MUZZLE and the flat plastic loop pointing outwards. Feed the clear end through the FRONT SLING LOOP and then through the FLAT PLASTIC LOOP on th e strap. Pull tight.

2. Take the SHORTER strap and, holding it parallel with the first strap and with the MALE clip end pointing outwards, feed the clear end of the LONGER strap through and over the RIDGED EDGE of the gate in the base of the male clip on the SHORT strap, connect the male and female parts of the clip together.

3. Ensure that the LONGER strap remains untwisted, then feed the CLEAR end through the REAR SLING LOOP on the weapon.

4. Check that the SHORTER strap is not twisted, then feed the clear end of the LONGER strap outwards through the main gate of the BUCKLE BAR.

5 & 6. Finally, thread the CLEAR END of the LONGER strap through the gate in the BUCKLE. TO REMOVE the SLING, reverse the fitting procedure as above.

USES OF THE SLING - see illustration - next page.

Essentially the SLING can be used in two ways, although other variations may be possible.

SKILL AT ARMS

CARRIAGE OF THE RIFLE — using the Sling.

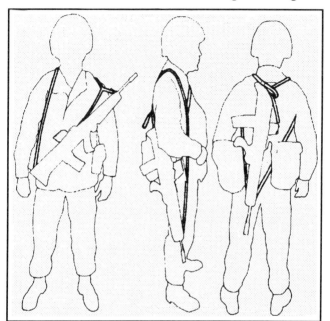

FRONT SLUNG POSITION.

Separate the two straps and insert your head, right arm and shoulder through the loop so formed.

The weapon will now be suspended from your left shoulder across your chest.

Adjust the position of the weapon by pulling down on the CLEAR end of the LONGER strap.

Pulling the QUICK RELEASE loop or releasing the CLIP will allow the weapon to be brought into the aim.

BACK SLUNG POSITION.

Separate the SLING to form TWO loops.
Put an arm through each loop to position the weapon, MUZZLE down, in the centre of your back, COCKING HANDLE uppermost.

THE RIFLE SIGHTS

The weapon has two sets of sights:-

1. **The IRON SIGHT which is mounted on a FORESIGHT BLOCK.**
2. **The CARRYING HANDLE, into which the APERTURE BACKSIGHT is built.**

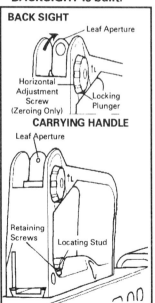

BACK SIGHT
Leaf Aperture
Horizontal
Adjustment
Screw
(Zeroing Only)
Locking
Plunger
CARRYING HANDLE
Leaf Aperture
Retaining
Screws
Locating Stud

THE FORESIGHT blade is protected on both sides by an extension of the block, it can be vertically adjusted for zeroing by a small screw.

The whole FORESIGHT BLOCK is secured by a small RETAINING SCREW, this must **not** be removed **or tampered with,** (see diagram over page).

THE BACKSIGHT & CARRYING HANDLE

The BACKSIGHT which is housed within the CARRYING HANDLE has adjustable range apertures from 100 to 500 m.
There is provision to adjust this sight for zeroing, but it must not be tampered with.

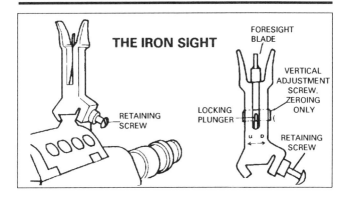

STRIPPING & ASSEMBLING

The sequence of stripping the rifle is important to prevent damage to the working parts.
The weapon will NOT be stripped further than taught.
The weapon is stripped into the following parts:-
The TRIGGER MECHANISM HOUSING (TMH)
The RECOIL ROD & COCKING HANDLE ASSEMBLIES.

CARE & CLEANING OF THE RIFLE

The regular care and cleaning of your rifle will ensure that it is in a serviceable condition at all times.
Your ability to look after a rifle will be reflected in the high standard of Weapon Training required to pass your APC Training Tests and also to use the rifle to achieve your marksmans shooting qualification.
A CLEANING TOOL KIT with a COMBINATION TOOL is provided to carry out all the cleaning that is required.
The THREE PIECE CLEANING ROD is issued one per five rifles.

THE RIFLE STRIPPED

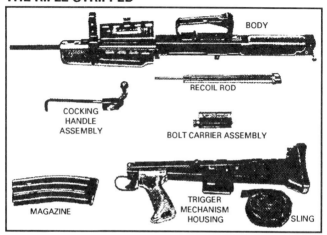

BODY

RECOIL ROD

COCKING HANDLE ASSEMBLY

BOLT CARRIER ASSEMBLY

MAGAZINE

TRIGGER MECHANISM HOUSING

SLING

THE CLEANING TOOL KIT

The CLEANING ROD is used with either the BORE or CHAMBER BRUSHES.

The ROD sections screw together. It is important that the screwed joints form a close, smooth surface that will not score the barrel, should there be any rough surface to the ROD it must not be used.

The ROD must be inserted through the MUZZLE, taking care not to rub it against the side of the bore at the MUZZLE.

If you have to twist the ROD, only twist it clockwise, or the ROD will un-screw inside the barrel.

The BORE BRUSH is only to be used to clean the BORE of the rifle.

Oil can be used with it to remove fouling and stains. It can be used with the PULLTHROUGH, but only drawn from the CHAMBER end of the BARREL.

The CHAMBER/BARREL EXTENSION BRUSH is to be used with the CLEANING ROD and only for cleaning the CHAMBER and the BARREL EXTENSION.

The PULLTHROUGH can be used instead of the ROD to draw a FLANNELETTE PATCH or the BORE BRUSH through the BARREL, it must first be stretched to remove any knots or kinks.

A FLANNELETTE PATCH can be fitted by folding it in half lengthways and putting it into the eyelet with equal parts of the flannelette protruding either side.

FLANNELETTE PATCHES are mainly used to dry clean or oil the barrel. They must not be used in a size larger than 50mm x 50mm or they will jam in the barrel.

The NYLON BRUSH is used with FLANNELETTE to clean the inside of the BODY.

A piece of lightly oiled FLANNELETTE is used to clean the outside of the weapon. CLEANING THE RIFLE

CLEANING THE RIFLE

a. FIRSTLY - CARRY OUT THE NSP's (Normal Safety Precautions)

b. Using the NYLON BRUSH remove any loose fouling or dirt from the BODY of the weapon and its component parts.

c. Lightly oil a piece of FLANNELETTE and clean the outside of the weapon

d. Fit the CHAMBER/BARREL EXTENSION BRUSH to the CLEANING ROD and insert it into the CHAMBER. Using a clockwise rotating action dislodge any fouling and debris. By holding the rifle with the MUZZLE pointing up, the fouling will fall out when the brush is removed.

e. Using the NYLON BRUSH and FLANNELETTE, clean the inside of the body.

f. Clean the barrel first with the BORE BRUSH, then pull it through with a dry clean FLANNELETTE.

g. Examine the barrel for cleanliness. Look through the MUZZLE end by holding it up to the light about 150mm away from your head, keep both eyes open and follow the lands and grooves in the rifle barrel throughout their length.

h. If required, clean the barrel again. If you find that you are unable to get it clean, show it to one of your instructors. Dry clean the whole weapon with FLANNELETTE, examine it for damage, stains or wear.

i. Lightly oil the RIFLE and MAGAZINE.
   NOTE. Do not oil the IRON SIGHT APERTURES and POST.

j. Assemble the weapon and test that it functions correctly.

Put the SAFETY CATCH to FIRE (F), operate the trigger, put the SAFETY CATCH to SAFE (S).

CLEANING IN ADVERSE CONDITIONS

Heavy Rain and Damp Conditions
Inspect frequently for rust and remove it.

Dry, Sandy or Dusty Conditions
Keep your rifle dry, this can be done by sweating it in the heat of the sun and wiping off any oil. If rust appears remove it as normal, but remember to remove any oil that you may have used.

MAGAZINES
The MAGAZINE can be stripped, but this should only be carried out if it has been exposed to conditions that will have allowed grit and mud to get into it. Rough handling or too much force to remove the BOTTOM PLATE of the MAGAZINE will soon make it unserviceable. Until you are fully trained, you would be well advised to do this with the help and supervision of your instructor.

DESCRIPTION OF AMMUNITION

It is very important that you are able to quickly recognise the different types of ammunition available for use with your rifle

The ammunition for the GP rifle is rimless; its calibre is 5.56mm. It is issued in cardboard boxes of 20 rounds. The types of ammunition are as follows:-

BALL - This has a smooth brass cartridge case, a jacketed bullet with a percussion cap in the base.

TRACER - Similar to BALL rounds with a Red painted tip.

BLANK - A black plastic cartridge case, with a brass base, or a brass case, both incorporating a percussion cap in the base, there is no bullet.

DRILL - A silver coloured grooved case, a copper jacketed bullet and no percussion cap.

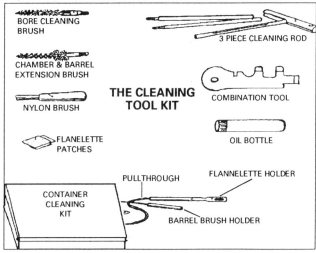

BORE CLEANING BRUSH

3 PIECE CLEANING ROD

CHAMBER & BARREL EXTENSION BRUSH

NYLON BRUSH

THE CLEANING TOOL KIT

COMBINATION TOOL

FLANELETTE PATCHES

OIL BOTTLE

PULLTHROUGH

FLANNELETTE HOLDER

CONTAINER CLEANING KIT

BARREL BRUSH HOLDER

CARE OF AMMUNITION

Always look after ammunition; keep it clean, dry and free from oil.

Never let it lie in the direct rays of the sun as this can cause inaccuracies when firing.

Do NOT use a round as a tool.

Do NOT apply pressure to the base of a round, either with a clip or another round. There is a possibility of detonating the percussion cap and thereby firing the round.

Tampering with ammunition is dangerous and strictly forbidden.

BASIC MECHANISM - HOW THE RIFLE WORKS

1. When the safety catch is at "S" the TRIGGER cannot be fully operated.
    2. Looking through the DUST COVER RECESS you will see that when the safety catch is at 'F' and the TRIGGER is pressed, the HAMMER is released and hits the rear of the FIRING PIN, driving it forward on to the CAP in the BASE of the ROUND. The ROUND is fired.
3. When the weapon is cocked the BOLT is unlocked by the rearward movement of the CARRIER forcing the CAM STUD down the CAM STUD SLOT.
4. Look through the EJECTION OPENING while cocking the rifle and hold back the COCKING HANDLE, you will see the CARRIER and BOLT go back together, cocking the HAMMER as they go.
    The DRILL ROUND is withdrawn from the CHAMBER by the EXTRACTOR and ejected out of the weapon to the right, through the EJECTION OPENING.
    The RETURN SPRING on the GUIDE ROD is also compressed at this stage.Rearward movement of the CARRIER and BOLT ceases when the rear of the CARRIER strikes the BUFFER.

5. When the COCKING HANDLE is released the RETURN SPRING re-asserts itself and drives the CARRIER and BOLT forward. As it does so the BOLT feeds the next DRILL ROUND out of the MAGAZINE and into the CHAMBER. The EXTRACTOR grips the DRILL ROUND and the EJECTOR is compressed.
6. The BOLT is rotated to lock into the BARREL EXTENSION by the continuing forward movement of the carrier, forcing the CAM STUD to slide up the CAM STUD SLOT.
7. It is only when the parts are fully forward and locked that the SAFETY SEAR can operate allowing the HAMMER into its ready position. This in turn can only happen on the TRIGGER being released. A distinct CLICK will be heard.
8. The action described above will be repeated each time the TRIGGER is operated and the weapon re-cocked, until the last round in the MAGAZINE has been fired and the weapon re-cocked. The working parts will then be held to the rear by the HOLDING OPEN CATCH being lifted up by the MAGAZINE PLATFORM. Operation of the BOLT RELEASE CATCH will depress the MAGAZINE PLATFORM allowing the working parts to travel forward.

USE OF COVER - MUZZLE CLEARANCE

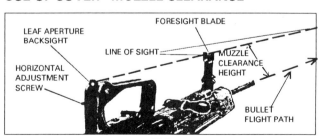

SKILL AT ARMS

The diagram - on the previous page - is produced to make you aware of the fact that the LINE of SIGHT on the rifle is high in relation to the axis of the bore of the rifle or flight path of the bullet when fired.

Firing from behind cover it may well be possible/ essential to have a clear line of sight to the target and at the same time have the path of the shot obstructed by cover. Obstruction may be less noticeable a few meters in front of the position than directly in front of the MUZZLE.

It is therefore important to always be mindful of the MUZZLE CLEARANCE and make allowance for it when selecting a FIRE POSITION, at the same time to consider the possible exposure to the view of the enemy.

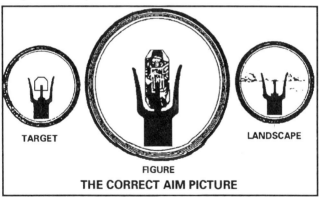

TARGET **LANDSCAPE**

FIGURE
THE CORRECT AIM PICTURE

AIMING WITH THE IRON SIGHT

1. With both your eyes open identify the target and roughly align the rifle adjusting the body position so that the rifle points naturally at the target without effort.
2. Position your cheek on the cheek piece so that the eye

is approximately 25mm from the aperture.

3. Look through the centre of the APERTURE and centralise the TIP of the FORESIGHT.

The BACKSIGHT will be too close to the eye for the edges of the aperture to be clearly seen; however a clear area in the centre of the aperture will be apparent.

Ensure that the FORESIGHT is upright and clearly in focus. Keep the left eye open.

4. It may be necessary to move your head slightly in order to achieve SIGHT ALIGNMENT; it is essential, however, once it has been achieved, that the position of your head remains unchanged.

5. Maintaining this alignment, focus on the tip of the foresight lining it up with the target or more correctly called the POINT of AIM (POA), this completes the 'AIM PICTURE'. You will find that when doing this the target will become blurred for a few moments.

6. Check that the tip of the FORESIGHT is still in the centre of the aperture

7. The adjustment of your sights can give you a more "COMFORTABLE AIM PICTURE" or eye relief, you must test and if necessary adjust your sights with the aid of your instructor. This will help you to be consistent with your aim and as a result improve your results.

IF after GENUINE attempts you are unable to aim keeping BOTH EYES OPEN, you should close the left eye. The "BOTH EYES OPEN" technique is generally recommended as better with the IRON SIGHT.

BE SECURITY CONSCIOUS AT ALL TIMES NEVER LET YOUR RIFLE OUT OF YOUR CONTROL

GP RIFLE TRAINING TESTS

INTRODUCTION

Throughout your Skill at Arms training you will become more proficient until you arrive at the THREE STAR LEVEL, when you will be required to take your TRAINING TESTS with the GP Rifle.

As you would expect, these tests are set to a very high standard and to pass them you will have to be well trained and practised.

The conditions and the levels of assessment are strictly observed.

The following sections set out the eight tests with their respective conditions, for you to know exactly what has to be learned to pass the tests.

TRAINING TEST No 1 SAFETY

CONDITIONS.

A rifle will be laid on the ground, with a MAGAZINE fitted, unloaded and the SAFETY CATCH NOT APPLIED. You will be told to PICK UP the rifle and put it on the table.

Keeping the MUZZLE POINTING in a SAFE direction, you should:-

First Stage of Test.

1. You pick up the rifle, adopting the LOW PORT position.
2. Put the SAFETY CATCH to **"S"**.
3. Remove the MAGAZINE, CHECK IT, and place on table COCK weapon and check that BREECH is EMPTY.
4. Allow the WORKING PARTS to go FORWARD.
5. Put the SAFETY CATCH to **"F"**.
6. Operate the TRIGGER.
7. Put SAFETY CATCH to **"S"**.
8. CLOSE the DUST COVER.

9. Place the rifle on the table, COCKING HANDLE
   UPWARDS, MAGAZINE NOT fitted.

Second Stage of Test

You will be ordered to pick up the rifle from the table and
hand it to the examiner.

You MUST pick it up with the MUZZLE pointing upwards
then :- Cock weapon, operate the HOLDING OPEN
CATCH, check for yourself, then show examiner that
BODY, CHAMBER and BOLT Face is clear, then hand rifle
over to examiner.

ASSESSMENT.

You will ONLY Pass this test if you carry out ALL the
actions correctly.

TRAINING TEST No 2 STRIPPING & CLEANING

CONDITIONS.

1. You will be told to STRIP the rifle.

NOTE: BOLT CARRIER ASSEMBLY is to be removed, but
   NOT stripped into its component parts.

2. You will be asked to answer or demonstrate the
   answers to three of the following questions:-

a. CLEANING the BARREL using the CLEANING ROD.

b. CLEANING the BARREL using the PULLTHROUGH.

c. What is the MAXIMUM size of the FLANNELETTE
   PATCH that can be used to CLEAN or LUBRICATE the
   BORE.

d. Show how you would remove any FOULING or
   DEBRIS from the CHAMBER.

e. Show how you would EXAMINE the BARREL for
   cleanliness.

f. When should MAGAZINES be STRIPPED.

g. STRIP and RE-ASSEMBLE a MAGAZINE.

3. You will be told to RE-ASSEMBLE the rifle.

ASSESSMENT
1. Main purpose is to test your ability to STRIP and ASSEMBLE the rifle.
2. You will pass if you make TWO OR LESS mistakes.
3. If you FAIL TO COMPLY with any RULE OF SAFETY whilst carrying out the test, you will fail regardless of success at 2 above.
4. NO TIME LIMIT to be set.

TRAINING TEST No 3 MAGAZINE FILLING
CONDITIONS.
Starting with an EMPTY MAGAZINE, you will be told:-
    1.To FILL 10 rounds.
    2. Told to EMPTY the MAGAZINE.
ASSESSMENT.
You will pass the test if you FILL and EMPTY the MAGAZINE correctly. (Target time of 20 seconds)

TRAINING TEST No 4 LOADING IN THE LYING POSITION
CONDITIONS.
You will be given a MAGAZINE, with 5 DRILL ROUNDS, put MAGAZINE in POUCH, FASTEN YOUR POUCH.
You will be in the STANDING POSITION.
1. You will then be given order "LOAD"
2. Adopt the LYING POSITION and load as taught.
3. Your action is complete when the SAFETY CATCH is applied, POUCH FASTENED and the LEFT HAND back UNDER HAND GUARD.
ASSESSMENT.
You will pass this test if NO MISTAKES are made.
While in this position you are ready to go on to the next test.

TRAINING TEST No 5 MAKING SAFE

CONDITIONS.

Following Test 4 you will be in the LYING POSITION.
You will be given the order " MAKE SAFE".
NO MATTER WHAT STATE of READINESS THE WEAPON
IS IN you should UNLOAD as taught, and then put on a
FULL MAGAZINE.

ASSESSMENT

You will pass this test if NO MISTAKES are made.
You remain in the LYING POSITION ready for the next
test.

TEST No 6 UNLOADING

CONDITIONS.

Following test 5 you will be in the LYING POSITION and will
be given the order "READY".
This will be followed by:-
1. Given the order 'UNLOAD'.
2. You UNLOAD as taught. Your final actions should be to
   CLOSE the DUST COVER, PICK UP the ejected rounds,
   CLEAN and REPLACE them in the MAGAZINE, put
   MAGAZINE in POUCH, FASTEN the POUCH, and then
   if ordered to do so, stand up and STAND AT EASE.

ASSESSMENT.

You pass this test only if NO MISTAKES are made.

TEST No 7 APPLICATION OF FIRE

CONDITIONS

You will be asked to indicate the correct POI (Point Of
   Aim) on each of the following three targets:-
   1. A RANGE TARGET.
   2. A FIGURE TARGET.
   3. A NATURAL TARGET.

ASSESSMENT

You pass this test if NO MISTAKES are made.

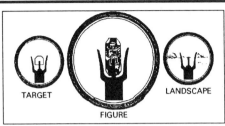

TARGET

FIGURE

LANDSCAPE

TEST No 8 FIRING FROM COVER

CONDITIONS

You will be advancing along a set route, where targets and suitable cover of different kinds will have been arranged for testing your ability to "TAKE - COVER" and select your "FIRE POSITION".

1. You will be given the order to LOAD in the STANDING POSITION.
2. When ready, you will be given the order to "ADVANCE".
3. As your near the selected positions, you will be given the order to "TAKE COVER".
4. When you have TAKEN COVER and selected your position, you will be given a FIRE CONTROL ORDER by your examiner on a target, followed by the order to "FIRE".
5. After one or two rounds have been fired, you will get the command to "STOP".
6. Then the order "PREPARE TO ADVANCE".

ASSESSMENT.

1. You are assessed on your speed in taking cover, your selection of a FIRE POSITION behind COVER, your ability to HANDLE YOUR RIFLE and MAKE SAFE before advancing.
2. You pass this test only if NO MISTAKES are made.

THE LIGHT MACHINE GUN

The LMG is a good light machine gun and has stood the test of battle. It can fire single rounds or bursts, it has a effective range of up to 600 yards and is very accurate..

You can set the change lever at "S" (safe), "A" (automatic) to fire bursts, or "R" (rounds) to fire single rounds. The gun is air cooled and fed by a magazine which holds 28 rounds. The flash when fired is reduced by a flash hider fitted to the barrel. The bipod legs can give adjustment for height or lowered, folded and locked for ease of carrying.

HOW THE GUN WORKS.

The gas from the fired round drives the piston group back and takes out the empty case, the return spring drives it forwards, loads and fires. This goes on as long as you keep the trigger pressed and there are rounds in the magazine.

THE BACKWARD ACTION

a. When the gas forces the bullet up the barrel, some of it goes through the gas vent, and gas regulator into the gas cylinder; it hits the face of the piston, drives the piston back on the piston buffer and compresses the return spring.

b. The extractor grips the empty case and carries it backwards as far as the ejector, which throws it out of the gun downwards through the ejection slot in the piston.

THE FORWARD ACTION

a. The piston buffer stops the piston, and the return spring drives it forwards again; the feed piece on the breech block meets the base of the next round in the magazine and pushes it into the chamber, and the extractor closes over the rim of the round.

b. The piston goes further forward and the piston drives the firing pin through the hole in the face of the breech block into the cap of the cartridge, and fires the round.

SAFETY PRECAUTIONS

Safety precautions must be carried out before and after using an LMG for any purpose.

Likewise all magazines, drill rounds and your pouches must be inspected to ensure that no live rounds are present.

The drill for carrying out LMG Safety Precautions is as follows:-

Put the CHANGE LEVER to "S", open the MAGAZINE OPENING COVER, open the EJECTION OPENING COVER; pull the COCKING HANDLE to the rear as far as possible and return it to its forward position.

This action is called 'COCKING THE GUN'.

Look into the BODY and CHAMBER and ensure that there is no obstruction present; put the CHANGE LEVER forward to "A" press the TRIGGER, close the MAGAZINE OPENING COVER, close the EJECTION OPENING COVER. Put the CHANGE LEVER TO "S".

This is a drill you need to practice until it becomes an automatic action when ever you handle the LMG.

LOADING AND UNLOADING

On the command "Load", lie down straight behind the gun, legs together and heels uppermost.

Hold the small of the butt with the left hand with an overhand grip, and the pistol grip with the right hand, forefinger lying outside the trigger guard.

LOADING: To load the gun:-

1. Put the change lever to "Safe" push the magazine opening cover forward.
2. Take up a magazine and, after ensuring that the top

round is correctly positioned, place it into the
magazine opening, toe first and rotate it backwards
until it is locked into position. Check that it is secure.
3. Position the hands as in the loading position. Hold the
gun upright.

UNLOADING.
1. Raise the butt into your shoulder.
2. Cock the gun and remove the magazine by pressing
the magazine catch using the bottom of the palm of
your hand. Put the magazine on the ground.
3. Push the change lever forward, if it is not already there,
align the sights roughly onto the target and press the
trigger.
4. Bring the butt out of the shoulder, close the magazine
opening cover and close the ejection opening cover,
lower the sights, put the change lever to "Safe" and
stand up.
5. If the order "Unload, clear gun" has been given, carry
out actions as taught, stand up, report "Gun clear".

ACTION ON BEING ORDERED, TO MAKE SAFE.
It is often necessary to return a gun, which has been loaded
and cocked, to a state in which it is loaded but safe.
To MAKE SAFE, you would be in the lying position
behind the gun, carry out the 'UNLOAD' -
BUT DO NOT CLOSE THE MAGAZINE OPENING COVER.
Re-load as taught.

HOLDING AND FIRING.
When you are told a range:

a. Set the sights, bring the butt into the shoulder and
cock the gun.
b. Pull the butt backwards and downwards with your left

hand; keep your left elbow well forward.

c. Hold the pistol grip with your right hand, with the forefinger on the trigger, and pull back into your shoulder.

d. To lock your hold, turn your wrists inwards and press your chin against the butt.

IMMEDIATE ACTION (IA)

If the gun will not fire, or stops firing, your immediate action is to cock the gun, change the magazine, aim and fire: this Immediate Action is called "IA" for short, and you must practice it until you can do it without thinking. The **IA** puts most stoppages right.

GAS STOPPAGE

If you try the IA and the gun fires one or two rounds and then stops again, it may be for lack of gas; to put it right.

a. Cock the gun, take off the magazine, and press the trigger.

b. Cock the gun again, and rest the butt on the ground.

c. Disconnect the barrel nut, and ease the barrel forward by the handle until you can turn the gas regulator.

d. Turn the regulator to the next larger hole; put the combination tool or the nose of a round in the upright slot, and turn it away from you.

e. Put the barrel on again, lower the carrying handle, put the same magazine back on if it is full enough, aim and fire.

f. Put the tool or round back in its place when you have the chance.

g. You have to decide whether it is better to move forward on the left of the gun or pull the gun back to you, to get at the gas regulator.

SKILL AT ARMS

MAKING SAFE

If you have to move with a magazine on the gun you
    must first make safe.
a. Unload, but do not close the magazine opening cover.
b. Inspect a full magazine and put it on the gun: make
    sure the change lever is still at "S".

SKILL AT ARMS LMG TRAINING TESTS

The purpose of these LMG Training Tests is for you to
measure the standard of safety and handling that you
should have attained through your training. LMG
Training Tests. In the Regular Army these tests are
carried out during initial training and anually thereafter.

TEST No 1. SAFETY.

Stores:
Gun loaded, cocked and the change lever at 'S', either in
the corner of a room or on the firing point.
Conditions: You will be ordered to bring the gun to the
centre of the room, or to another position on the firing
point. You will be expected to carry out the normal safety
precautions on the gun.

ASSESSMENT:

You will FAIL if the safety precautions are not carried out
correctly.

TEST No 2. STRIPPING, CLEANING AND ASSEMBLING.

Stores:
Gun. Spare Parts Wallet. Conditions: You will be ordered
to strip the gun for daily cleaning and asked the following
questions:-
   1. What size flannelette is used to clean the bore.

2. What size flannelette is used to oil the cylinder.
3. What spare parts for the gun are contained in
   the spare parts tin.

You will then be ordered to assemble the gun.

ASSESSMENT:

The main purpose is to test your ability to strip and
assemble the gun, you will be assessed with this in mind
SKILLED - No mistakes. AVERAGE - 1 to 3 mistakes.
FAIL - More than 3 mistakes.
NOTE. No qualification awarded if any mistake affects
safety.

TEST No 3. LOADING

Stores:
Gun. Magazine. Spare Parts Wallet. Stop Watch.
Conditions:
This is a TIMED test. You will be lying behind the gun;
magazine in a pouch and the change lever at "A". You
will be given the order "LOAD". Time is taken from the
order "LOAD" until you have both hands in their proper
positions on the gun and the gun is upright.

ASSESSMENT:

SKILLED - 8 seconds or less. AVERAGE - 9 to 12 seconds.
FAIL over 12 seconds. Add 2 seconds to the overall time
for each mistake.
NOTE. No qualificatioin awarded if mistake affects safety.

TEST No 4. IMMEDIATE ACTION AND GAS
STOPPAGE.

Stores: Gun. Magazine filled. Spare parts Wallet. Stop
Watch.

Conditions: This is a TIMED test. You will be lying behind
the gun; gun loaded and firing. Given the order "GUN

STOPS". When IA has been completed, order "GUN FIRES A FEW MORE ROUNDS AND STOPS AGAIN". Time is taken from "AGAIN"until you have aimed and fired the gun.

ASSESSMENT:
Skilled - 12 seconds. AVERAGE - 13 to 17 seconds. Fail - over 17 seconds. 2 seconds are added to the overall time for each mistake.
NOTE. No qualification awarded if any mistake affects safety.

TEST No 5. UNLOADING
Stores: As for Test No 4.
Conditions: This is a TIMED test. You will be lying behind the gun: gun loaded and firing.
Ordered "STOP" and when you have carried out the correct actions, given order "UNLOAD".
Time is taken from "UNLOAD" until you are standing up behind the gun.

ASSESSMENT:
SKILLED - 12 seconds. AVERAGE - 13 to 17 seconds. FAIL - over 17 seconds. 2 seconds added to the overall time for each mistake.
NOTE. No qualification awarded if mistake affects safety.

TEST No 6. PREPARATION FOR FIRING.
Stores: Gun. Spare Parts Wallet. Flannelette. Oil.
Conditions: You will be order to prepare your gun for firing. You should immediately:-
a. Strip the gun for daily cleaning.
b. Remove the extractor stay, spring and barrel nut.
c. Clean the gun and leave it dry.

d. Oil the locking shoulder of the breech block and piston, the piston guide ribs and the guides in which they run.

e. **EXAMINE**:-

1. The numbers on the barrel, body, butt slide and barrel nut.
2. Bipod, magazine, magazine opening cover, barrel nut catch and back sight.
3. Change lever, trigger and ejection opening cover.
4. The bore, foresight, foresight protectors and carrying handle.
5. The firing pin and spring, the extractor stay and spring and the feed piece.

f. Push in the return spring rod and pour a little oil in to the recess.

g. Check that the gas regulator is set to the correct mark.

h. When the gun is assembled, put the change lever at **"A"**, and, keeping the trigger pressed, move the cocking handle backwards and forwards a few times.

ASSESSMENT:

The sequence you use need not be as laid down above, but all aspects are to be correctly completed.
SKILLED - Up to 2 mistakes. AVERAGE - 3 to 5 mistakes.
FAIL - over 5 mistakes.
NOTE No qualifications awarded if mistake affects safety.

QUESTIONS

1. How many rounds does the GP Rifle magazine hold.
2. What is the TMH.
3. What reason do you adopt the LOW PORT POSITION.
4. What do you insist before someone hands a weapon to you.
5. Carrying the Rifle in the BACK SLUNG position, is the MUZZLE up or down.

6. Name the parts of the IRON SIGHT.
7. Where is the BACK SIGHT located.
8. What is the name of the tool in the Cleaning Kit.
9. How many pieces is the CLEANING ROD made up of.
10. Using the CLEANING ROD , which way do you turn it.
11. Looking inside the BARREL, what do you see.
12. What has a Green and Red painted tip.
13. How should AMMUNITION be kept and cared for.
14. What stops the rearward movement of the CARRIER and BOLT.
15. What hold the working parts to the REAR.
16. What do you understand by Muzzle Clearance.
17. WHEN IN THE AIM, what space should be between your eye and the Iron Sight.
18. How many training tests are there for the GP Rifle.
19. Name the LMG CHANGE L:EVER positions.
20. What do you understand by the term; "GAS and SPRING OPERATED.
21. What causes the Piston to be driven back.
22. When the round is in the Breach, what closes over the RIM of the Round.
23. What is carried out at the start and finish of every weapon training lesson.
24. How can you identify a DRILL ROUND.
25. What size is the FLANNELETTE used to CLEAN the BARREL of your rifle.
26. What is the "overall important thing to remember when doing your Training Tests.
27. Complete the saying; "It's better to be safe than ___.
28. Never use a round of ammunition as a _ _ _ _ .
29. What do you watch out for on your rifle in damp weather.
30. Do you oil the IRON SIGHT, APERATURE and POST.

THE DUKE OF EDINBURGH'S AWARD

INTRODUCTION.

When the scheme was first started the Army Cadet Force was one of the organisations that took part in the Pilot Scheme, this was not surprising as the Duke of Edinburgh was then and still is the Colonel-in-Chief of the Army Cadet Force.

To gain the award is a personal achievement that takes a great deal of self discipline to see it through, it was the Duke of Edinburgh who said that anyone who was determined to gain the award would have to have 'STICKABILITY' to see it through all the way.

THE MAIN PRINCIPLES

1. THE AWARD SCHEME IS ENTIRELY VOLUNTARY FOR YOU TO JOIN.
2. THE AGES ARE FROM 14 TO 25 YEARS OLD.
3. THE AWARD SCHEME HAS FOUR COMPULSORY SECTIONS:-

SERVICE — EXPEDITION — SKILLS — PHYSICAL RECREATION

There are three levels of the Award:-

| BRONZE. | SILVER. | GOLD. |

4. The minimum time for completing each level is:-

Bronze	Silver	Gold
6 MONTHS.	12 MONTHS.	18 MONTHS.

THE CHALLENGE

There is no question of you being made to take part in the Award Scheme, it is entirely voluntary at each stage, Bronze, Silver and Gold Award. It is an individual effort on your part, your unit does not enter a "team", nor are you expected to follow exactly the same elements as one another. You have to choose what you would like to do and then go for it. If you don't see it through, then you will be one of those lacking the 'stickability' required.

YOUR CONTACT

The County Duke of Edinburgh Award Officer. In your County ACF there will be a Duke of Edinburgh's Award Officer, find out who that is and make contact to enrol in the scheme.

You will have to buy your **Entrance Pack** which will include your **Record Book**, this is your first commitment to the scheme and gives you a personal stake in it.

It has to be YOUR EFFORT that "sets the ball rolling". Every help will be given to you, but as you progress, you will be expected to choose, design and develop your own programme from the many options available.

ADVANTAGES

Taking part in the scheme can add an extra dimension, excitement and purpose to your cadet career and beyond to your 25th birthday.

The award will bring you into closer contact with many other young people and you will no doubt develop lasting friendships.

The self confidence, awareness, determination and enthusiasm displayed by successful participants in the scheme has given the award holders a deserved reputation, which like your training in the ACF - PROVIDED you have attained the required standards - gives you a distinct advantage when setting out on your adult career.

Make no mistake about it, if and when you go for a job interview wearing your Duke of Edinburgh's Award Gold badge, it will be recognised that you have already spent a considerable amount of time improving yourself and helping others to do the same.

To a potential employer, this alone is sufficient evidence that you have the makings of a valuable addition to their staff, a factor you should never forget.

YOUR OPPORTUNITY

As a cadet this offers you a great opportunity and an advantage to take part in the scheme, while at the same time continuing with your cadet career.

This has been made possible by many of the subjects within the APC Syllabus fitting in with the requirements of the scheme.

Referring to the chart ON PAGE ***: having completed your ONE STAR training, it can be seen that if you decide to enrol as a participant in the scheme, you can with some extra effort, gain the BRONZE Award by completing APC 2 Star First Aid, Expedition Training, Shooting/Skill at Arms and Physical Activity.

It must be stressed, that it is not compulsory/mandatory for you to only count ACF related activities towards your DofE award, nor is the list of activities mentioned in the chart the only ones accepted, there are a great many more that your County DofE officer will be able to tell you about.

However, any aspect of ACF activity can, with some help and imagination on the part of your instructors, working with the County DofE officer, be brought into a DofE Award programme; this is most likely to be the case in respect of the Expedition option in the Silver and Gold Awards.

THE DUKE OF EDINBURGH'S AWARD

Your County Duke of Edinburgh's Award Officer will have several leaflets and books that you will be allowed to read. It is advisable that you do just that before making up your mind to take up the challenge.

All that we can tell you, is that if you do join the Award Scheme, and see it through all the way, you will never regret it.

THE REQUIREMENTS OF APC (ACF) IN ORDER TO QUALIFY FOR THE AWARDS THROUGH ACF TRAINING

BRONZE AWARD

SERVICE SECTION
Requirement:
Passed Casualty Code Test in APC.(2Star First Aid)
EXPEDITION SECTION
Requirements:
To have been trained and passed APC TWO STAR Expedition Training.
To have learned Map and Compass (including Route Cards) and Fieldcraft at 2 Star level.
You will be required to produced a report (oral or written) in some detail of a venture that you have taken part in. This will include sketches, Route Cards, diagrams and be presented in a neat and acceptable manner.
Note: If you are to take part in your 2 Star expedition, then, provided you make arrangements with your County DofE Officer and all the conditions are complied with it can be counted as your Bronze Expedition.
SKILLS SECTION
This requires you to take up an approved topic as a hobby/interest.
You will need to talk to your DofE officer to help you

decide what you are to do.

He will have the approved list of topics to choose from. You will be required to take a keen interest in this and study it in some depth, during which time you will become quite an expert in your own right.

Note: Should you wish to take up a skill not listed, then it can be submitted by your DofE Officer through the proper channels for approval.

You must wait for approval before proceeding.

This applies to all levels of the Award Scheme.

As examples, some of the Military topics are:-

Skill at Arms, Drill, Drumming, Bugling, Forces Insignia.

You will be assessed as to how well you have done, by someone who is recognised as an expert in the topic you have chosen. At the Bronze level you would normally be judged as a 'beginner'. Should you be taking Skill at Arms as a choice , then you may be judged as "having some knowledge".

PHYSICAL RECREATION

Requirements:

To have passed APC 2 Star Physical Achievements Test. Scoring 24 points; at least 12 for participation, the rest from the standards set out in the Physical Achievement Tests at the end of this section. Two participation points can be gained per week, for one hour's work.

RESIDENTIAL PROJECT:

No requirement at Bronze level.

SILVER AWARD

SERVICE SECTION

Requirement:

You are able to use your 'Service' in the ACF as a qualification for the Silver Award, provided:-

THE DUKE OF EDINBURGH'S AWARD

1. You have attended and performed satisfactorily at a Junior Cadet Instructors Cadre.

2. You have successfully completed the THREE STAR syllabus for the Cadet and The Community.

3. Know the history of the ACF, and its organisation in your own detachment, area and county, plus the history of the Regiment/Corps to which you are badged. This must be to a higher standard than required by APC at 2 Star.

4. The total period of involvement in these activities must be at least 16 weeks.

ALTERNATIVE OPTION

As an alternative to the above "Service in the ACF option, the following may be undertaken:-

To have qualified for the Public First Aid Certificate of St Johns Ambulance or its equivalent, or any First Aid Certificate approved for the purpose of the Health and Safety (First Aid) Regulations. (4 Star First Aid) To have taken part in active first aid duties.

EXPEDITION SECTION

Entry requirements:

4 Star Expedition standard is required at this level (48 km with two nights out) **OR** you have the option of undertaking an EXPLORATION 2 nights out, PLUS a project to be carried out, to include 10 hours journeying - this could be extended 3 Star training. Your expedition can be on foot, by canoe, boat, bicycle (or horse).

SKILLS SECTION

As in the Bronze Award you must participate for a minimum of 6 months if you have gained your Bronze Award. If you are starting the Award for the first time at Silver, then you must follow your Skill for 12 months.

THE DUKE OF EDINBURGH'S AWARD

The conditions are the same, except you will be expected
to carry it out with some degree of study and in detail,
making significant advances in the quality of your project,
over that of your Bronze; you may well be working at a
level of "those with some knowledge" or even "the more
advanced"

This does not mean that you keep to the same topic,
although there is no reason why not, provided you are
able to prove to your assessors how much you have
improved.

The Military subjects in addition to those mentioned in
the Bronze are:-

Map Making, Military Brass Bands, Military Flautists,
Model Soldiers, Piping, Small Bore Shooting, Shooting,
Signalling.

These skills will be assessed by an expert in that particular topic you have selected.

You will be judged according to the amount of effort and
quality of your project as someone who has some specialist knowledge of the subject.

PHYSICAL RECREATION SECTION

Qualification required: to score 30 points as set out in the
Duke of Edinburgh Award Physical Achievement Tests. (12
points minimum for participation)

RESIDENTIAL PROJECT SECTION

No requirement at Silver level.

GOLD AWARD

SERVICE SECTION
Requirement:

You are able to use your cadet 'service' as a qualification
at this level, provided you have:-

THE DUKE OF EDINBURGH'S AWARD

1. Attended and performed satisfactorily at the Senior Cadet Instructors' Cadre **OR** for a cadet who has not used the ACF Service Syllabus at Silver level, has attended and performed satisfactorily at a Junior Cadet Instructors Cadre.
2. Carried out tasks of special responsibility or given some specific service to your detachment, e.g making training aids, organising fund raising events, responsible for training specific group of cadets.
3. Held at least the rank of Corporal for not less than 12 months or if as a Cadet where there is no NCO vacancy, be a 3 Star cadet.
4. The period of training and practical service to be at least 12 months and to include at least three counselling sessions with the assessor during the practical service period.

EXPEDITION SECTION

Expeditions at this level are only permitted to take place in specified areas of the country providing suitable "wild country". It is normal practice for the expedition to be linked to an exercise to be carried out en-route or some adventurous project.

At Silver level, you have the option of carrying out an EXPLORATION, over the same period of time, but not necessarily in Wild Country, with a requirement of a project and 10 hours journeying. And at Gold level only, there is the option of "Other Adventurous Projects" when the venture you want to undertake departs from the normal conditions for an expedition or exploration.

A great deal of preparation is required to ensure correct training is carried out and equipment checked and you have had some practical experience with it.

THE DUKE OF EDINBURGH'S AWARD

The expedition is very much a **team effort**, practising Leadership, Map Reading, Camp Craft and First Aid Skills.

SKILLS SECTION

As at other levels of the award, you set your project in liaison with your DofE officer who will advise you of the standards required for the work you are to do.

As before, it may be a continuation of a previous skill, but you will be expected to take it to a higher level of knowledge with a more professional approach to the presentation of the project.

PHYSICAL RECREATION SECTION

Qualification: to carry out the APC 4 Star Physical Achievement Test or APC 4 Star Orienteering

RESIDENTIAL PROJECT SECTION

The intention is for you to work with a group which is largely comprised of people who are unknown to you. Attendance at many of the normal cadet activities can qualify you for this as long as you are spending the time mainly with people you would not normally spend time with.

Annual Camp over a period of more than five days. Satisfactorily completing courses at The Cadet Training Centre, or UKLF Cadet Leadership Course or attachment to a Regular Army unit in BAOR.

If you are unable to have time off to carry out the above, you may qualify by a series of weekend camps, your DofE officer will advise you.

SEE THE CADET SUPPLY DEPARTMENT CATALOGUE FOR A FULL RANGE OF TENTS AND EXPEDITION EQUIPMENT

THE DUKE OF EDINBURGH'S AWARD

CHART SHOWS HOW ACF ACTIVITIES CAN QUALIFY FOR D of E AWARD

	SERVICE	EXPEDITION (FOOT)	SKILL	PHYSICAL RECREATION	RESIDENTIAL PROJECT
BRONZE	APC 2 star APC 2 Star First Aid	ACF related Expedition Trg plus Report of Venture 1 night and 24 km.	APC 2 star activities:- Ceremonial Drill Drumming Bugling Signalling Forces Insignia Shooting Map Making Military Brass Bands Military Flautists Model Soldiers Piping Skill at Arms Small Bore	Physical Achievements Test DofE 24 points	No requirement Bronze
SILVER	Service in the ACF (Silver) or APC 3 Star Cdt & Community or APC 4 Star First Aid plus Practical Service	Expedition 4 Star Expedition Training (2 nights & and 48 km) or Exploration: 2 Nights + Project to include 10 hours journeying i.e. expanded 3 Star Expedition Trg)	Levels of ability are:- 'For beginners' 'For those with some knowledge' 'For the more advanced' - as appropriate.	APC 3 Star Physical Achievement Test NOTE: APC 2, 3 & 4 Star are now identical to Bronze, Silver and Gold Award respectively	No requirement at Silver
GOLD	Service in the ACF (Cadets) or Service in the ACF (Adult)	Post 4 Star Programme *NOTE: Expeditions can also be by other means, e.g. Canoeing, cycling, on Horseback etc.		APC 4 Star Physical Achievement Test or APC 4 Star Orienteering	Possible attendance at Annual Camp. CTC and UKLF Leadership Courses. Canadian Leadership/ Challenge. Sen Cadet Instructors Master Cadet CTC Adult Training MOD Attachments

FITNESS TRAINING

SPORTS and PHYSICAL FITNESS

Sport and Physical Fitness are important activities in the Army, it is the duty of every soldier to keep fit at all times, likewise as a Cadet it is your personal responsibility to be physically fit and in turn, mentally alert.

Much of the training you do requires you to have a high level of fitness to attain the standards to pass your APC.

Team Spirit

Taking part in sport and physical training as a member of a team teaches you team spirit and to work with others. Individual sports such as swimming needs a great amount of self discipline to keep it up and constant practice, especially if you get into serious competitions. This will then require practice every day and that does need a great amount of self discipline.

All Sporting activities in the Army are governed by the Army Sports Control Board.

Many years ago they drew up their definition of a Sportsperson, which we reproduce below, as it is perhaps more relevant today than when it was first written, we recommend you to learn it off by heart.

You may find it difficult to 'measure-up' to this definition, just think about it, but nothing that is easy to attain has

much value.
Keep this definition of the SPORTSPERSON in mind at all times, - especially when taking part in sporting activities - it may help make YOU a better sport.

FITNESS TRAINING

THE SPORTSPERSON
A SPORTSPERSON IS ONE WHO:-
PLAYS THE GAME FOR THE GAMES SAKE.
PLAYS FOR THE TEAM AND NOT FOR THEMSELVES.
IS A GOOD WINNER AND GOOD LOSER;
I.E.; MODEST IN VICTORY AND GENEROUS IN DE-
FEAT ACCEPTS ALL DECISIONS IN A PROPER SPIRIT.
IS CHIVALROUS TOWARDS A DEFEATED OPPONENT.
IS UNSELFISH AND ALWAYS READY TO HELP
OTHERS TO BECOME PROFICIENT.
AS A SPECTATOR APPLAUDS GOOD PLAY ON BOTH
SIDES.
NEVER CHALLENGES UMPIRES, JUDGES OR
REFEREES - NO MATTER WHAT THE DECISION

ALWAYS TAKE PART IN PHYSICAL TRAINING

ALWAYS LOOK FOR OPPORTUNITIES
TO PLAY ENERGETIC GAMES -
ESPECIALLY AT CAMP
If you work hard at your exercises -
play games hard and enter into sport
with a will and the right spirit — you
will not have any fitness problems.

Sport and Fitness
Fitness is a matter of self-discipline.
Good health is one of the greatest gifts that you can have,
The care you take of your body will help you to keep
physically and mentally fit at all times.
If you are over weight or if you are too thin your stamina
will be affected.

156

watch that you get your proper treatment and medicine and see to it that you don't do anything silly.

EXERCISE DISCIPLINE

To keep fit all you need to do is a few simple physical exercises every day, on your own or get others to join you.

You don't need to join a Health Club or build a 'home gym' in your bedroom where your Weight Lifting kit goes through the floor, just practice some of the simple exercises you will know already; Sit-Up's, Press-Up's, Running on the Spot, Arms Swinging Forwards and Sideways and many others, not forgetting to jog a couple of miles twice a week.

THE FITNESS FEELING

Once you have attained a level of fitness you will feel great, more alert, willing and able to take part in many other activities, and of course, as a cadet you will undertake Physical Achievement Tests for your APC stars, and possibly for your Duke of Edinburgh's Award as well.

Use the Duke of Edinburgh Award Fitness Tests as the measure of your ability, you should improve your speed and stamina in the tests as you become more fit.

It's a great personal achievement to keep fit, and there is no better feeling to know that you are at the peak of your performance, all you need is the SELF DISCIPLINE to do it.

A WORD OF CAUTION

Remember that you are ONLY INSURED when taking part in officially organised events and activities, supervised by qualified coaches and/or instructors.

You will personally take the consequences if you participate in any activity not approved by your County Cadet Commandant.

THE DUKE OF EDINBURGH'S AWARD

PHYSICAL ACHIEVEMENT TESTS

Points required to qualify for your APC Star Grades

One Star - 6 points. Two Star - 12 points.

Three Star - 18 points. Four Star - 24 points.

NOTE: For the Award Scheme you are required to undertake all SEVEN events and select SIX to count. At least ONE point must be scored in each event. Maximum score in any event - FIVE points. A reasonable rest is allowed between each event. Tests may be spread over TWO days.

SCORING BOY CADETS

Event	Points				
	1	2	3	4	5
Speed Test Time (secs)	30	28	26	24	23
Sit-ups No in 60 secs	30	45	60	75	90
Burpees No in 30 secs	14	16	18	21	23
Stamina Run Time (Mins & secs)	4.20	4.00	3.40	3.20	3.10
Ball Speed Bounce No caught in 30 sec	30	35	40	45	50
Standing Broad Jump Distance (metres)	1.4	1.8	2.2	2.4	2.5
Push-ups or Bailey Bridge, Number in 30 secs	10	18	26	32	38
	18	22	28	32	36

SCORING GIRL CADETS

Event	Scoring				
	1	2	3	4	5
Speed Test Time (secs)	24	23	22	21	20
Sit-ups in 60 secs	28	36	44	52	60
Burpees No in 30 sec	11	13	15	18	20
Stamina Run Time (mins & secs)	4.50	4.30	4.10	3.50	3.40
Ball Speed Bounce Number caught 30 secs	20	26	32	36	38
Standing Broad Jump Distance (metres)	1.2	1.4	1.8	2.2	2.4
Push-ups or Bailey Bridge	8	14	22	28	34
Number in 30 secs	14	18	24	28	32

Note: Scores may be counted for either Push-ups or Bailey Bridge, but **not both**.

DESCRIPTION AND CONDITIONS OF TESTS

Speed Test Boys: Cross **TEN** times; **Girls** cross **EIGHT** times - between two lines marked on ground or floor NINE metres apart. Each line crossed or touched by one foot.

Sit-ups

Lie on the back with legs bent and feet about 50 cm apart. Place hands to the side of the head. Ankles should be held (e.g. under wallbar or by partner) so that the heels are kept in contact with the ground.

Sit up curling trunk and head and turn until one elbow touches the opposite knee and then return to the starting position. Repeat the exercise to the opposite side. Scoring ceases if a rest is taken.

Burpees

This is a four-count movement.

Start standing upright, then bend to crouch position placing both hands flat on the floor, jump both feet backwards and together to front support position (NB - the distance between the hands and feet in this position to be at least 70cm).

Jump feet forward to return to crouch and then stand upright.

Score is counted by the number of times you stand upright in 30 seconds.

Stamina Run

Twenty laps of a regular circuit 12 metres by 8 metres, each corner marked by a small object.

Ball Speed Bounce

Using a Netball or a size 5 Football, stand behind a line 2 metres from a wall. Hold the ball with two hands against the chest. Ball must be thrown with two hands so as to rebound from the wall into the hands behind the restraining line. Count each successfully caught ball in 30 seconds. It is recommended that a brick or similar solid surface is used for this event to ensure a satisfactory rebound.

Standing Broad Jump

Your feet may be placed in any position behind the edge of the take-off line or board, but may leave the ground only once in making an attempt to jump onto the feet.

You may rock backward and forward, lifting heels and toes alternately from ground, but may not lift either foot clear from ground or slide it along in any direction on the ground.

THE DUKE OF EDINBURGH'S AWARD

Measure from the front edge of the line or board to the nearest point on the gym mat or in sandpit touched by any part of the body or limbs.

CHOICE of TESTS either:-

Push-Ups

Lie face down on the floor, hands under shoulders, palms flat on the floor.

Straighten arms to lift body, locking elbows and leaving only palms and toes on floor.

Bend elbows until nose only touches the floor, then push up to straighten arms.

Repeat, keeping body straight from head to ankles.

The activity must be continuous, scoring ceases if a rest is taken or if your body sags.

Girls may find it easier to lie face down on the floor, hands under shoulders, palms flat on the floor with legs bent upwards from the knees on the floor.

or: Bailey Bridge

Start in the front support position with shoulders near to and facing a chair, stool or box on which is placed a small object, bean bag, keys, a stone etc.,.

The seat of the chair should be 45cm from the floor.

Take the object from the chair seat with one hand, place it on the floor, pick up the object with the other hand and replace it on the chair seat.

Continue the cycle, using alternate hands.

If you need any help or information for your Duke of Edinburgh's Award, get in touch with your County D of E Award Officer

---

THE DUKE OF EDINBURGH'S AWARD

QUESTIONS

1. What are the four compulsory sections of the Award Scheme.
2. What is the age you can enter the Bronze, Silver and Gold Award
3. At what Star level of your APC training would you qualify for the Bronze Award.
4. Give two examples of where a Senior Instructors Cadre might fit into an Award.
5. What is the upper age limit for gaining an Award.
6. If you are taking First Aid at Silver what is required to qualify.
7. How many miles (kilometres) are specified for Bronze, Silver and Gold Expeditions on foot.
8. Before going on an Expedition what do you leave behind.
9. What is the minimum period of time you must undertake for a particular Skill at Silver level.
10. The standard expected to be achieved for a Skill at Bronze is as "for beginners", what is it for Silver and Gold.
11. In a week how many points can be earned in a week.
12. In the Physical Recreation section what is the minimum period of time you must take to qualify.
13. What is the important proviso which enables you to count Annual Camp as your Residential Project (apart from the time requirement).
14. During Expeditions the minimum recommended calorie intake per day is 1000, 2000, 3000 or 4000.
15. Can Drill be taken as a Skill in the Award.
16. What do you have to buy to start on the Award Scheme.

17. Do you all enter as a team in your unit for the Duke of Edinburgh's Award Scheme.
18. Who is the Award officer in your County.
19. Are you permitted to do an expedition other than on foot.
20. Can Skill at Arms be counted as a Skill towards the Award.

COULD THIS COUNT AS PART OF AN EXPEDITION

EXPEDITION TRAINING.

This is perhaps the most important part of your training, it is also when you can have more fun and excitement while doing it than most other subjects.

It is important because it brings into practical use so many of the other skills and training that you will have been taught.

Throughout your life you will be able to use and benefit from the skills learned during your Adventurous Training, not to forget that it is also one of the Sections of the Duke of Edinburgh's Award Scheme.

THE COUNTRY CODE.

At times you may take part in expeditions that are not over Military Training Areas, but land to which the public have access or privately owned property.

This will require you to observe the normal courtesy expected when in contact with the public or moving over other peoples private property.

We must all try and preserve the natural beauty of our countryside and the wildlife that lives there, if we don't then areas of the country will not be available for us or the public at large to enjoy.

The COUNTRY CODE is a series of ten reminders based on common sense - and common failings.

It applies to everyone who use the countryside at any time of the year, there is no need to break it, lack of thought and care can cause untold trouble and prevent you and others from using a landowners ground.

Currently, farmers in the UK are facing serious financial losses due to their animals being killed through picking up the metal ring fasteners from tins of drinks, condoms disposed of thoughtlessly, and litter dumped in the countryside.

"YOU LEAVE NOTHING BUT YOUR FOOTPRINTS"

THE COUNTRY CODE

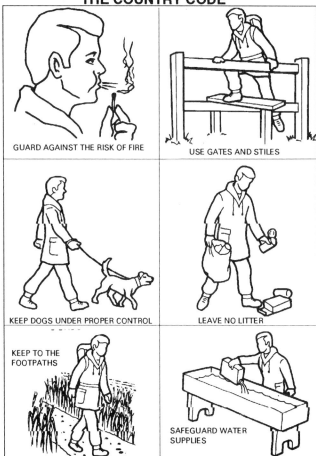

GUARD AGAINST THE RISK OF FIRE

USE GATES AND STILES

KEEP DOGS UNDER PROPER CONTROL

LEAVE NO LITTER

KEEP TO THE FOOTPATHS

SAFEGUARD WATER SUPPLIES

EXPEDITION TRAINING

RESPECT THE PEOPLE AND LIFE OF THE COUNTRYSIDE

PROTECT ALL WILD LIFE

GO CAREFULLY ON COUNTRY ROADS

SECURELY FASTEN ALL GATES

DISCIPLINES OF PERSONAL HEALTH and HYGIENE
HOW TO WALK — FEET and BOOTS

You only get one pair of feet, therefore they are worth looking after. Some of you reading this may be sitting there with sore feet through badly fitting shoes, or shoes that your feet hate the sight of.

When it comes to BOOTS then it is more important than ever that you are comfortable in them and that they give you the support required.

We all know that boots should be Polished for parades, but boot for Expeditions do need different treatment, as they are for a different purpose.

This is difficult for a Cadet, even if you can manage TWO pairs of boots, you grow out of them so fast and at the age of 16 trying to walk in boots that you had when 14 is a very painful experience!.

Should you get your boots wet, they should be dried out naturally not over or close to heat. Stuff them with paper to draw out the damp, changing it often.

Leather boots dried by heat will go hard and crack, making them useless.

FITTING BOOTS

When you go to buy a new pair of boots take a thick pair of socks with you or two pairs of normal socks to wear when trying on your boots.

Make sure you can wiggle your toes and they must not be touching the toes of the boot.

A method of testing the fitting is to be able to get a finger down between your heal and the back of the boot, if you can do this and your toes just touch the toe of the boot that is a good fit.

Fully lace up the boot to check that the uppers have enough room for your foot and that it's comfortable.

Remember, your feet have some of the most delicate bones in your body that need protection.

Good quality, well fitting shoes or boots are a wise investment, not only will they last longer, but will protect your feet and prevent problems later on in your life.

If you are to take part in any expeditions and to get the most fun out of it, then you had better make sure that you wear boots that are in a good and serviceable condition, not training shoes or 'wellies'.

HILL WALKING SKILLS

Any walk over a reasonable period of time requires you to have a rhythm in the way you walk. This is especially so when HILL WALKING and carrying a loaded rucksack. You should start out at a speed that you feel capable of keeping up for at least a few hours. While walking you should be able to talk or sing, if you cannot due to being short of breath, then you are walking too fast.

To get to the top or where you planned to stop for a "bite", means that you must keep going, if you keep stopping it will break your rhythm. The best way it to have a slow, plodding pace, it will get you there without undue effort. If you use too much effort it will make you over-heat and sweat, making your clothes wet and dehydrate you.

So if you are wise; conserve your energy, stay in good condition, not getting tired , too hot or too cold.

Climbing a hill

If you place you feet properly when going up hill it will prevent your calf muscles from aching.

This is mainly caused by pointing your feet directly up the hill, which puts strain on your calf muscles and Achilles tendon.

| WRONG | RIGHT |

Walk in a "zig-zag" fashion across the slope, your feet will be happier, being in full contact with the ground , with less chance of slipping, this may be slightly further, but far less tiring.

EXPEDITION TRAINING

Going down a hill
You don't need telling that running down a hill can be
dangerous and tiring. When decending a slope carrying a
full rucksack it requires some skill to do it safely. It is a
matter of confidence and adopting the right attitude to
tackling a decent.
Your balance plays a great part, the main thing to

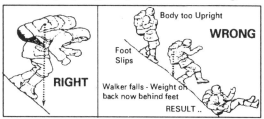

remember is to bend both your knees and lean well
forward. By adopting this stance your legs act as springs
and absorb the shaking-up your body would have had.
NEVER attempt to slide down a hill — it will end in
disaster as you cannot control yourself.
If you decend by traversing across the slope, keep your
hand on the uphill side and near to the ground for
support should you slip. Keep off any slopes with loose
stones or scree, and if any slope frightens you too much
— find another way down.

Crossing rivers or streams.
Never attempt to cross a river or mountain stream in
flood. Water is very powerful and easy to under estimate
its force. It may often be reasonable to cross streams or
small rivers, but , if you do so in your boots you will
regret it, better to take them off first, not forgetting your
socks!.

EXPEDITION TRAINING

CARE OF YOUR FEET

To go with you boots you need clean, well fitting woollen socks, without holes in them and a similar spare pair in your pack, plus a darning needle and wool to mend them if required.

Woollen socks ventilate your feet and keep them happy. Always remember that the extra weight you carry on your back is equivalent to more than three times the same weight on each foot.

Your balance is more critical and therefore you have to adjust to a different 'gait' with the weight of your body transferred onto the flat part of your foot rather than your heel.

This will become more apparent when you carry all your kit on your back.

Don't halt for more than five minutes or your muscles will stiffen up.

BLISTERS

You can help to prevent blisters - as already said if your boots are well fitting and "broken in", you are wearing well fitting woollen socks, but your normal "civilian pedestrian" feet are not prepared to perform over a long period, so you will have to do some training and treat them.

You need to harden the skin on your feet. This can be helped by rubbing them with surgical spirit during your training and preparation period well before any long expedition.

Every morning when on a march dust your feet with a foot powder (Mycil), but the main thing is to keep them clean and change your socks as often as is practical to do so. Wash your feet every night, preferably in hot salted water, rub them DRY and check your toe nails that they are cut reasonably close.

Never soak your feet when on the march, wash them if you wish — quickly and dry them well, changing socks from one foot to the other.

TREATMENT of BLISTERS

When you discover a blister it should be opened in the right way, so that the skin is not rubbed off and becomes infected.
Sterilize a needle by holding it in the flame of a match. When it has cooled, prick the blister, not directly, but through the skin at the side, and gently press out the fluid until the blister is flat. Cover it with a small sterilized dressing secured by two strips of plaster over it like a cross.
A raw blister would be treated with the dressing adding a smear of antiseptic cream to the raw blister.

WET FEET

Should you get your feet wet, if at all possible dry them and your boots, putting on fresh socks, do not "march to dry them" it will make your skin tender which will then rub off, and you will then become a casualty.

CRAMP

If you have been walking for a long period, without any warning you may get "CRAMPS", this is very painful spasm in your leg muscles which are best treated by massage, which after a few minutes disappears.

THIRST

In hot weather, after the first few hours on a march you may find that you develop a great thirst, not caused by your stomach's demand for water, but by your mouth feeling very parched.
The immediate thought is to drink more water, but this is not the answer. It is better to chew a piece of grass, or carrying a non-absorbent pebble in the mouth; a much better thirst-quencher is to suck a prune or carry a bit of raw onion in the mouth.

You can go on a long time without drinking at all if you have an onion with you, it also helps to prevent your lips from cracking.

WATER SHORTAGE

There may be a shortage of water and a requirement to ration it carefully.

Should water have not been available for any long period and then you have plenty of it, be careful, sip it slowly, so as not to chill your stomach.

If you drink until you feel no more thirst, then you may well get cramps in the stomach which are very painful. If you drink ALL the water you are carrying, you may not be able to replace it for some time. To be without it would be courting disaster if an emergency situation came up. Never try to satisfy thirst by swallowing snow or ice; melt it first by heating it in the mouth - if no fire is available. It is best to eat a biscuit or something with it as snow or iced water is bad for the stomach.

DANGER OF ALCOHOL

The consumption of alcohol in any form increases the rate at which your heart beats, thus increasing the flow of blood through the body, it follows that during cold weather veins near the skin surface cool at a quicker rate, thus increasing the speed at which exposure (hypothermia) may set in.

Another disastrous affect of alcohol is that it slows down your reactions and impairs your thinking, this could only lead to a disaster.

CLOTHING & EQUIPMENT

You are never certain what sort of weather you may be faced with in the UK, in a matter of an hour it can change from bright warm sun to a cold damp wind and rain. This makes it difficult to be dressed in the right gear.

If we remember that what ever we wear needs to:-
" Keep water out " - keep our body heat in. "
Allowing any water vapour to escape.

COMBAT JACKET/ANORAK

If your Combat Jacket/Anorak lets in water, your
pullover, shirt and under clothing will get wet/damp.
Wet clothing will not insulate your body, in fact it will
help it cool quicker, as a result your chances of becoming
a casualty through Hypothermia increases.
The answer is to have a fully waterproof Combat Jacket/
Anorak, but if you did it would be too hot due to not
letting your body heat evaporate, which in turn would
produce condensation making your clothes wet !!
Fortunately modern materials are now available that are
fairly waterproof and at the same time do allow your
body to breath.
This material is called GORTEX, it is expensive I, but if you
want to save up for anything - save up for a GORTEX Anorak.
Another useful waterproof outer garment is a CAGOULE,
this is ideal for wet weather and has a ventilated yoke at
the back. It packs into a very small space, and can be
neatly rolled on top of your kit for quick access.

SHIRTS and UNDERWEAR

On an Expedition it is always advisable to wear clothing
made of wool, as this has the best insulating/breathing
properties.
Many of you will not normally wear a vest, but we assure
you that it is good advice to do so "when out on the
hills", it is easy to take it off and "prevention is better than
a cure"

BALACLAVA - WOOL HAT

One third of our body heat can be lost from our heads,
therefore it is very good sense to cover our heads.

The easiest garment is a BALACLAVA hat which can be pulled well down over your ears if it is very cold.
A SKI hat would be ideal, but not so practical.

PERSONAL KIT LIST

Wear your personal Combat Jacket as issued, your county may have CAGOULES to loan you for expeditions.
A wool cap comforter. Underclothes - loose fitting for good insulation.
To be carried on you personally:-
Map. Compass. Pathfinder Protractor/Romer. Whistle on lanyard. Matches in a waterproof container. Elastic adhesive dressings. Pencil and notebook.
Packed in your Ruck Sack:-
Mess Tins with knife, fork & spoon, plus reserve food such as raisins, chocolate, Kendal Mint Cake.
Mug - metal preferred - plastic would do, but it cannot be heated up!. A water bottle with secure top. Towel and washing kit. Groundsheet and a Length of strong string.
Spare pair of thick wool socks. Torch - a small one.
Survival bag or blanket. A sleeping bag liner.
In a kit bag or equivalent to be delivered to camp site -
Two blankets or a sleeping bag. Spare change of clothing. Spare boots/shoes if available. Gym shoes or light weight trainers. Wool Pullover. Six blanket pins.

PACKING YOUR RUCKSACK

Packing your RUCKSACK correctly can make or break your comfort on a journey.
The type of RUCKSACK and capacity you are able to use can make all the difference to the way you pack it.
If it does not have a frame to it that fits the shape of your body, you will have to be careful not to overload it.
The reason being that in trying to pack everything into it you may have hard or odd shaped items that will stick into your back when carrying it.

PACKING YOUR RUCKSACK

The emphasis is on packing "into" the Ruck Sack - not hanging boots or other odd items on the outside until you look like a Christmas tree on the move.

Pay attention to LOAD CARRYING and the DISTRIBUTION of the load as illustrated in the diagrams. Practice PACKING and LOAD DISTRIBUTION then wear/carry it to ensure that it is comfortable to carry on a journey.

Stove Fuel should be packed in a well sealed polythene bag stored well away from rations.

All clothing and your sleeping bag should also be kept in polythene bags and the sack itself would benefit from a strong quality polythene bag as a liner.

LOAD CARRYING — The RIGHT and Wrong methods

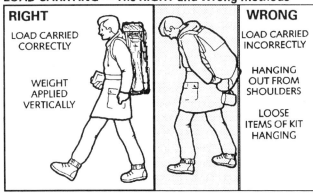

RIGHT

LOAD CARRIED CORRECTLY

WEIGHT APPLIED VERTICALLY

WRONG

LOAD CARRIED INCORRECTLY

HANGING OUT FROM SHOULDERS

LOOSE ITEMS OF KIT HANGING

CHOOSING A CAMP SITE - in the first place your officer will have to get permission for you to camp on private land or in fact any area that you might think of using. It is only good manners and common courtesy to ask permission to use someone's property.

Make sure that is carried out as part of your pre-expedition preparation, and you are positive that permission has been given before you arrive to set up camp for the night.

The ideal camp site, is one offering shelter from the prevailing wind, on a well drained fairly level soil, facing East to hopefully catch the early morning sun.

It should be as far away as possible from any houses, be close to a good clean water supply and be in the open.

CAMP SITE LAYOUT

Having chosen a suitable site, the following should be points should be considered and then if satisfactory, the camp should be laid out in accordance with the following

SAFETY FIRST - is it safe?

1. Is the site below the level of a river, lake, dam or reservoir, whose banks could burst or overflow in the event of a severe storm, or in a dried-up stream which "comes to life" in a storm.
2. Is the site under overhanging rocks or cliffs.
3. Ensure that the ground does not slope down from the bivi area to where the fire or cooking area is set out, and that the tents are not close enough to be a fire risk.

CAMP LAYOUT

a. Can the Tents/bivi's be correctly pitched in the area and sheltered from the wind and not under trees.
b. If a platoon or section camp, a COOKING AREA properly set out for the purpose to be conveniently close to the bivi's, but again, not too close in case of fire risk.

c. Latrine/washing area defined and sited down wind and away from tent site and cooking area and afforded some privacy.
d. Where there is running water, a drinking water point up-stream from a washing water point.
e. Some access for a vehicle if possible.

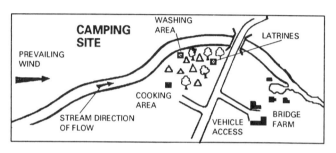

LATRINES

One of our normal, everyday occurrences is the use of a latrine, you sit in solitary confinement, with the door secure, not disturbed and very often in a cosy situation, with a chain or handle as the final act of the operation. You will not find it quite so civilised when living in the field, but there are a few important things to remember.
Hygiene; in spite of being "in the field" you have to exercise more care in washing your hands.
The digging of a hole in the ground is essential as any exposed excrement will attract flies who then can quickly spread disease.
The whole idea of this might not be to your liking, but the alternative could lead to a disaster with everyone going down with a serious illness.

CONSTRUCTION OF A FIELD LATRINE

You must make provision for a latrine by digging a hole not less than 44cm (one foot six inches) deep.

Some form of seat or bar if time permits the making of it.

The earth taken from the hole is piled up ready to be used by each individual to cover their excrement, and finally to fill the hole before leaving the site. All ground used in this way must be marked with a sign 'Soiled Ground'.

Even living in a "bivi site", in the open air, it must be recognised that privacy is important to every individual, therefore some form of screen or concealment is desirable. Your instructors should be very much aware of the privacy factor, and introduce some form of control.

If you are an NCO in this situation, the most simple form of "discipline" is to have a container which holds the toilet paper, left in a prominent position. ALL those when using the toilet take the container with them - remembering **to return it after use**.

The message - when the toilet is "engaged" the container is not there, simple, and effective.

PERSONAL HYGIENE

This would appear to be of low priority when you are in the field, yet the reverse is the fact.

It requires considerable self discipline to maintain a high standard of personal cleanliness when "living in the field". **Strict Routines** and personal discipline are essential if you are to maintain your health and energy, and keep friends.

WASHING

Regular washing and drying of all parts of your body with soap and water - even if it is cold water.

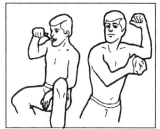

Particular attention should be given to those parts which collect sweat, such as armpits, crutch area, the waist and feet. Dirty and long hair can harbour lice and cause skin diseases. Teeth and gums must be brushed properly every day with tooth paste to avoid decay, clean and dry your tooth brush and keep it in a special holder

Take care of your washing kit, keep your towel clean and dry.
Use a container for your soap to keep it dry and not waste it.
They are all best kept in a polythene bag to help keep them clean and dry.
Wash out your underclothes and socks (weather and time permitting) so as not to be carrying dirty kit.

PREPARING FOOD IN THE FIELD

Your experience of cooking may be restricted to keeping something warm that has just been fetched from the nearest "take-away" and is now in the microwave.
Perhaps you live on pre-prepared meals from the Super Market, that just have to be heated up at the right temperature for a specified time, so long as you can read the instructions - you will feed!.
You will not be surprised that "cooking in the field" when on an expedition takes on a very different meaning.
Bottles of lemonade or tins of Coke are out !.
During cold weather, it is essential to stop and "brew-up" for the whole group of you on an expedition.
Once you get into a camp site, one of the duties to be performed must be to "brew-up".
Your body needs well cooked, hot food to sustain it.
There is no excuse to eat food out of a tin not having cooked it.

EXPEDITION TRAINING

COOKERS

You may use butane gas cookers, or more probably 'tommy cookers' which use small blocks of solid fuel in a folding tin container.

They are best used by scraping a hole in the ground so as to keep any draughts away from them to prevent them being blown out.

The hole needs to be deep enough to shield your mess tins when they are on the 'tommy cooker' to prevent cooling.

OPEN FIRES

The problem of cooking on an open fire is not so much the actual cooking, but finding a place where you can safely light a fire.

You will be aware of the dangers of fires in the countryside, where woods, forests and crops can be destroyed, causing untold damage taking years to replace. Therefore landowners are not at all keen to give you permission and the Forestry Commission strictly forbid fires on land that they look after. The warmth of a fire, the thought of hot, well cooked food is something to look forward to on an exercise, especially if the weather has been bad and you are wet through and cold!!, in which case you will certainly have to know how to produce hot - good food on an open fire.

STRICT RULES TO BE OBEYED

You will only light a fire when your officer has obtained permission.

You are on a recognised and organised exercise - not something you have set up between yourselves.

You have been trained how to light and care for a fire sufficient for your needs to be able to cook with.

You observe the safety rules - cooking area away from bivi's or any other fire hazards.

That all fires are out before going to sleep.

BUILDING a "COOKING FIRE"

If you rake together a pile of leaves, cover it "higgledy-piggledy" with dead twigs and fallen branches off the trees, and set a match to it, you will have a roaring fire that apart from being useless to cook on, will be a serious danger, as well as letting everyone know where you are.

If you are to have good meals cooked in the field and wish to save time and "hastle", you must learn how to produce a quick, hot little fire that will boil water in a jiffy, and that will soon burn down to HOT EMBERS with no smoke.

To light this type of fire you need small dry twigs, that will blaze up quickly and give you the heat to burn larger twigs and set your fire going to give you the correct hot bed of embers for cooking.

It is as well to remember that all trees are, in some sense, in the process of dying, and upon any tree it is possible to find dead twigs and sometimes dead branches.

Even in the wettest weather dead wood from a tree or hedge row will be found to be dry inside and easily lit.

If you build a fire on grass, carefully cut and remove the turf and soil, keep it to one side.

When you move out, clean out the fire ashes, water the ground well - make sure it is **not still warm** - replace the soil and turf.

Leave no litter behind you, ensure that the whole camp site has no trace of anyone being there.

If you do this you will have no problems if you want to use the site again.

MESS TIN COOKING

Mess Tin cooking is usually carried out with two of you "teaming up", as a small fire or cooker is very efficient to produce hot food for two.

To build a small cooking fire , look for a "rut" made by vehicles in soft ground, or make a "scrape" in the ground, see the diagram on the next page

EXPEDITION TRAINING

It needs to be deep enough to light a small fire that will quickly burn down to embers, at the same time rest your mess tin below the surface of the ground on the embers. If you are able to do so, have your "scrape" with the breeze blowing through its length, this will keep the embers glowing, giving you a gentle heat — the best possible heat to cook on.

The points to remember are :-

Check the direction of the wind, make a small trench in the ground about the size of your mess tin and six inches deep, with one end facing the wind.

The draught will blow along the length of your "trench" and help to keep the fire alive.

Build up a fire with plenty of **dead wood**, let it burn until all the smoke has disappeared and the trench is filled level with the ground with hot embers that glow as the breeze catches them - it takes time, but it is worth it.

The deep - hot ashes do not smoke, never cook on a fire with a lot of smoke, it makes less work in cleaning your mess tins.

The heat is gentle - not so likely to burn your food and without smoke much more pleasant to work with.

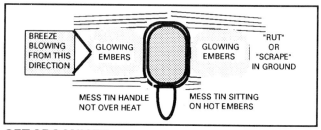

GET ORGANISED

Without any system or thought of getting yourself properly organised to do this simple job, you will waste an hour

182

messing about over a smoky fire, getting your eyebrows singed, finishing up with a 'burnt offering' for your dinner. Prepare your food while the fire is settling down - don't sit there watching it burn.

Make maximum use of the heat once it is the correct fire to use. Put a mess tin of water on while you are eating to make a hot drink, at the same time provide the hot water to wash your mess tins.

The use of cooking foil on an open fire is very efficient, by wrapping the food in foil and then raking the hot embers over the top of the wrapped food. Baked potatoes (in their jackets) are good cooked like this and also banana splits.

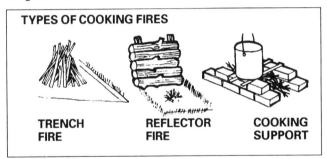

TYPES OF COOKING FIRES

| TRENCH FIRE | REFLECTOR FIRE | COOKING SUPPORT |

SAFETY

You will now realise that there is no need to light a "bonfire" to cook in the field.

The last word on this must be to stress the need for safety precautions at all times and we repeat, keep fires well away from bivi's and be sure the fires are out before settling down to sleep for the night.

Should you set up a camp site for a section or platoon, then you may need a larger fire - or several small ones to cook with, the same principles apply, removing the turf

and replacing it when clearing the camp site etc.
The illustrations on the previopus page show three
different types of fires for cooking.
These would be for a section or platoon to cook centrally,
not all at once though!

WARNING
DON'T LIGHT A FIRE ON PROPERTY,
UNLESS YOU HAVE BEEN AUTHORISED
TO DO SO BY YOUR OFFICERS OR
INSTRUCTORS, WHO WILL HAVE
FIRST OBTAINED PERMISSION
FROM THE LAND OWNER.

THE HARDEST TASK TO TACKLE.
ON RETURN FROM AN EXPEDITION, WHEN YOU
ARE TIRED AND EXHAUSTED — THERE IS A
GREAT DEAL WORK TO BE DONE BY *EVERYONE.*
WITH NO EXCEPTIONS — DIFFICULT, BUT ;
     "POST EXPEDITION ADMINISTRATION"
HAS TO BE DONE — THEN — NOT LATER.
TO CHECK FOR; DAMAGE OR LOSSES.
EQUIPMENT TO CLEAN AND CHECK.
TENTS, SLEEPING BAGS AND CLOTHING HUNG
UP TO DRY — PREVENTING DAMAGE AND
COSTLY REPLACEMENT.
SPARE RATIONS AND EQUIPMENT TO BE
RETURNED TO STORES.
ALL FOLLOWED BY; SHOWERS, FOOD, FOOT
INSPECTIONS AND DE-BRIEFING ON THE
EXPEDITION - IN THAT ORDER.
THIS IS A PART OF YOUR APC EXPEDITION TEST

CARE OF THE ENVIRONMENT

At any time you are able to use wood for a fire, or for that matter any time you use wood, just remember that growing trees are a valuable natural resource which take many years to mature.

In Britain we cannot grow enough to meet our needs and import many millions of pounds worth every year.

It follows that we must take great care in preserving what we have, not to cause damage by carving names on trees, or breaking down small saplings or branches off growing trees to build a fire. Find dead wood and use that — provided you have permission to do so. Read the following old poem, it will remind you just how valuable wood really is.

THE PRAYER OF THE TREE

You who pass by and would raise your hand against me, hearken ere you harm me.

I am the heat of your camp fire on a cold night, the friendly shade screening you from the summer sun.

My fruits are refreshing draughts quenching your thirst as you journey on.

I am the beam that holds your house, the board of your table, the bed on which you lie, the timber that builds your boat.

I am the handle of your hoe, the door of your homestead, the wood of your cradle, the shell of your last resting place.

I am the gift of God and the friend of man. You who pass by, listen to my prayer,

                              harm me not.

FOOD-RATIONS

The need for a balanced diet becomes more important as the distance you travel increases.

If a journey is to take several days you will have to plan your menus giving variety at the same time a balanced diet.

The amount of food you require daily will depend upon th type of country you are moving over.

If it is mountainous then your body will use more energy for you to replace by more food.

Food has to be carried, too much will add unnecessary weight to your load; too little and you will go hungry and that will cause problems.

The use of dehydrated foods can be very useful, especially as emergency rations. They are light to carry but are expensive to buy.

If you can take dehydrated food with you select the items that give you the most carbohydrates (sugars, starches) and fats.

Only take food that you like and enjoy eating. Keep all your meals simple to prepare.

All in stews are very good as you only need one mess tin to cook it in and it will be hot which is important.

Ensure that you have sufficient to drink. In the hot weather water in small quantities is alright, but not freezing cold

COMPOSITE RATIONS

As a cadet you will very often have Army Composite Rations **(COMPO)** issued to you while carrying out Field Training.

These rations have been developed over many years to give the soldier a high quality, balanced diet to ensure that they are always in the peak of fitness.

CONTENT OF "COMPO" RATIONS

Compo is issued in a Ration Pack, in this instance we are dealing with the 24 hour Ration Pack which is produced in four different menu selections, as set out on the next page.

EXPEDITION TRAINING

24 HOUR RATION PACK

MENU "A"	MENU "B"
BREAKFAST	**BREAKFAST**
Porridge	Porridge
Bacon Grill	Baconburger
Biscuits Brown	Biscuits Brown
Chocolate Drink	Chocolate Drink
SNACK	**SNACK**
Biscuits Brown	Biscuits Brown
Ham Spread	Beef Spread
Chocolate Full Cream	Chocolate Full Cream
Boiled Sweets	Boiled Sweets
Chocolate Covered Caramels	Chocolate Covered Caramels
Nuts and Raisins	Dextrose Tablets (Orange)
MAIN MEAL	**MAIN MEAL**
Biscuits Fruit Filled	Biscuits Fruit Filled
Instant Soup	Instant Soup
Chicken Curry	Steak and Kidney Pudding
Rice	Beans in Tomato Sauce
Apple Flakes	Apple & Apricot Flakes

MENU "C"	MENU"D"
BREAKFAST	**BREAKFAST**
Porridge	Porridge
Bacon Grill	Baconburger
Biscuits Brown	Biscuits Brown
Chocolate Drink	Chocolate Drink
SNACK	**SNACK**
Biscuits Brown	Biscuits Brown
Chicken Spread	Chicken & Bacon Spread
Chocolate Full Cream	Chocolate Full Cream
Confectionery Bar	Boiled Sweets
Chocolate Covered Caramel	Chocolate Covered Caramel
Dextrose Tablets (Lemon)	Dextrose Tablets (Orange)
MAIN MEAL	**MAIN MEAL**
Biscuits Fruit Filled	Biscuits Fruit Filled
Instant Soup	Instant Soup
Steak & Onion Casserole	Minced Steak
Beans in Tomato Sauce	Mixed Vegetables
Fruit Salad	Mixed Fruit Pudding

NOTE: The contents of Compo Rations may vary from time to time, depending upon the availability of items at the time of packing.

DRINKS	SUNDRIES
Beverage Whitener, Sugar, Tea Coffee, Beef Stock Drink, and Orange or Lemon Powder.	Chewing Gum, Toilet Paper, Book Matches, Waterproof Matches, Can Opener, Water Purification Tablets and a Menu Sheet.

COOKING INSTRUCTIONS

ROLLED OATS for PORRIDGE - Oats contain MILK already mixed.

ALL MENUS - Add the Rolled Oats mixture to a little cold water until it makes a paste, add a little more water and bring it to the boil, let it simmer and stir for 4 to 5 minutes. Add sugar to taste.

May also be flavoured with some Chocolate Drink Powder if desired.

BACON GRILL - Slice thinly to the thickness of a bacon rashers.

Fry on a LOW heat, turning them over until golden brown on both sides. Can also be eaten cold IF sliced thinly.

BACONBURGERS - Slice it in two for quick cooking.
Use the fat from the can to fry them in on a low heat, turn them over, cook until golden brown.

They can also be eaten cold if thinly sliced.

INSTANT SOUP Empty the contents of one sachet into your mug. Add half a pint of boiling water and stir well. The variety of soup will depend on the availability at the time of packing.

PRE COOKED RICE Put rice in mess tin, cover it with boiling water, bring it back to boil and let it simmer for FIVE minutes. Allow it to stand for TWO minutes, during which time it will soak up the water.

APPLE FLAKES and APPLE/APRICOT FLAKES Put sachet in mess tin, pour boiling water over the flakes and leave for TWO minutes - while the flakes are soaking up the water. The flakes are then ready to eat.

DRINKS The ingredients for the different drinks in your pack will make up the following quantity of drink:-

Tea - THREE pints. Coffee - TWO pints.
Drinking Chocolate - ONE pint.
Orange/Lemon Drink - ONE or TWO pints.
Beef Stock Drink - ONE THIRD pint.

TO HEAT CANS

You can cook COMPO rations "in the can" by piercing
TWO holes in the lid of the can, stand the can in your
Mess Tin with the holes at the top, fill the mess tin with
water until it is half submerged.

Bring the water to the boil and let it boil for TEN
minutes. Handle carefully when opening the hot can.
Although this is an easy method of heating the can, the
food does not taste quite as good if you cook it in the
way suggested, bearing in mind that this is a very good
method for a soldier who may have to cook under very
difficult conditions.

> **SAFETY - BE SURE YOU MAKE TWO HOLES IN
> THE CAN AND THAT THE HOLES ARE AT THE
> TOP WHEN BOILING IT IN YOUR MESS TIN.**

WATER PURIFICATION TABLETS

These are a part of your Ration Pack and it is important
that you know how to use them.
For Drinking Water, add one purification tablet to each
litre (ONE and THREE QUARTER pints) of water.
Leave for TEN MINUTES before use.
Leave for at least THIRTY minutes if using to make up
your Lemon or Orange Drink.

WINDPROOF/WATERPROOF MATCHES

These matches MUST be kept for lighting your Hexamine
blocks in bad weather conditions.
Don't use them for any other reason or you will be in
great difficulty if bad weather sets in and you have:-

— *NO WINDPROOF/WATERPROOF MATCHES*

— *NO HOT FOOD — NO HOT DRINK — NO WARMTH*

USEFUL MEASURE TO NOTE

Examine your small mess tin, if you fill it up to the bottom rivet that holds on the Mess Tin Handle hinge, you will have a PINT of water in the mess tin.

IMPROVISED SHELTER

Construction of improvised Shelters for use when BIVI'S are not available.

There will be occasions when you do not have a tent to shelter in. The British soldier has a reputation to be able to improvise, it is said that "any fool can rough it, but a good soldier will make himself comfortable under any conditions", the illustrations give you a few ideas of how to put up improvised shelters.

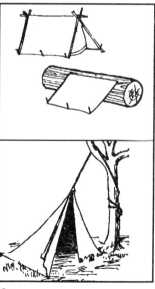

A shelter with two ground sheets constructed on the same principle as a BIVI for two.

A groundsheet shelter against a fallen tree trunk for one person.
The ground sheet must be on the side of the trunk away from the prevailing wind.

Another groundsheet type of shelter for one person. The rope must be strong and the open side of the groundsheet away from the prevailing wind.

IMPROVISED TENT

Using a string between two supports, tie groundsheets over the string, pegging the bottom edges to the ground. This type of "tent" can also be put up against a fence or wall using one half of the tent as shown on the right as a triangle A - B - C.

To make a Basha for two you need two groundsheets, string or bungees (6 at least), meat skewers or tent pegs are useful (6 or 8 are needed).

A length of strong string is always useful to have in your kit.

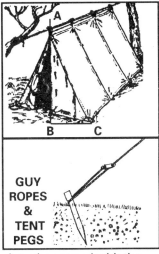

GUY ROPES & TENT PEGS

Tent pegs must not be driven into the ground with the head of an axe, use the proper mallet.

They must be put in at an angle as the diagram above and not so far in the ground that they cannot be seen.

ADVENTUROUS TRAINING & PHYSICAL ACTIVITIES

You must have a responsible attitude to all activities you take part in, to prevent yourself and others becoming casualties through your own lack of care and preparation. The rescue services invariably report that "the party was totally unprepared for the expedition" or they "had not been trained in map reading", or even worse the Coroner at the inquest reported "they had no idea that the deceased was suffering from Hypothermia".

There are many activities that you may take part in as a group, but they will only be organised provided the officers and instructors supervising are currently

191

qualified in that activity or other people who are to assist
hold a valid certificate to organise and run the event.

OFFICIAL PERMISSION

On No Account will you organise activities without the
knowledge and assistance of your officers or instructors.
This is not to "spoil your sport", but to make sure that
you are properly organised and prepared with the correct
equipment, and that it is carried out to the highest
standards.

**REMEMBER - YOU ARE ONLY COVERED BY
INSURANCE IN THE EVENT OF AN ACCIDENT, IF
IT IS OFFICIALLY PLANNED AND ORGANISED.**

ADVENTUROUS & PHYSICAL ACTIVITIES

To remind you, the activities that are considered as
adventurous and physical are as follows:-

**Mountaineering - including Hill Walking, Rocking
Climbing, Absailing, Skiing, Caving, Canoeing, Off
Shore Sailing, Rafting, Swimming, Gliding or
Hang-gliding, Para-cending, Sub - Aqua Diving and
all activities involving the hazard of water.**

There is no substitute for good training and planned
preparation to ensure that you will be able to cope with a
crisis.

You must carry out fitness training, practice using and
testing your equipment - to include cooking practice.
Make sure that you ARE properly organised and DO have
the correct equipment, have a "dress rehearsal" - doing it
to a high standard and safely.

PREVENTION OF ACCIDENTS
ON OUTDOOR ACTIVITIES

Before you set out:-
Don't overdress, leave off that woollen pullover - carry it
on top of your pack until the harder part of the march is over.
Do not carry too much kit.

EXPEDITION TRAINING

Plan the kit you will carry, reducing non essentials like two sweaters where one will do.

As an individual, always carry a map, compass, protractor, pencil, whistle, first-aid kit and a torch.

Always carry spare warm clothing.

Carry emergency rations such as chocolate, glucose tablets, dried fruit etc. with you, and don't eat them except in an emergency.

Always leave a detailed Route Card showing your intended route out and back, check points, RV's, camp sites and your Estimated Time of Arrival (ETA), all supported by accurate Map References.

Know the location of local mountain rescue posts and their procedures and map references of telephone boxes.

Report to the local Rescue Post letting them know your route and time expected back, give them a copy of your route card.

Decide on a Lost Drill e.g., "go West till you strike the main road" or "keep walking down-stream".

PLANNING YOUR ROUTE.

Plan your route beforehand, and ensure all members of the group are fully briefed and all have copies of the route, map refs, check points and RV's.

Take into account weather conditions and the forecasts for the duration of your exercise.

Treat hills and mountains with very great respect.

OUT ON THE HILLS

Always stay together, unless there is an injured person, in which case half of the party should stay with the casualty, while the other half goes for help.

Walk at the pace of the slowest person.

Remember to observe the Country Code.

If you go out as a group, never travel in groups of less than FIVE.

Carry at least one polythene survival sack or sleeping bag per two persons.

Stick to the route you agreed with the local Rescue Post. Make one decision among the group as to the direction to take.

If a compass bearing is used, have others check it, then trust your compass.

PRECAUTIONS —

DO NOT SPLIT UP - DON'T LEAVE ANYONE BEHIND.

If weather conditions deteriorate - DON'T PRESS ON - TURN BACK.

Do not throw stones; these can dislodge bigger ones and you could cause an accident.

IF YOU DO GET LOST :-

1. **DO NOT SPLIT UP.**
2. **DO NOT PANIC.**
3. **DO NOT FORGET TO USE YOUR MAP, COMPASS AND YOUR COMMON SENSE.**
4. **REMEMBER THE INTERNATIONAL DISTRESS CALL - SIX BLASTS ON YOUR WHISTLE OR SIX TORCH FLASHES PER MINUTE.**

PREVENTION OF ACCIDENTS.

Walking by day or night as an individual, when moving on foot you must:-

Use a footpath or pavement or, if there is not one, walk on the side of the road facing the nearest traffic (normally the right hand side) and keep as close to the side as possible.

Cross motorways by bridges and railways by bridges or level crossings.

When dark, keep an extra sharp look-out and wear a high visibility jacket or white arm band or white patch (a handkerchief if nothing better is available) which will show up in the lights of a vehicle.

SAFETY and EMERGENCY PROCEDURES
Emergency Messages
The Police are responsible for calling out the rescue services. The information they will require is as follows:-

a. The exact location of the injured person(s), with a six figure grid reference and a description/landmarks of the area for a Helicopter Pilot to identify.

b. The number of persons injured and their name(s).

c. The nature of their injuries.

d. The time of the accident.

Those going for help must remember the area and landscape with any particular reference point to help find the site on return with a rescue party.

Waiting for help to arrive.
Those looking after the injured would set up shelters and carry out emergency first aid, with special reference to the prevention of hypothermia/exposure.

It will be necessary to mark the site with light coloured clothing or bandages on sticks where they can easily attract attention.

There are International **Ground to Air Signals** that can be used to communicate with rescue aircraft. They are shown on the next page.

In addition to these signals, **A RED FLARE, A RED SQUARE OF CLOTH** or a **FIRE** are also recognised **International Alarm Signals.**

The shape of each signal can be made by setting out clothing or items of kit, or a person taking up the shape of the letter standing up or lying down.

Get help, attract attention in any way you can.

Be alert and watch out for the rescue party to guide them in the quickest route.

Make yourselves comfortable as possible, "brew-up", eat HOT food, keep together, keep warm, keep up the morale.

GROUND TO AIR SIGNALS

letter	signal	
V		**REQUEST ASSISTANCE**
↑		**WE ARE PROCEEDING IN THIS DIRECTION**
X		**MEDICAL ASSISTANCE REQUIRED**
N		**NO WE DO NOT NEED ANYTHING**

WIND CHILL FACTOR

Not sufficient attention is paid to the combined effect that
the air temperature and the speed of the wind has on the
human body, especially exposed surfaces, such as the
face, head and hands.

The wind speed is often given during weather forecasts
and you would be well advised to take note of this if you
are to embark on an expedition or extended hill walk.
These factors, the combined effect of the wind speed and
air temperature on your body reduces the natural heat.
As the as the wind speed increases it reduces your body
temperature more quickly.

This is most apparent at lower wind speeds between 0 to
24 k.p.h. (15 m.p.h.) at these speeds even a small
increase in wind speed causes more rapid cooling of the
body. Wind speeds above 24 k.p.h. (15 m.p.h.) cool the
body slower, but this does not mean that you can ignore
high wind as in addition to the wind chill factor it makes
you use a lot more energy and can blow you over the
edge off a path or hillside.

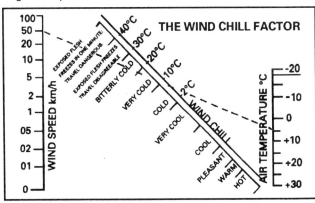

EXPEDITION TRAINING

The diagram on the previous page is reproduced from the book Mountaincraft and Leadership by Alec Langmuir and illustrates graphically how important it is to be aware of the Wind Chill Factor.

In the diagram as an example it shows:-

The air temperature at +5 degrees C, at a wind speed of 50 k.p.h. (31 m.p.h.) it crosses the Wind Chill Line at "very cold".

Protection from wind alone is not sufficient, you must try to keep yourself dry, as wet clothing combined with the Wind Chill Factor can rapidly bring on the conditions for you to suffer from Hypothermia (exposure), you will then most certainly become a casualty.

HYPOTHERMIA or EXPOSURE

Hypothermia - describes the serious effect which may result from exposure to climatic conditions where the heat content of the body is so reduced to the point where the deep body temperature begins to fall - this is a serious condition.

Ignorance of a victims condition can lead to dangerous incorrect treatment. It is not easy to recognise a mild case of exposure, but, just the same very important to do so to avoid a crisis.

It is vital to preserve the heat already in the body, but NOT to increase the heat rapidly on the surface of the body.

SIGNS AND SYMPTOMS.

1. Unexpected behavior, complaints of coldness and being tired.
2. Physical fatigue - failure to understand questions/ instructions.
3. Failure of vision - a usual symptom and serious.

4. Some slurring of speech.
5. Sudden shivering fits.
6. Violent outbursts of unexpected energy, violent
   language and physical resistance to help.
7. Falling over - stumbling.
Other symptoms may sometimes be muscle cramp, very
grey face, dizzyness and fainting fits.

TREATMENT - HYPOTHERMIA.

1. Put victim into a sleeping bag or wrap blankets all
   round body.
2. Put fit companion into sleeping bag with victim or
   lying close by them.
3. Shelter victim from wind or draught,
4. Get rest of the party to build a shelter.
5. If victim is able to eat, give them sugar in easily
   digestible form, for example condensed milk.
6. If breathing ceases - perform artificial respiration.
7. When victim recovers they MUST be treated as a
   STRETCHER CASE, in spite of apparent recovery or
   protests of being 'all right'.
8. Seek medical aid immediately.
   a. Prevention is better than cure.
   b. Better to take action to prevent exposure.
   c. Make sure that clothing, including headgear, is
   windproof and wear it early enough on your journey.
   d. Eat small quantities of energy giving food before
   and while on a expedition, such as glucose sweets or
   Kendal Mint Cake.

FROSTBITE

Frostbite is the freezing or partial freezing of parts of the
body, more often than not the extremities of the body,
ears fingers toes.

If the supply of blood to those parts is sufficient and the tissue keeps warm there is little chance of frostbite. However, if the person is in the early stages of hypothermia, is exhausted or has poorly insulating clothing, their circulation will drop and parts of the body susceptible to frostbite will cool rapidly.

The tissues will freeze, the initial stage of "frostnip" will show itself in the form of the nose, hands or ears turning white.

They must be re-warmed immediately. Feet and hands will feel warm and then cold. This is a sure sign of "frostnip" and if not treated will be followed by frostbite.

TREATMENT — Frostnip

For "frostnip" is to warm the affected part on a warm part of the body. Hands warmed under the armpit, ears and nose with hands and feet on the stomach of your buddy.

Superficial frostbite can be skin deep or surface tissues which are a white/grey colour, frozen on the surface yet soft beneath.

Immediate action and the correct treatment can lead to full recovery and no damaged tissue. Deep frostbite affects not only the skin, but also the muscles, tendons and bone in a limb.

Recovery is a very slow and painful process and nearly always leads to some loss of tissue or worse.

TREATMENT - Frostbite.

Introduce warmth to the casualty and maintain the warmth protecting the damaged limb from the weight of blankets etc with some form of rigid support over it, preventing physical damage or contact with the affected limb.

Make sure that cooling does not take place. Immediate

evacuation is essential. If there is any delay treat for exposure, give shelter and continuous warmth.

DO NOT ATTEMPT TO RE-WARM FROSTBITTEN PART BY EXERCISE OR ANY OTHER MEANS - THIS WILL GIVE THE CASUALTY THE BEST CHANCE OF RECOVERY LATER

W A R N I N G

**IT IS A COMBINATION OF CAUSES THAT MAKE YOU VULNERABLE TO THIS DREADED KILLER, WHICH CAN AFFECT YOU IN MANY CIRCUM-STANCES, NOT ONLY IN WILD COUNTRY. SINGLY, THESE CAUSES ARE NOWHERE AS DEADLY, BUT GIVEN THE RIGHT CONDITIONS ALL FOUR "GANG UP" ON THE UNSUSPECTING, WHO RAPIDLY BECOME VICTIMS OF HYPOTHERMIA. REMEMBER:
COLDNESS + WIND + WETNESS + FATIGUE = HYPOTHERMIA**

IF YOU DO AS YOU HAVE BEEN TRAINED TO DO, YOU MAY NOT BECOME A "DISASTER FOR THE EMERGENCY SERVICES"

SUMMARY

Accidents ARE CAUSED.

Most accidents and related problems on Adventurous type outdoor activities, no matter where it is taking place, in hills or mountains or even in your local countryside are due to one or more of the following reasons:-

1. Not involving senior, more experienced members of your unit and getting permission in the first place to carry out an "expedition".

2. Insufficient detailed preparation, planning and training - RECCE not done properly, no rehearsals. Menu not planned for type of area travelled.

3. Not being properly equipped or dressed - especially wearing "jeans" and useless footwear.

4. Carelessness or casualness by you and those taking part.

5. Over estimating your own and others physical strength and the stamina required.

6. Not having enough practical experience and practice - especially map reading and camp craft.

7. Not paying enough attention to detail, not being observant - failing to notice soon enough to take action due to changes in the weather conditions.

8. Not turning back early enough - when common sense said "turn back".

9. Not noticing a member of the team "flagging"- getting left behind.

10. Failing to work together as a team - getting in a panic.

11. Not accepting advice from experienced people, while en-route.

12. Failing to give Route Cards, Map References of RV's and timings and other information IN WRITING to anyone before departing.

QUESTIONS

1. What are the ten Country Code Rules.
2. What sort of socks should you wear on an expedition
3. The weight you carry on your back is equal to ....times the weight on your feet.
4. What do you dust your feet with.
5. How do you open a blister and what with.
6. If you are very thirsty, should you eat snow.
7. What do you carry on the outside of your ruck sack.
8. When looking for a camp site, what do you have to have from the owners.
9. What do you check out for safety when choosing a camp site
10. Is it a good idea to put up a tent under trees.
11. If you have to use water from a stream, what do you first do with it.
12. Where would you site the latrine and washing area, and why.
13. In a camp for several days you construct a latrine, how is it done and what are the important sizes.
14. When sighting a latrine what do you do about providing privacy, and how important is it.
15. If allowed to build a fire for cooking, what sort of fire do you cook on.
16. Why is the advantage of digging a small hole to put your cooker into.
17. What should you leave at a camp site.
18. You cannot go off on your own expedition as a Cadet, why not.
19. Five of you are on an expedition, one is injured, how many would normally go for help.
20. When planning a route what must you produce and give someone a copy of .
21. The weather is getting bad on an expedition, do you go on or turn back.

22. What is the distress call/signal with: a. Whistle. b. Torch, and the Emergency Ground to Air Signals.
23. What do you understand by the Wind Chill Factor.
24. What added danger is there if you get wet on a cold and windy day.
25. You use ONE Water Purification Tablet to how much water.
26. Making Porridge, simmer and stir for how many minutes.
27. Describe three types of improvised shelters..
28. What happens if you walk for some distance with boots full of water.
29. How can you test that a pair of boots are about the right size.
30. Without anything covering your head, how much body heat can you lose.

MAP and COMPASS

INTRODUCTION

We are fortunate in Britain to have first class maps produced by the Ordnance Survey Department of Her Majesty's Stationery Office.

All military maps are produced for the Army by the RAOC in flat sheets.

A map should be protected by either being folded in a plastic bag when in use or by being placed on a piece of hardboard and covered with a transparent sheet, although this is not very satisfactory if you are walking any distance, but essential to use for training and route planning.

If maps are not carefully handled they quickly become useless, it follows that you must not write directly on a map or use it without protecting it in some way.

Map cases are available from the Cadet Supply Department, and are a useful item to have.

Your map should be folded lengthwise and then folded again like a concertina.

RELIABILITY OF MAPS.

A map is virtually a 'birds eye view' of the ground drawn on paper. It is absolutely accurate only at the time it is drawn. Today maps are produced from aerial photography which ensures their accuracy, but as time goes by much of the 'picture' of the ground soon changes, villages grow, new roads are made, some woods are cut down and others planted etc, etc. For practical map reading purposes this will not affect the accuracy as far as you will be concerned, any map produced within the last few years may be relied upon unless specifically stated otherwise.

MAP READING

MARGINAL INFORMATION.

On most maps you will find a part of it set aside for 'marginal information', you should find this as soon as you unfold your map as it provides a great deal of guidance as to how to read the map and how to interpret the detail.

You will need to constantly refer to this until you have a complete understanding of what all the symbols (usually called Conventional Signs) and other information mean to you.

The number of your map and its scale will be found at the top of the map. The index to ajoining sheets is shown as a diagram near the bottom right hand corner of the map. You will need to find out which sheet number you require to cover the particular area that you are using and the next sheet if your route goes "off the map".

Most maps now use metres as the "unit of elevation", check your map by looking in the margin at the bottom of the map as "ELEVATIONS IN METRES".

THE GRID SYSTEM.

The British National Grid System divides the whole country into large squares, which are sub-divided and finish up as GRID LINES printed on the maps that you will normally use.

For your purpose the GRID LINES are a method for you to 'pin-point' a specific spot on a map, by using the numbers of each line as shown in the margins around the outside of the map as co-ordinates.

Maps are printed with the North at the top of the sheet, one set of GRID LINES run up and down the map (North and South), the others run across the map (East and West).

It is important that you are able to find a point on the map and then be able to go out and find it on the ground, also to be able - at all times - to indicate on the map the exact place that you are standing on the ground.

MAP READING

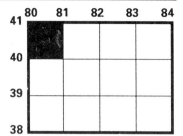

To assist in the accurate use of the grid system it is advisable to obtain a Pathfinder Protractor/Romer, it provides two of the different scales of GRID SQUARES found on Ordnance Survey Maps.

This Romer is made of rigid plastic which you place on the GRID SQUARE of the map and read off the figures as described below, to pin-point the exact position.

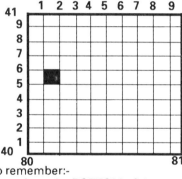

FOUR and SIX FIGURE REFERENCES

When giving a reference there are a few simple rules to remember:-

1. FIRST - count the figures along the BOTTOM of the map, from left (west) to right (east) these are called **'EASTINGS'**.

   Next count the figures up the sides of the map, from bottom (south), to top (north) these are called **'NORTHINGS'**.

2. A reference must always contain an even number of figures

3. GRID REFERENCES are always given with the **'EASTINGS'** value first, followed by the **'NORTHINGS'** value.

The example in the diagram at the top of this page,

shows a black square, that can be given the reference as sqaure 8040 (a four figure reference). This square could represent a whole square kilometre of ground, not exactly a 'pin-point' location on a map or ground. Should you use a four figure reference you must add a feature to indicate where you mean.

To get an exact position, the square is further sub-divided into 10 squares in both directions. The bottom diagram on the previous page illustrates this sub-division, the black square is "square 2 - 5", these figures when added as explained below make up a six figure reference.

The first two figures the EASTING value, followed by the sub divided square figure, then the two NORTHING value figures, followed again by the sub divided figure, making up a six figure reference 802405

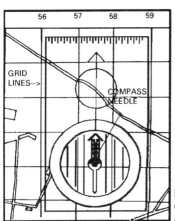

SETTING A MAP

This is useful if you are in mountain country or on a featureless plain.

You must always read your map in relation to the ground, therefore as soon as you unfold a map it must be automatically 'SET' or 'ORIENTATED'. This can be done both with and without a compass.

By Compass

1. Turn the COMPASS HOUSING until the ORIENTING ARROW lies under the NORTH (RED) end of the compass NEEDLE - pointing to NORTH.

Remembering that NORTH on a map is at the TOP of the map sheet, place the compass on the map, with it's edge parallel to the GRID LINES running NORTH to SOUTH on the map.

Turn the map and compass together until the ORINENTING ARROW again lies under the NORTH (RED) end of the Compass NEEDLE - see diagram on previous page.

SETTING A MAP WITHOUT A COMPASS BY CAREFUL OBSERVATION

This can be easy, once you have identified exactly where you are on the map, and if you are standing on a straight road, line up the road on your map with the road you are standing on. Make certain that the map is pointing in the right direction, i.e the right way round.

If not on a road, you will need to find other objects on the ground such as a road/track junction, church, prominent hill top or farm buildings. You must also find the same objects on your map, using them as shown in the diagram by turning your map to set or orientate it in relation to the ground

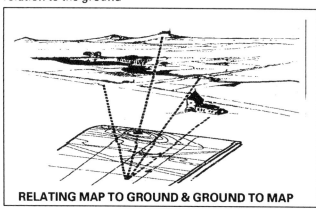

RELATING MAP TO GROUND & GROUND TO MAP

MAP READING

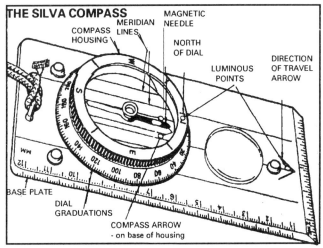

THE SILVA COMPASS

CARDINAL POINTS OF THE COMPASS

North, East, South and West are known as the cardinal points of the compass.

There are 32 points of the compass, but only 16 of them are normally used in map reading for the description of direction. These 16 are the four cardinal points and 12 intermediate points as shown in the diagram on th left The letters **N, E, S** and **W** stand respectively for **NORTH, SOUTH, EAST** and **WEST**. In the intermediate points these letters are combined, eg **SE** is South East. **NNW** is North North West, etc.

These points describe direction only to within one sixteenth of the full circle: for more accurate indication of direction it is necessary to use sub-divisions of the circle using "mils" or "degrees".

POINTS OF THE COMPASS

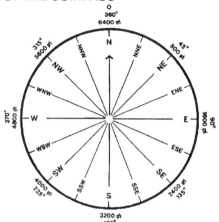

The mils system is used by the Army to give much greater accuracy than degrees.

The MILS SYSTEM divides the circle of the compass into 6400 MILS, the zero being at the North Point.

The four quadrants or quarters of the circle are each 1600 mils, and so the East, South, and West points fall at 1600, 3200, 4800 mils respectively, as illustrated.

The symbol normally used for mils is m, with a / across them.

NORTH POINTS.

There are **THREE** NORTH points:

1. **TRUE NORTH** - The actual direction of the geographical North Pole..
2. **GRID NORTH** - The direction of the vertical GRID LINES on a map. For all practical purposes TRUE and GRID NORTH are the same.

3. MAGNETIC NORTH -

The direction towards which the compass needle is attracted is the MAGNETIC NORTH POLE, see the diagram on the right.

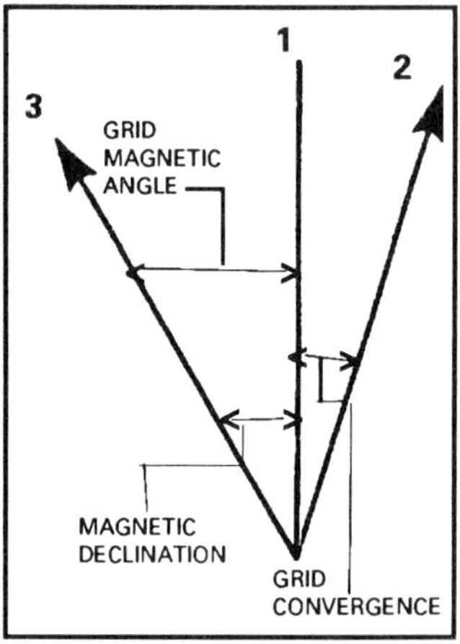

ANGLES BETWEEN NORTHPOINTS

Grid Magnetic Angle. (GMA)
This is sometimes called the magnetic variation, is the angle between GRID NORTH and MAGNETIC NORTH and it depends on two factors:

1. **TIME**. As the position of the Magnetic North Pole moves slightly eastwards, so the GMA (Grid Magnetic Angle) changes. This is called the Annual Magnetic Change and must be taken into account when converting magnetic bearings to Grid Bearings and vice versa.

2. **PLACE**. The GMA (Grid Magnetic Angle) also varies from one part of the country to another. These two factors are included in the marginal information on the map.

Magnetic Declination

This is the angle between MAGNETIC and TRUE NORTH as shown on the diagram.

Grid Convergence

This is the angle between GRID NORTH and TRUE NORTH which can, in practice be ignored since for practical map reading purposes TRUE NORTH and GRID NORTH are the same.

BEARINGS - TYPES OF BEARINGS

As there are three types of North points, there are three kinds of bearings, according to the North point from which they have been measured:

1. A MAGNETIC BEARING is one taken with a compass (an accurate compass needle always points towards MAGNETIC NORTH).

2. A GRID BEARING is one measured on a map with the Silva compass used as a protractor or using your Pathfinder Protractor/Romer.

3. A TRUE BEARING cannot be measured direct, but must be calculated from the other two. However this can be ignored for practical map reading purposes.

NOTE. INDIVIDUAL COMPASS ERROR (ICE)

The accuracy of each individual compass is subject to error, it is important that you should check your own compass to establish the INDIVIDUAL COMPASS ERROR (ICE), do this by checking it against other compasses. Having done so make a note of it on your compass base with a small sticky label, don't forget to allow for it.

TO TAKE A MAGNETIC BEARING

1. Point the compass direction of march arrow at the object.

2. Turn compass housing until the red arrow is under the needle.

3. Read off the MAGNETIC BEARING on the compass housing.

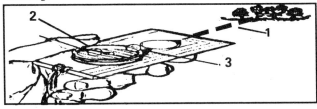

MAP READING

TO TAKE A GRID BEARING

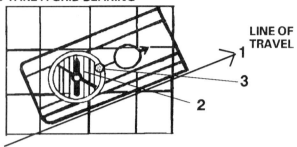

LINE OF TRAVEL

One of the most common uses of taking bearings is to take one from the map to find the bearing to march on With your SILVA compass or your protractor it is quite simple.

NOTE: IGNORE THE COMPASS NEEDLE.
1. Place the long edge of the compass along the desired line of travel, making sure that the DIRECTION OF TRAVEL ARROW on the compass POINTS IN THE DIRECTION YOU WISH TO GO.
2. Turn the COMPASS NEEDLE HOUSING, so that NORTH on the housing rim points to NORTH on the map. You will notice that the MERIDIAN LINES on the COMPASS are parallel to the GRID LINES on the map - or they should be.
3. Read the number of mils/degrees against the DIRECTION OF TRAVEL LINE, this is the GRID BEARING. Having taken a GRID BEARING from the map, you must take into account and make allowances for the GRID MAGNETIC ANGLE (GMA)

MAP READING

FINDING YOUR POSITION WITH A COMPASS RE-SECTION

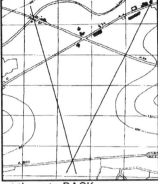

Select two identifiable features or landmarks that you can take a bearing onto, and identify the two features on your map.

They should be some distance apart, preferably at right angles from you - see diagram.

The method is that you take FORWARD BEARINGS on to the features, then convert them to BACK BEARINGS.

Not forgetting that these are MAG BEARINGS, convert them to GRID BEARINGS and plot them on your map using your PROTRACTOR or your SILVA compass as a Protractor.

By plotting these bearings and drawing lines ON THE PLASTIC COVER of your map, the TWO lines meet and cross over.

Where the two lines cross is your approximate position - provided you have carried out the following correctly:-

Assuming you have taken the bearings on the TWO landmarks, they need to be converted to GRID BEARINGS by subtracting the MAGNETIC VARIATION.

Then convert these two bearings into BACK BEARINGS and plot them on the map by placing the compass on the map with the CENTRE OF THE COMPASS DIRECTLY OVER EACH FEATURE ON THE MAP and with the ORIENTEERING LINES on the COMPASS housing parallel to the GRID LINES.

Turn the compass BASE so as the DIRECTION of MARCH
arrow is set at the converted bearing..
Mark your map cover at the POINT of the DIRECTION of
MARCH ARROW, draw an extended line from the
FEATURE on the map THROUGH the mark you have
made and beyond a few inches.
Repeat this for the second feature, you should find that
the TWO extended lines you have drawn cross each other
- this should be your approximately position.

IDENTIFYING A FEATURE

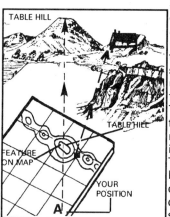

Set your map, use the
edge of your protractor or
a pencil, place it on the
map with the edge running
through your position,
swing it across the map
until it lines up with the
feature on the ground.
The feature should be easy
to pick out, provided it is
not too far away and that it
is on your map!.
This like so many Map
Reading skills need
constant practice until you
carry it out as a "drill" and
second nature.

After a while you will be able to locate and identify
features by just looking across the map.
In setting your map, no matter what method you use, it is
the constant relating and comparison of the map and
ground which will build a good foundation for your
navigational skills.
We remind you that this skill above all will go a long way
to prevent you getting lost on your DofE Expedition.

MAP READING

GRID MAGNETIC ANGLE
(GMA) in UK
GMA = 8 degrees,15' West
or145 mils West in
June 1980
Annual change approx
10' East MN GN GMA
145mils, 8 degrees

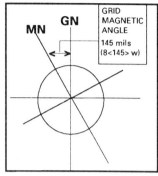

| **REMEMBER** |
| "Grid to Mag - ADD" |
| "Mag to Grid get RID" |

CONVERTING A GRID BEARING TO A MAGNETIC BEARING

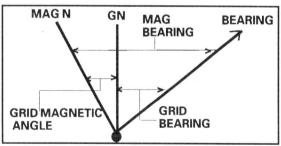

Remember all bearings are measured in a clockwise
direction from the NORTH point. A MAG bearing will
always be GREATER than the GRID bearing taken, by the
amount of the GRID MAGNETIC ANGLE.
Therefore to convert GRID to MAG ADD the GRID
MAGNETIC ANGLE.
To convert a MAG bearing to a GRID, SUBTRACT the
GRID MAGNETIC ANGLE.

MAP READING

TO MARCH ON A BEARING

Having converted your GRID BEARING to a MAGNETIC BEARING, set the graduated circle to read the MAGNETIC BEARING at the DIRECTION OF TRAVEL line.

Then turn the whole compass until the NORTH end of the NEEDLE coincides with the NORTH ARROW and is parallel to the MERIDIAN LINES on the COMPASS HOUSING, holding the compass in front of you, march in the direction indicated by the LINE OF TRAVEL ARROW. So long as the compass needle and the NORTH ARROW are kept together, the DIRECTION OF TRAVEL ARROW will remain on the required bearing.

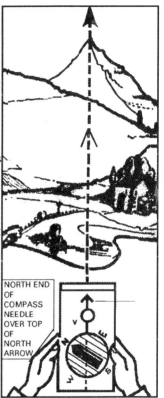

NORTH END OF COMPASS NEEDLE OVER TOP OF NORTH ARROW

BACK BEARINGS with a SILVA COMPASS

When marching on a bearing - especially at night - over some distance you may often have a doubt in your mind that you may go wandering off course and finish up being lost.

MAP READING

The ability to use your compass and to **trust it** by taking a back bearing on to the point from which you started, will prevent you getting into difficulties. The simplicity of the Silva compass makes the use of back bearings an easy navigational aid. To use the compass for a **BACK BEARING**, keep the compass on the bearing you have taken (as **'X'** to **'Y'** in the diagram), rotate the **COMPASS HOUSING** through **3200 mils (180º)**.
The compass is now **set** to march on the **BACK BEARING** (in the direction of **'Y'** in the diagram) of your original **FORWARD BEARING**.
To retrace your route - (from **'Y'** to **'X'** march on the bearing given as your **BACK BEARING**.
This is a very important skill - easily learned with a compass, it is one of the best methods of preventing yourself from getting lost.
Practice makes perfect.

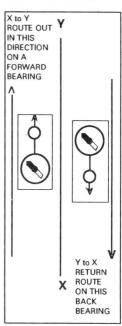

FORWARD AND BACK BEARING

X to Y
ROUTE OUT
IN THIS
DIRECTION
ON A
FORWARD
BEARING

Y to X
RETURN
ROUTE
ON THIS
BACK
BEARING

HILLS AND VALLEYS

The method of showing how the ground is shaped in terms of the hills and valleys which are expressed as the RELIEF, are shown by CONTOUR LINES. These appear as thin brown lines on the map and are described as "an imaginary line joining all points of equal height above sea level".

MAP READING

You must check the information at the bottom of the map near the scale diagram to find the "Contour Interval", that is the height between each contour
To give you a better understanding of contours the following pages of information and diagrams will explain them.

UNDERSTANDING and INTERPRETING CONTOURS

Contors are quite easy to follow, provided you understand the fact that they follow the same height, round hills, into re-entrants, and over the spurs.
They do not provide a picture of the shape of the land, but with practice and using contours you will be able to do so.
Something that always puzzles cadets is to know from a contour whether the ground is rising or falling, whether the feature is a spur or a re-entrant.
A spur projects out from the land mass, while a re-entrant is exactly the opposite - a shallow valley running up into the mass.
It is not always possible, however, to tell which is the top of the slope and which is the bottom, without being able to find the contour figures.
When the contour figures can be read with both the map and the figures the correct way up you would be able to tell if the ground is rising or falling.
A general idea of which way the slopes run can be obtained by looking at other features - particularly lakes, ponds, rivers, streams, and railway lines.
A stream running near a set of contours indicates at once which is the bottom of the slope.
Similar features such as railways, villages and large woods are more likely to be found at the bottom of a hill than at the top.
These skills of recognising the ground from the map go towards making Map Reading become an 'alive' and enjoyable hobby for most of your life.

CONVEX and CONCAVE SLOPES

A CONVEX slope is one that bulges outwards, and a CONCAVE slope is one that curves inwards - see the diagrams on the right. Standing at the top of a CONVEX slope you would not be able to see all the way down to the bottom, because the outward slope would obscure your view. This is important to recognise as ground that you cannot see - "dead ground" can conceal the enemy or give you cover from view.

When standing at the top of the CONCAVE slope, however, there would be a clear view the whole way down the slope.

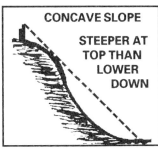

CONCAVE SLOPE

STEEPER AT TOP THAN LOWER DOWN

CONVEX SLOPE

BULGES OUT AT TOP

STEEPER AT THE LOWER END

CONTOUR VALUES

If you had several paths right round a hill, each one keeping at the same level, and were walking round one of them, you would find that where the paths were near to each other the ground would be steep between them, and where the paths were some distance apart, the ground would slope gently, the further they were apart, the less the slope would be.

> **ONLY WITH PRACTICE WILL YOU LEARN TO TRUST YOUR COMPASS**

MAP READING

UNDERSTANDING VERTICAL INTERVAL (V.I.)

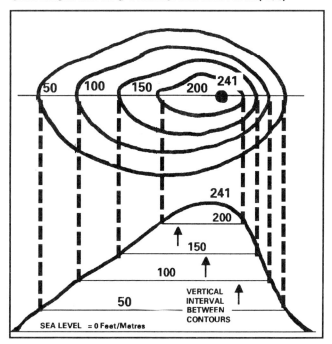

SPOT HEIGHTS
Apart from contours, height is shown by **SPOT HEIGHTS** which is marked on a map by a dot and number ●241. This is the exact height in metres or feet above sea level. You will also find **TRIG POINTS**, shown on the map as a small black triangle with a number next to it ▲576, this again is the exact height above sea level.

MORE ABOUT CONTOURS

On gentle slopes the CONTOURS are far apart, on steep slopes the CONTOURS are close together.

You do not need to find the figures on the contour lines to give you a 'picture' of the ground in an area, the contour lines show quite simply the comparative steepness of the slopes, the SPURS and RE-ENTRANTS.

If the ground is broken and rugged there will be many SPURS and RE-ENTRANTS and your path will be constantly turning in and out.

Broken and rugged country is shown by irregular, sharply turning contours.

Where the slopes are smooth, your path will curve gently, bending out as it follows the line of a SPUR and swinging in at a RE-ENTRANT. On gentle slopes the contours appear as smooth flowing curves.

The contours may appear to wander about all over, but if you follow them they natually come back to where they started from, the only exception to this is when you find a cliff face with a shere drop, then all the contour lines are so close together they appear to be one.

Every curve or bend in a contour indicates a SPUR or a valley, a rise or fall in the ground, just as it does on the side of a hill. Remember - the distance apart the contours are still indicates the steepness or flatness of the ground

Heights of Contours - see illustration on previous page
Understanding Vertical Interval (V.I.)

Each contour is drawn at a specific height above sea level and each one is the same vertical height above the one below. The difference in height between contours is called the Vertical Interval (VI).

These heights are written into the contour lines at intervals along their length.

MAP READING

Contours and the shape of ground

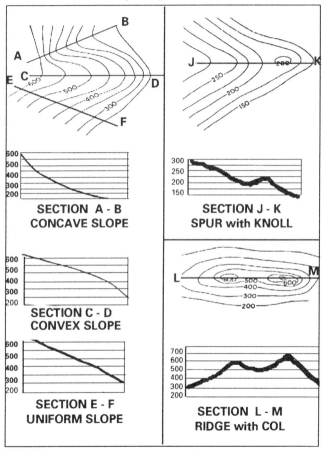

SECTION A - B
CONCAVE SLOPE

SECTION C - D
CONVEX SLOPE

SECTION E - F
UNIFORM SLOPE

SECTION J - K
SPUR with KNOLL

SECTION L - M
RIDGE with COL

MAP READING

On Ordnance Survey maps these figures showing the height of the contours are always written so as they read facing up hill, it is important to remember this as, you can very quickly find out which direction the ground is sloping.

Check the information in the margins of the map to find out if the VI (Vertical Interval) is in Feet or Metres.

Whenever you are "out and about", look at the ground in the area, draw those imaginary contour lines around the hills and valleys, make a rough sketch and then get a map of the area and see how well you have been able to intrepet the ground. This is a very important skill to use when you are planning the route of an expedition or trying to find a different route out of a difficult area you may have wandered into.

Practice as much as you can, it will improve your skill and interest in map reading and make every journey you take into new country all the more rewarding.

The Shape of Ground

RUGGED COUNTRY

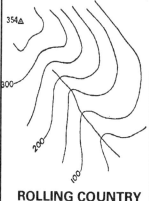

ROLLING COUNTRY

MAP READING

KNOW YOUR CONTOUR PATTERNS

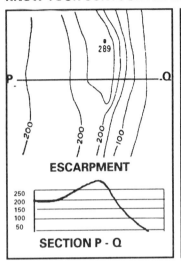

ESCARPMENT

SECTION P - Q

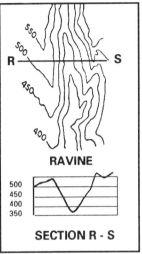

RAVINE

SECTION R - S

1. Contours close together mean steep slopes.
2. Contours far apart mean gentle slopes.
3. When contours are evenly spaced the slope is uniform, thes slopes have small undulations and poockets of dead ground.
4. When the spacing of the contours, reading from high ground to low, decreases, the slope is convex. Convex slopes mean short visability; dead ground becomes very close.
5. When spacing of contours, reading from high to low, increases, the slope is concave.
   Concave slopes mean good visability and little dead ground.

6. Wandering contours at various distances apart and never close, mean undulating ground. Important to note the general direction of the fall in the ground.

7. Gently curving contours indicate an area of country of rounded slopes. As the ground becomes steeper the contours come closer together; as it becomes more rugged the curves disappear and the contours take on 'jagged' shapes.

SCALES AND MEASURING DISTANCE

The scale of a map is the relationship between the actual distance measured from one point to another on the ground and the distance between the same two points on a map.

The way that the 'scale' of a map is expressed is by the Representative Fraction.

It used to be expressed in words, eg, "one inch to one mile", or "four miles to one inch".

This is now being superseded by the **RF** method.

The Representative Fraction (RF) is the standard method used on all continental maps and wherever the metric system is used.

Most British maps are now expressed in metric. It is simple to use if you remember that the RF is 1/X, one unit of distance on the map represents X units of distance on the ground.

For example, a scale of 1/50,000 means that one inch/ centimetre/metre on the map represents 50,000 inches/ centimetres/metres on the ground.

The essential connection is that the SAME unit of measurement applies both to the map and to the ground measurement.

A distance of 2cms on a 1/50,000 map therefore represents 2 x 50,000 cms on the ground = 100,000 cms = 1000 metres.

MAP READING

All maps are printed with graphic linear scales, usually
in the centre of the bottom margin, from which any
horizontal distance may be measured on the map in
kilometres and metres, or in miles and yards.
A linear map scale is always shown in the form of a
diagram.

SCALE

1 : 50 000
2 Centimeters to 1 Kilometres (one grid square)

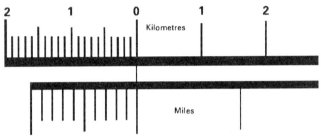

1 Kilometre = 0.6214 mile   1 Mile = 1. 6093 Kilometres

**NOTE: The above diagram is NOT to scale, but to
illustrate the scale found on a 1: 50 000 map.**

You will notice that the zero mark is set from the left of
the scale by one major division, which is then
subdivided into ten (or other suitable) sub-divisions
usually not longer than about 4 mm each.
Any measurements falling between these sub-divisions
must be estimated.

PROTECT YOUR MAP BY FOLDING IT CAREFULLY ROUND A
PIECE OF CARD, PUT IT IN A POLYRTHENE BAG — YOU CAN
WRITE/DRAW ON IT WITH A CRAYON, OR YOU CAN BUY A
MAP CASE FROM THE SUPPLY DEPARTMENT

MAP READING

LINEAR MAP SCALE.
How to measure distance.

Make a mark on the straight edge of a piece of paper, put the mark on the point you wish to measure from and make successive marks along the edge of the paper as you follow the route from your starting point to the final point.
This is easy if you just want to measure along a straight road, but if it means going round corners you will have to pivot the paper and make several marks as you progress. The total distance is then recorded along the edge of the paper.

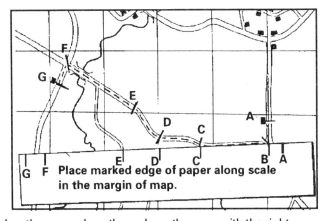

Lay the paper along the scale on the map, with the right hand tick against one of the major divisions, so that the left hand tick lies against the sub-divisions to the left of the zero mark. The total distance is then the number of major divisions plus the distance to the left of the zero.
With practice this is quite an accurate method of measuring distances.

MOVING ROUND OBSTACLES

Obstacles are often found on a route and in order to keep a really accurate direction you should go round them by plotting a series of right angles and measuring by paces as illustrated in the diagram, 200 x 500 x 200.

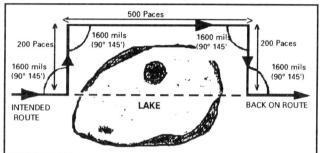

FINDING TRUE NORTH FROM THE SUN USING A WATCH.

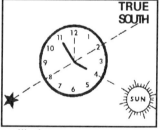

When you do not have a map or are map reading without a compass, it can help if you are able to find the rough direction of TRUE NORTH or SOUTH.

The method explained below will give you an approximate direction - not accurate enough for reading bearings or other measurements.

INFORMATION - as the sun rises in the EAST, and moves (in the northern hemisphere) through the southern sky, setting in the WEST, the position of the Sun, when visible, is always a rough guide to the direction of NORTH.

MAP READING

A watch when set to Greenwich Mean Time (GMT) for UK (or to local time for other areas some distance EAST or WEST of Greenwich) may be used.

If summertime or other artificial time is in local use your watch should be adjusted to Greenwich Mean Time (GMT) or to the local standard time.

METHOD - lay your watch flat, with the HOUR HAND pointing to the sun.

In the NORTHERN hemisphere, TRUE SOUTH will then be midway between the hour hand and twelve o'clock on the watch - see the diagram on the previous page.

In the SOUTHERN hemisphere, lay your watch with twelve o'clock pointing to the sun.

TRUE NORTH then lies midway between the hour hand and twelve o'clock.

When the sun is high up in the sky, this method cannot be used with any success. In any case the result is unlikely to be accurate to better than five degrees.

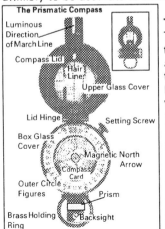

The Prismatic Compass

Luminous Direction of March Line

Compass Lid

Hair Line

Upper Glass Cover

Lid Hinge

Setting Screw

Box Glass Cover

Magnetic North Arrow

Compass Card

Outer Circle Figures

Prism

Brass Holding Ring

Backsight

THE PRISMATIC COMPASS

This is the compass that the Army uses. It is a very accurate instrument and therefore costly to make. Not issued to cadets, but we include it for interest.

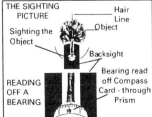

THE SIGHTING PICTURE

Hair Line

Object

Sighting the Object

Backsight

READING OFF A BEARING

Bearing read off Compass Card - through Prism

MAP READING

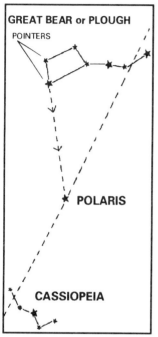

GREAT BEAR or PLOUGH
POINTERS
POLARIS
CASSIOPEIA

FINDING TRUE NORTH

By the stars (Northern Hemisphere)
In latitudes less than 60° the **POLE STAR** is never more than about 40 miles away from **TRUE NORTH**.
The position of the **POLE STAR** is indicated by the "pointers" of the Great Bear or Plough - see diagram. All stars revolve round the POLE STAR and the Plough may be either below it low down near the horizon and "right way up", or above it in the sky and "upside down" or in any position between.
If the Plough is obscured or below the horizon, **Cassiopeia** which is shaped like a **W** and is on the opposite side of the POLE STAR from the Plough, may be visible; the POLE STAR is the nearest bright star within the arms of the W.
Above 60° latitude the POLE STAR is too high in the sky to be a good guide to NORTH.
At the NORTH POLE it is vertically overhead.

The only way to learn night navigation is to get out in the dark, identify the constellations shown in the above diagram and practice moving in different directions by using stars and checking with your compass. As with all map reading — practice makes perfect.

ROUTE CARDS

The purposes of a ROUTE CARD is to ensure that you plan the route you are taking and from the start become aware of the distances you are proposing to travel, the obstacles that you will encounter, either overcoming them or taking action to find a route round them, RV's and the locations for your bivi sites, also to ensure that in an emergency - assuming you have had the sense to leave a copy - someone will know your approximate position at any given time.

The illustration of the ROUTE CARD below is self explanatory, you need plenty of space in each column to write information. Never be short of detail, it is better to have more than you need than not enough.

If you are in a group make sure each person has an accurate copy and leave a copy behind for someone who you will be in contact with during your expedition.

The importance of CHECK POINTS and the TIMES that you are to be there must be shown on the ROUTE CARD.

ROUTE CARD

Date_____

Produced by_____   Start Point Grid Ref_____   ETD ___
Date finish_____Finishing Point GridRef_____ETA___

| Leg | From | | To | | Bearings | | Distance | Remarks Landmark Hazards |
	Location	Grid Ref	Location	Grid Ref	Grid	Mag		
			EXAMPLE OF HEADINGS AND LAYOUT FOR A ROUTE CARD					

THE 24 HOUR CLOCK SYSTEM

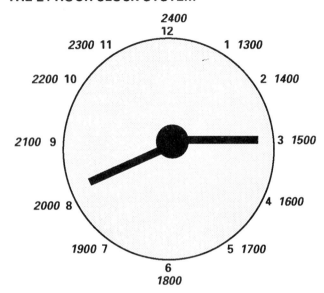

The hands on the clock face are pointing to quarter past eight. If it was in the morning (Ante Meridian - **AM** - before noon) you would call it 0815 hours. If it was in the evening (Post Meridian - **PM** - after noon) you would call it 2015 hours.

The importance of using the 24 hour clock system cannot be ignored as it avoids any confusion over timings and is explicit in its meaning.

The Armed Services use what is known as the date/time group, which includes the date as two figures in front of the time, see examples on the next page.

EXAMPLES:-

122200 June would be 2200hrs on the 12th of June, ie 10pm in the evening on the 12th of June

This is used when timings cover several days, eg START Exercise 170600 END Exercise 201000

The exercise will begin at 6am on th 17th and end at 10am on the 20th.

It is important that you learn how to use the 24 hour clock system as all timings in the services are based on it. Use it every day until it becomes automatic.

ORIENTEERING

Orienteering is like a car rally on foot, and as a sport has become well established in the UK. It can be over a mile or two or made to cover a vast area.

It can be a mornings fun, last all day or several days.

It can be toughened up to cross mountains, or be "improved" by introducing rafting or even canoes. It can be a treasure hunt or finding "escaped prisoners".

It can be carried out by day and night. It is a competitive activity putting your map reading skills to the test and your ability to think quickly on your feet.

You need to be fit and have plenty of determination, to safely navigate around a set course laid out by the organisers.

The 'event' is judged by the shortest time it takes the competitors to navigate and complete the course with the most points scored.

You have to record your progress on a Control Card.

HOW IT IS ORGANISED

A MASTER MAP of the area in which the orienteering is to take place will be set up for all competitors to see. Normally you will be given a list of MAP REFERENCES

ORIENTEERING

which are the CONTROL points. You will be issued with a map of your own in a plastic cover or Map Case.
You plot the CONTROL references on your map from the Master Map and then set off for your first CONTROL.

CHECK POINTS or CONTROLS

The CHECK POINTS or CONTROLS which make up theroute are usually marked in some way to distinguish between them.
In some Forestry Commission areas for instance these markers are diamond shape painted red and white, fixed to posts each one being separately numbered.
In competitions moveable CONTROLS are put out before the competition. This allows the organisers to use different areas and different courses.
To prove that you have been to the CONTROL you have make a note of the number or symbol carved into the top of each post or use a special punch called a Swedish marker punch on your event card.
These will be checked when you return.
The Controls are not easy to find, more often than not they can only be seen from a close distance, usually less than 30m, therefore accurate map reading is essential if you are to find them.
It is a good idea to choose an easily identified point like a track junction near to the CONTROL (this is called an ATTACK POINT) and then to pace the distance on a bearing to the CONTROL.

EQUIPMENT

To orienteer safely you would normally require the following:- Map and map case. Compass (Silva type). Pen. Whistle. Suitable Clothing.
The type of clothing you wear depends to some extent on the time of year, the location of the course and how long the event is likely to last.

ORIENTEERING

Your cadet combat kit is adequate, especially in wooded areas or in rough terrain.
If you buy your own kit, of course it will depend on how much you want to pay and the quality of the kit.
Set out in the paragraph below is the minimum kit required. However, you would be advised that experienced people take what they need and nothing more - what you take - you have to carry:-

Wool or cotton shirt or vest.
A lightweight waterproof Kagoule.
Long trousers/track suit bottoms to protect your legs against thorns, nettles etc.
Cotton or wool socks.
Strong walking/running shoes.
A towel for when you return to your transport.
A change of clothing (you may be very wet and or dirty) including shoes.

KEEPING DIRECTION

To orienteer successfully you must be able to keep going in the correct direction. This can be achieved in two ways :-

1. USING A COMPASS.

This will always tell you where NORTH is and by SETTING the compass you can find the direction in which you want to go. This is however only really useful in open country like moorland.

2. USING THE MAP.

This is perhaps the best method since it is hard to get lost if you use this method correctly. The compass is also used in this method, but only to orientate the map (point the map North).
Once the map is orientated always use known features to get you to your destination.
This involves planning your route in advance and in a number of short easily navigated "legs". If there is a leg

with no easily identified features trust your compass.
When either of these methods are used, keep in mind
the orienteering techniques mentioned below, they wil
help you to navigate by the quickest and safest methoc

GETTING LOST

Even the best navigators can sometimes get lost,
however this is not usually the disaster it may seem,
since it is not too difficult to find yourself again.
If you get into a situation where you are lost, **STOP** ar J
THINK IT THROUGH, bearing in mind the following:-

1. Don't Panic - a cool head is needed.
2. Use the compass and orientate your map, try and
   trace your route.
3. Try to identify the ground around you and match to
   the map, if you succeed then you have found you self,
   plan your route onward.

If you cannot, then try to retrace your route to the
previous check point.
If this also fails, set your compass and walk towarc a
road or other easily identifiable line on the ground hen
stay there until found.

THE ORIENTEERING MAP

The map is a large scale (usually 1:10000 or 1:150 0
scale) representation of the land, the information iround
the margin of the map will tell you what the colo rs and
symbols means.
Study your map and identify all the different ma ings
and colours.
Colours on the SPECIAL ORIENTEERING MAPS re used
to indicate the speed at which you can MOVE, not the
TYPE of GROUND, for instance an area shaded dark
green might indicate ground which would be very
difficult to move through, - usually known as "FIGHT"

because you would have to fight your way through it, whereas a light green area could indicate close woodland or very rough ground through which you could walk.

White may indicate where you could run, perhaps grassland or very mature woodland where the trees are well spaced.

The orienteering map, because of its scale shows great detail and will accurately position depressions in the ground, holes and mounds, earth walls and embankments which would normally not be shown, learn these new symbols as soon as you can, identifying them on the ground could be the difference between being 'lost or found'.

As you know, you must know exactly where you are at all times, you will only achieve this by constantly checking the map and always keeping it orientated.

To remind you, maps are made with NORTH at the top, the black grid lines which run up and down the map run approximately NORTH to SOUTH, line up the compass needle with these lines, the red end of the needle pointing to the top of the map.

NAVIGATING TECHNIQUES AND CHOOSING A ROUTE

When you choose your route try and find the best way of getting to the first CONTROL by selecting a good, easily identifiable **ATTACK POINT** like a track junction and then plan your route to this ATTACK POINT using easily followed features like tracks, fence lines, forest edges and streams these features which you will meet on your route are known as **COLLECTION POINTS** (because as you move around the course you can 'collect them').

It is not a good idea to go directly for the CONTROL since they are easily missed.

When you begin to select your route start by choosing a good **ATTACK POINT** near to the next **CONTROL**.

A track junction or corner of a wood will do but it should be as close as possible to the **CONTROL** and easily identifiable.
Next select a route which will have as many COLLECTION POINTS on it as possible.
The more the better since these are the way in which you will

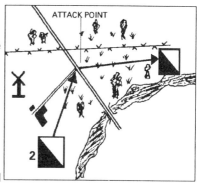

navigate from one CONTROL to another, however remember to check direction from time to time with the compass.
Try to avoid bogs, dense forest and very steep hills as these will slow you down and may even be impassable.
It will often be better to go round an obstacle even if the distance covered is greater because it will be easier and faster.
To help you decide which route you should take remember the following.

The Short Hard Route v The Long Easy Route -
Swim across the lake or go round it. Climb up and over the mountain or go round the valley.
There are usually several ways to get from one point to another, two points may be separated by different types of terrain which will take different amounts of time and energy to get through.

ORIENTEERING

A good runner will typically take the following amounts of time to complete 400 metres over different terrain:-

    a. Path 2 mins
    b. Heathland 4 mins
    c. Open Forest 6 mins
    d. Thick Firs 10 mins or more

It may be the case that it will be quicker to run twice or three times the distance on tracks, than to try and fight your way through a thick forest.

The Steep Short Route v The Long Flat Route -
You will often find when orienteering in hilly country that the course has a number of CONTROLS at opposite sides of a steep hill or valley.

You must then make the decision whether or not it will be quicker to go over the top or to 'contour' round.

If you remember that a 25 ft height gain will be equivalent to 100m on the flat, in the amount of effort used, you should be able to make the choice.

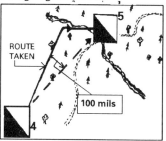

AIMING OFF

Sometimes the CONTROL you are aiming for is on a linear feature at right angles to your line of approach such as a track or stream.

This will mean that the CONTROL may be difficult to find if you aim straight for it since if you miss it, you will not know for sure whether it is, for instance, to the North or South.

This problem can be overcome simply by aiming off to one side of the CONTROL, say the North, then when you reach the stream/track you will know that the CONTROL is to the South.

241

MAP READING

This will cut down the time that you spend searching for the CONTROL.

Orienteering is great fun and an exciting sport with the added benefits of practicing and improving your Map Reading and sharpening your wits, at the same time keeping you physically fit.

TERMS USED IN MAP READING

BEARING The angle, measured clockwise, that a line makes with a fixed zero line. It may be a True Bearing, measured from True North - a Magnetic Bearing measured with a compass from Magnetic North, or a Grid Bearing measured from Grid North.

COL (SADDLE): The low land or ridge, connecting two hilltops.

CONTOUR: An imaginary line on the surface of theground at the same height above mean sea level throughout its length. Contour line are drawn a map to show the shape of the ground.

CREST: The highest part of a hill or range of hills.

DETAIL: All the topographical information on a map.

ESCARPMENT: The steep hillside formed by a drop in land level, usually at the edge of a plateau.

GRADIENT: A slope described by a percentage, mostly used on roads to indicate a steep hill.

GRID: Lines drawn on the map forming squares as a basis for a system of map references.

LEFT or RIGHT BANK: The appropriate bank of a stream or river when facing DOWN stream.

LOCAL MAGNETIC ATTRACTION: Attraction of the compass needle due to presence of metal or magnetic iron ore. NOT to be confused with Magnetic Variation.

MAP READING

MAGNETIC VARIATION or DECLINATION: The angle between True North and Magnetic North.

MAGNETIC NORTH: The point in far north of Canada, to which a compass needle points. MERIDIAN: A true north and south line.

ORIENTING a MAP: Placing it so that its True North line points True North (or Magnetic or Grid North line points to Magnetic or Grid North). This is also called "Setting the Map".

PLATEAU: A raised plain, usually quite flat, above a level of the land.

PLOTTING: Transferring to a map bearings and other measurements.

RAY: A line drawn from the position of an observer to fix the direction of an object.

RE-ENTRANT: A shallow valley running into a hill, usually between two spurs, found where a stream runs off a hillside.

RE-SECTION: The process of finding a position by taking bearings on two identifiable points and plotting them on a map, also by fixing a position by observation of at least two previously fixed points.

SPOT HEIGHT: A point on a map whose height has been found by survey methods, identified on a map by a dot with figure against it.

SLOPES (Concave and Convex): Convex "bulges out", Concave "caves in".

SPUR: A hill feature or low ridge, running out from a hill or high ground, often found between two re-entrants.

MAP READING

TRIG POINT: A concrete pillar with a brass mounting used by Ordnance Survey for their survey work. The correct name is a Triangulation Point. Marked on a map by a small triangle with the height above sea level shown next to it.

TRUE NORTH: The direction of the North pole from that point.

VERTICAL INTERVAL (V.I.) The difference in height between two adjacent contours.

WATERSHED: The line, usually mountain range where waters divide to flow in different directions.

QUESTIONS.

1. Who produces maps for the Army.
2. Where will you find the Map Sheet number.
3. What is the Grid System used for.
4. Do use normally use a four or six figure reference to pin point a item.
5. On a map sheet where is North.
6. What is a Romer used for.
7. What is to Orientate a map for.
8. Where do you find Meridian lines on a Silva compass.
9. How can you set a map without a compass.
10. Name eight Cardinal Points.
11. How many North's are there.
12. What do you understand by the GMA.
13. What is Grid Convergence.
14. How many types of Bearings are there, and what are they called.
15. What is I.C.E, and what do you do about it.
16. Taking a bearing, which two arrows on a compass do you "line-up".

17. Taking a Grid bearing, what do you do with the compass needle.
18. Complete the sentence: "Grid to Mag Add, _ _ _ _ _".
19. What is the reverse of a forward bearing.
20. What use has a contour line, give a definition.
21. Concave and Convex slopes, which "bulges" out, which has good visibility.
22. Where are you most likely to find a re-entrant.
23. What type of ground will you find if contours are close together.
24. What is the name given to the height between contours.
25. It says; "one unit of measure on the map, equals X on the ground". Explain what is this about.
26. When finding North with a watch (that has hands) which hand is pointed to the sun.
27. Without a compass, how would you find North on a clear night.
28. You are to make out a Route Card, give the headings required to do so.
29. When do you use a Master Map.
30. When Orienteering, why do you "Aim Off".

MAP READING

PROTRACTOR/ROMER

IMPROVE YOUR MAP READING SKILL

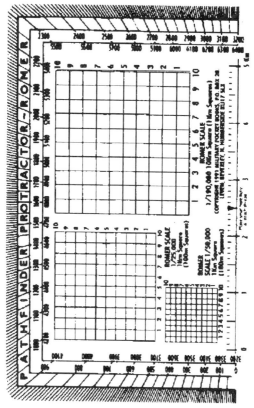

£1-50p + P&P

Available from:-

SUPPLY DEPARTMENT

Duke of Yorks HQ, Kings Road, London SW3 4RR Tel 071-730-0179

FIRST AID

INTRODUCTION

Casualty Code is your introduction to First Aid training at 1Star. As you progress in your training it will become more advanced as shown in the syllabus.

Given the opportunity to learn this skill, the chances are, that during your lifetime you will help to prevent someone dying.

It is therefore not just another APC subject to have to pass, it is a skill that — provided you keep it up to date — is a "life skill" you can always have ready and waiting to use.

We are not suggesting that once you have passed your examinations it will last you for the rest of your days. You have to re-sit exams as required by the examining authorities , **The British Red Cross Society, St John's Ambulance and St Andrews Ambulance Association**.

As a qualified "First Aider" it will be to your advantage in many ways, apart from the obvious one of helping those who are injured, but many employers are required to have **Qualified First Aiders** as members of their staff. If you are going for a job interview — and are **currently qualified**, then tell them so.

First Aid does require you to spend time studying the important lessons to be learned, it can be the difference between life and death, there is nothing more important than that — especially to the casualty.

In the following pages we give you an outline of some of the more important facts and actions to remember.

Nothing takes the place of good instruction and practice, give your instructors the chance to teach you by attending ALL the lessons.

You never know who's life you might be able to save.

ASSESSING THE EMERGENCY

An efficient First Aider will:-
1. Be calm and take charge.
   Ensure the safety of the casualty and themselves
3. Prevent further casualties arising by:-
a) Road traffic accidents - instruct someone to control
   traffic .
b.) Collapsing buildings and fires - remove casualty to
   safety.
c) Poisonous fumes/gas - turn off at source
d) Electrocution - where possible, switch off at source
   and take precautions against electric shock.
4. Reassure the casualty, listen, give confidence
5. Get others to help

DIAGNOSIS

History

This is the story or report given by the casualty or a
bystander as to how the accident occurred or illness
began.

Signs

Obtained by the first aider giving a thorough
examination of the casualty using sight, touch, hearing
and smell to gain maximum information.

Symptoms

Details given by the casualty concerning what they can
feel.

THE AIMS OF FIRST AID ARE TO:-

Preserve Life

Open Airway, apply artificial ventilation if casualty not
breathing, continuing until qualified medical help
arrives. Control Bleeding.

Prevent Condition Deteriorating

Dress wounds. Place casualty in the correct and
comfortable position.

Promote Recovery

Reassure, handle casualty with care and consideration:-
GAIN QUALIFIED MEDICAL ASSISTANCE AS SOON AS POSSIBLE.
FIRST AIDERS CAN SAVE LIVES BY MAINTAINING A CASUALTIES VITAL NEEDS.
(Remember "Key Letters" ABC)

> AIRWAY - - - - - - - - OPEN
> BREATHING - - - - - ADEQUATE
> CIRCULATION - - - -SUFFICIENT

UNCONSCIOUS CASUALTY

In an unconscious casualty, the protective mechanism which prevents food or fluid entering the windpipe does not function. This means that there is a danger of blood, vomit or saliva entering the windpipe and blocking it.

There is further danger if an unconscious casualty is left lying on their back which may allow their tongue to fall to the back of their throat blocking the AIRWAY

Noisy bubbling gasping breathing means possible obstruction to the AIRWAY.

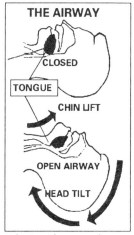

THE AIRWAY

CLOSED

TONGUE

CHIN LIFT

OPEN AIRWAY

HEAD TILT

Do not delay, remove any obvious obstructions and loosen clothing from around the neck.
LIFT THE CHIN FORWARDS WITH THE INDEX AND MIDDLE FINGERS OF ONE HAND, WHILST PRESSING THE FOREHEAD BACK WITH THE PALM OF THE OTHER.
In this position, any foreign matter that can be seen should be removed where possible.

Turn the casualties head to one side and sweep inside the mouth with two fingers.

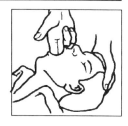

> **DO NOT WASTE TIME SEARCHING FOR HIDDEN OBSTRUCTIONS**

ARE THEY BREATHING?

Place your ear above the casualties mouth and look along the chest. If the casualty is breathing you will hear and feel any breaths and see movement of the chest. If the casualty is breathing, check for further injuries and place in the **Recovery Position**.

RECOVERY POSITION
NON-BREATHING CASUALTY

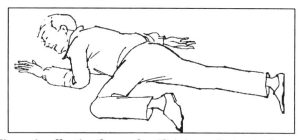

The only effective form of artificial ventilation is the MOUTH TO MOUTH OR MOUTH TO NOSE VENTILATION.
Obviously, this is easiest when the casualty is lying on their back, but ventilation should be started immediately whatever position the casualty happens to be in.

FIRST AID

NOTE: THE FIRST TWO VENTILATIONS SHOULD BE GIVEN AS SOON AS POSSIBLE.

1. Ensure that the casualties head is in the **OPEN AIRWAY** position. **TAKE A DEEP BREATH**

2. Pinch the nostrils together with your fingers and seal your mouth around the casualties mouth. (for mouth to nose close the mouth with your thumb and seal your lips around the casualties nose).

3. Blow into the casualties lungs until you can see the chest rise.

4. Remove your mouth well away and breathe in clean air. Repeat inflation.

5. After two successful inflations check to make sure the heart is beating (See External Chest Compression).

6. If the heart is beating, continue to give inflations every six seconds until natural breathing is restored or qualified medical help is obtained.

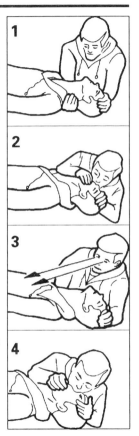

1

2

3

4

NOTE
IN THE INTERESTS OF YOUR HEALTH AND SAFETY, IF YOU HAVE A DISPOSABLE VENTILATION AID USE IT

IS THE HEART BEATING?
Before starting **EXTERNAL CHEST COMPRESSION** it is important to establish that there is **NO HEART BEAT**. This is done by checking the **CAROTID** pulse at the neck. The **CAROTID** pulse must be checked after the first two inflations, after the first minute and then every three minutes thereafter.

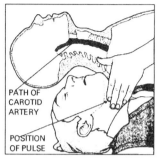

PATH OF CAROTID ARTERY

POSITION OF PULSE

IF THE HEART HAS STOPPED BEATING, START EXTERNAL CHEST COMPRESSION WHILST CONTINUING TO GIVE ARTIFICIAL VENTILATION.

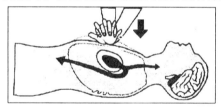

1. Ensure the casualty is on their back and on a firm surface, take position at the side of the casualty.
2. Find the junctions of the ribs at the bottom of the breast bone.
3. Place the heel of the hand two fingers above this junction, cover this hand with your other hand, interlocking the fingers.
4. Lock elbows and keeping your shoulders directly above the hands press down vertically on the breastbone moving it 4-5 cms for the average adult. Compressions should be regular and smooth not jabbing or jerking.

5. 15 compressions should be given (rate of 80 per minute) followed by two inflations. Repeat the cycle, checking the Carotid pulse after the first minute and then every three minutes.
6. When there are two first aiders present, one should undertake five compressions (rate 80 per minute), the other gives one lung inflation. This should be performed so that there is a pause after the fifth compression to allow the lungs to be inflated.

VARIATIONS - EXTERNAL CHEST COMPRESSION

YOUNG CHILDREN
Light pressure, one hand only, at a rate of 100 times per minute.

INFANTS
Very light pressure, two fingers only, at a rate of 100 times per minute.

Infants — mouth to mouth ventilation.
For an infant or young child seal your lips around the mouth and nose, blow gently into lungs until chest rises at a rate of 20 breaths per minute.

> NOTE: FIVE COMPRESSIONS ARE GIVEN TO ONE INFLATION PER CYCLE.

THE RECOVERY POSITION

An unconscious, breathing casualty should be positioned to ensure that there is no danger of their AIRWAY being blocked with saliva or vomit.

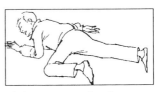

Providing there is the space and there are no further injuries that might be made worse by moving the casualty, gently move the injured person into this position.

MODIFIED RECOVERY POSITION

BLANKET

Used for a casualty with:—
1. Fractures to upper or lower body.
2. Casualty is in a confined space.
3. Bent limbs cannot be used as props

If injuries or space does not allow the normal
RECOVERY POSITION to be used, a rolled up blanket
placed down the side of the body can be used as shown
in the diagram above.

SEVERE BLEEDING

When large amounts of blood are lost from the body,
the vital organs are deprived of essential oxygen and
nutriments, causing **SHOCK** to develop.

TREATMENT

1. Lie the casualty down.
2. If the bleeding is from a limb, unless there are further
   injuries such as a fracture, raise the limb as high as
   the comfort of the casualty will allow.
3. Using a dressing, apply direct pressure onto the
   wound, ensuring it completely covers the area.
   Bandage with whatever is available, maintaining
   direct pressure.
4. If bleeding comes through the dressing, remove the
   bandage and place a further dressing on top of the
   original dressing. Re-bandage and maintain direct
   pressure for up to 15 minutes.
   DO NOT REMOVE ANY DRESSING ONCE APPLIED.

FIRST AID

SEVERE BLEEDING - FOREIGN BODY PRESENT
DO NOT REMOVE FOREIGN BODY,
DO NOT APPLY DIRECT PRESSURE ONTO THE WOUND.

TREATMENT

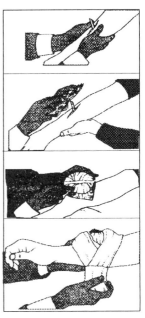

1. Lie casualty down, where possible elevate the injured part.
2. Gently place a piece of gauze over or around the foreign body.
3. Apply pressure by squeezing the edges of the wound together along the foreign body.

4. Using dressings if available, build up around the wound, until the padding is high enough to prevent pressure on the foreign body.

5. Secure the dressings with bandage avoiding pressure over the foreign body.

BURNS AND SCALDS
As with severe bleeding, large area burns and scalds mean loss of vital body fluids causing SHOCK.
TREATMENT
1. QUICKLY remove anything constrictive from the injured area, e.g.., rings, watches, boots, before injured part starts to swell.

2. Place injured part into cold water, preferably gently running water for at least ten minutes. If a large area is injured, gently pour cold water over it.
3. When the heat has been removed from the injury, cover and secure LOOSELY with a non-fluffy sterile dressing.

> **DO NOT USE CREAMS OR SPRAYS,**
> **DO NOT BURST BLISTERS,**
> **DO NOT USE PLASTERS.**

NOTE: IN A WORK SITUATION, ANY BURN OR SCALD OVER 2.5cm OR OF CONSIDERABLE TISSUE DAMAGE, OR CAUSED BY ELECTRICAL INCIDENT, MUST BE REFERRED TO A DOCTOR OR HOSPITAL.

TYPES OF FRACTURE

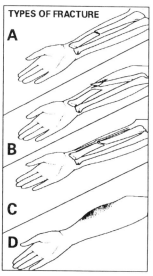

TYPES OF FRACTURE

A. Closed Fracture. Skin not broken.
B. Open Fracture. Bone has broken surface of skin. Dangerous; external loss of blood and serious risk of infection.
C. Complicated Fracture. When internal nerve or organ is also injured and when fracture is connected with a dislocated joint.
D. Symptoms and Signs. Casualty heard it break. Pain at site of injury. Swelling, bruising later. Deformity, bone grating and shock.

256

TREATMENT OF FRACTURES

If an ambulance is available within 15 minutes, it is preferable to support the injured part in the most comfortable position by use of blankets and other materials, or supporting the injured limb by holding it with one hand above and one below the site of the fracture. However, when medical assistance is not readily available, or the casualty has to be moved for their own safety, the following steps should be taken:-

TO IMMOBILISE AN ARM

1. Dress any wound.
2. Place arm in position comfortable to casualty and retain in position with a triangular bandage or improvised sling.
3. If possible, secure the injured arm to chest by binding a folded triangular bandage or piece of broad material over the injured arm and around the chest, taking care not to put pressure on the injured area.

TO IMMOBILISE A LEG

1. Advise casualty NOT to move.
2. Dress any wound.
3. Gently bring the 'Good' leg towards the injured one, place padding between the legs, ankles and knees.
4. Where available, select improvised splints long

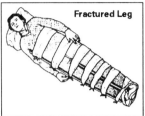

Fractured Leg

enough to extend from the casualties chest to their feet. Pad the splints and place on injured side.
5. Tie feet and ankles together with a figure of eight bandage, place further bandages above and below site of the fracture, around the chest, hips, upper leg and above the knee.

Ensure that the bandages are tied off over the splint, and no pressure is placed on the site of the fracture.

SHOCK

This is a condition resulting from a lessening of the activities of the vital functions of the body arising from a lack of blood supply.

Shock is present in severe bleeding, burns and scalds, recurrent vomiting or diarrhoea, severe pain, which occurs in many injuries and illnesses, such as heart attacks, acute abdominal emergencies , e.g.., ruptured appendix.

TREATMENT

1. Deal with the injury or cause of shock.
2. Lay the casualty down, head turned to one side, lower limbs raised when possible.
3. If casualty is unconscious, place in the Recovery position. Keep a check on the breathing.
4. Loosen clothing at neck and waist, moisten lips if casualty complains of thirst.
5. Keep comfortably warm, remember a blanket underneath is worth two on top when outdoors.
6. If removal to hospital is likely to be delayed, keep ten minute records of pulse and respiration details.

7. REASSURE - talk to your casualty.

8. NEVER LEAVE AN UNCONSCIOUS CASUALTY ON THEIR OWN.

Any casualty that has been unconscious even for a short period of time must be hospitalised.

HEAD INJURIES

Signs.
Bleeding from the nose
Straw coloured liquid sometimes spotted with blood from ears.
Bloodshot eyes and signs of "black eye" developing.
Pupils of eyes unevenly **dilated** (when in direct light), see illustration below.

DILATED PUPILS

Effects of a head injury.
Damage or disturbance to the brain.
Consciousness may be clouded or lost.
Symptoms of any other injury or condition may be masked.
Other serious injuries may develop from a head injury, it always advisable to hospitalise a casualty under these circumstances.

EXTREMES OF TEMPERATURE

Extremes of heat or cold can cause severe damage to skin and underlying tissues. The bodys ability to control the "core" temperature may be lost through extremes of heat or cold and unconsciousness my occur.

Hypothermia causes many casualties especially on expeditions, consequently it is fully dealt with in the Expedition Section.

EFFECTS OF HEAT

The bodies defences against excessive heat are:-
1. Increased blood flow.
2. Increased sweating.
3. Increased respiratory rate.

The last two cause increased evaporation of water resulting in a cooling effect.

The results of overheating may be mild or severe.

HEAT EXHAUSTION

This is caused by a loss of salt and water in the body. It primarily affects those who are not used to hot environments and may be proceeded by an attack of diarrrhoea and vomiting.

Heat exhaustion can occur in violent exercise such as running or long distance walks even in this country, especially if clothing prevent free circulation of air near your skin.

Symptoms and Signs

1. Casualty feels faint.
2. Dizziness, nausea.
3. Moist, clammy skin.
4. Pulse, rapid weak.
5. Temperature not much above normal.

Treatment

1. Lay casualty down in a cool place.
2. Give sips of water to which salt has been added (half a teaspoon to one pint of water).

HEATSTROKE

1. Casualty feels hot, restless, complains of headache.
2. Sudden loss of consciousness.
3. Skin flushed warm and dry.
4. Pulse rapid and strong.
5. Body temperature 40°C or more.

FIRST AID

Treatment
1. Place casualty in a cool situation.
2. Wet casualty all over with cold (NOT ICED) water. The cooling process is helped if a sheet is wrapped around the casualty and kept wet to increase heat loss.
3. Gain urgent medical assistance.
4. If unconscious, place in RECOVERY POSITION.

EMERGENCY USE OF A TELEPHONE

Many of the disciplines learned in Signals Training apply when using a telephone.
The following important points are made:-
1. Speak directly into and close to the mouthpiece.
2. Do not shout.
3. Speak slowly and clearly, separating your words.
4. When in contact, state who you are and who you wish to speak to.
5. In the event of calling an exchange, ask for the number required and NOT the person.
6. When replying, state who you are and the number from which you are speaking.
7. Always ask the caller their name and write it down.
8. If disconnected it is the CALLERS responsibility to re-establish communications with you.
9. When taking a message — make a note of the contents, name of the caller, their telephone number and the time of the call.
10. Always have something to write with/on by the telephone.

"IF IN DOUBT — SPELL IT OUT" USE THE PHONETIC ALPHABET

QUESTIONS

1. Who are the principal First Aid authorities in the UK.
2. What are the AIMS of First Aid.
3. Give the factors to be considered when Assessing the Emergency.

4. Diagnosis, three "key words", what are they and explain the meaning of each one.
5. You can save a life by maintaining a casualties vital needs, what are they.
6. What could cause "noisy, bubbling, gasping breathing".
7. Is the casualty breathing, how can you tell.
8. Ventilation: how soon should you give the first two ventilations.
9. Where is the Carotid artery.
10. How do you carry out Chest Compression and when is it done.
11. Why is the recovery position important.
12. If the casualty has severe bleeding their vital organs are deprived of what.
13. What will severe bleeding induce in the casualty.
14. A casualty with severe burns or scalds will lose vital body fluids — causing what.
15. What do you understand by anything constrictive in the injured area.
16. When the heat has been removed from an injury and it has been covered, name what you MUST NOT DO OR USE.
17. Name four types of fracture.
18. How do you immobilise an injured arm.
19. How do you imobilise an injured leg.
20. What is SHOCK.
21. What must you NEVER DO with an unconscious casualty.
22. Explain what DILATED PUPILS look like.
23. What affects the "CORE" temperature in the body.
24. What causes HEAT EXHAUSTION, what is the treatment for it.
25. What is HEATSTROKE, what is the treatment for it.

YOU AND THE FACTS OF LIFE.

INTRODUCTION - FACING THE FACTS.

This section of the Cadet Pocket Book, has been especially written for you, not to be taken as a "subject" or "instruction", but based on the need for it to be said by someone, some of it you may not like, or approve of — hard luck, it still needs to be said just the same.

Parts of it are intended to shock you into accepting that for some of you, life may be short lived, for others, to be a guide, to help you think more carefully about yourself, to find the strength and determination to cope better with your life than some of those you may see around you. Help you to make correct judgements and the right decisions on the route you take in developing your own identity, life style and career.

The choice of relationships, the effort you should put into a career/job to make a success of it and some of the things that can affect it on the way.

Perhaps make you think how you might broaden your mind, have consideration for others less fortunate than you, listen to others points of view, opinions, facts about different cultures and their life styles.

Life is a great gift and can be a great adventure, the quality of your life is up to you, how you use your time to live a meaningful and honest life, giving joy to those who have looked after you and brought you up over the years - the choice is yours.

EDUCATION FOR LIFE

Having left school you then think that it is all behind you. How wrong you are. In fact you are only just starting your "education for life", how to apply all you should have learned, gaining from experience how to use your knowledge, it won't be very long before you

are saying 'if only.... I had worked harder at school'.
Hopefully, you will quickly realise how little you know
and will have the good sense to take up every chance
that comes your way to improve your education,
knowledge and skills.

Being a cadet will help, but opportunities are available
to everyone, no one will make you go out and look for
them or do anything about it about finding them for you,
YOU will have to find them yourself.

CONTINUED EDUCATION

Colleges of Further Education offer many courses to
improve your levels of education and skills, to gain
qualifications by day release or evening classes in
subjects that most interest you.

Now is the time, because when you are young, your
mind is more receptive to learning, so do something
about it, find out what is on offer and go about
improving your own education standards.

You will have to be prepared to carry out private study
and give up spending some of that 'spare time' to use it
more productively by investing it in a better 'you', (time
should never be spent - it should always be invested).
That is how many thousands of students of all ages
study every year through the Open University for
Degrees in their chosen subjects.

SELF IMPROVEMENT

If you are seen to be making an effort to improve
yourself and making the most of your life by the
example you are setting, you will earn the respect of
those around you. No matter what job or occupation you
have at any given time, you will know that through your
own efforts you are on top of it, your value as a person
will have increased and so will your potential to an
employer.

YOU AND THE FACTS OF LIFE

MANNERS — DO OTHERS SEE YOURS?

It might be a sound advice for you to look to your manners when it comes to employment or where you come into contact with people you have not met before. It is often said "that its the little things that matter", for instance; when you are out and about, do you open a door for a lady, do you always say "please" and "thank you" at the right time, do you know the correct way to behave at a meal table - holding your KFS correctly, not sitting with your arms on the table, not talking with a mouth full of food - its the little things that matter, manners and social skills are noticed — especially by employers.

If you don't have good manners would you expect your boss to let you look after one of his customers? — would you?.

Would you expect your Detachment Commander to let you look after an important visitor if they had doubts about your manners — would you?.

'MILESTONES' TO REMEMBER

Your achievements can be looked upon as 'milestones' in your life, they are stages in your learning experience. Make no mistake about it some of the 'milestones' will not be a pleasant experience, they may cost you dearly as broken relationships, the start or end of a particular job, or even when you have to part with something you value. The important outcome for you as a person, is to be able to draw lessons from them to improve your own ability, knowledge, skills, attitudes and understanding.

YOUR CONTRIBUTIONS and HELP

Stop for a moment and think of the contribution you make at home. If you are at school you help create dirty clothes to be washed, a bath to be cleaned behind you, its like an assault course to get at your bed to change the sheets.

Your bike is dumped outside the front door, the dirty dish you had your supper in last night is still in your bedroom; so are several Coke tins, your new shoes are covered with dried mud and there is a heap of your clothes on the bathroom floor - that's probably the contribution you make at home.

If you are working then you should be making a contribution from your wages/salary to help pay your way with the housekeeping and other expenses, good, provided it is paid on time and the amount is not short, but there is a chance that you too are contributing like your younger brother/sister above.

If you are to be a good cadet/citizen then you should not need reminding that you have to make a meaningful contribution in helping with the "chores", whether at home, at work, or in the cadet hut. It's a part of your 'life skills' to show other people that you do your share in helping others.

LEAVING HOME

The 'milestone' that most of us remember vividly throughout our lives is when we leave home for the first time.

To some it is an action that is forced upon them through unhappy home circumstances, or after some row they have had, followed by an action taken on the spur of the moment. It is a difficult experience to say the least.

Even those who have had a caring family home and been a complete unit, sharing all the joys and sorrows of life, find it difficult when it comes to the time to 'fly from the nest'.

Feelings run high and are very powerful, causing heartache and "home-sickness" which takes a lot of coping with.

YOU AND THE FACTS OF LIFE

Those of you who have been to Annual Camps or on courses, will have already had the experience of being away from your home and normal surroundings, and will appreciate and understand these feelings.
Leaving home will not present you with quite so much of a problem, but you will be in a position to help others, who have not had your experience to cope with theirs.

CONSIDERATION for OTHERS

You must also consider the feelings of those you leave behind you.
The parents, brothers and sisters and relatives that have watched you grow up, they will have very real feelings of losing you.
The fact that you leave an empty space in the home, although it may be a lot more tidy than when you were there, but that was a small price to pay in having your company, the noise of your music, the problems you bought home etc.
Remember, that someone has spent a great deal of their lives, their work and effort, the problems you have caused, the great laughs you will have had at times, all as a part of life's pattern of "bringing you up", therefore, it's very little to ask you to stop by sometime and say hi!, how are you doing, or if away from home - do remember to write or telephone.

WHAT IT IS TO BE A UK CITIZEN.

First consider that as a member of this nation you belong to a family of nations across the world - the Commonwealth.
Some parts of our history we are perhaps not so proud of as to how we initially became possessed of other lands. However, today the individual countries of the Commonwealth do operate independently of us in Britain, yet keep close ties in many ways through trade

and other agreements and recognise Her Majesty The Queen as the head of the Commonwealth.

Our traditions that have been built up over many hundreds of years are the envy of many countries abroad, whose people visit us in their millions every year.

Let there be no doubt in your minds that many of them would gladly like an opportunity to change places with you, to become a Citizen of the UK.

The role that you play as a citizen, how you use the opportunities that others do not have is entirely up to you.

It is important that whatever you do, you maintain the traditions and standards that so many people have fought and died for in our past history.

YOUR FREEDOM

The freedom and the laws of the land which have been handed down from generation to generation are now in your hands. Future generations will expect you to have have taken care of this task in preserving our freedom and way of life that we all enjoy.

Our democratic system is not for your particular benefit, but for the nation as a whole. Your responsibility is to uphold the law and to assist those who's job it is to administer it.

Should our laws need changing then this is done through the democratic process by the people making representations to their local Member of Parliament. There are those who are not satisfied with the "way things are done" and will resort to their own remedies. Today we are often faced with people who have a mission in life, through misguided political or other reasons who try to make changes through subversive and regretfully terrorist activities, in attempts to undermine the government of the day, threatening our

peaceful, established way of life and the prosperity of
the nation.

You will no doubt be quick to recognise those who fall
into this category and their associates and as a result be
guarded against becoming exposed to their influences.

A CHALLENGE

There are many responsibilities that you have to accept
as a citizen. You may be called upon to act as a member
of a jury, you will be asked to fill in endless numbers of
forms for all manner of reasons from T.V. Licences to
Application Forms and Tax Forms!!

Your time will be called upon to assist with many
voluntary organisations as you are already doing. There
are very few people who at some period of their lives
have not given some of their spare time as a volunteer,
to help others in one way or another.

Consider what time and effort you are prepared to put
into helping others, particularly those who are physically
or mentally handicapped — remember one day you
might be the one who needs the help.

INFORMATION — WE ALL NEED IT.

It is often said the "it's not what you know, but who you
know", knowing who to ask or where to find out about
something you want to know can be very frustrating,
also if you want some advice on a subject can also be
difficult.

The ability to get the right information at the right time
can make yours and other peoples lives a lot easier.
There are a few simple rules about getting help, the first
thing is to sort out exactly what it is you need to know,
then to be able to communicate in such a way that the
person you are asking will gladly want to help you.

THE RIGHT APPROACH

We are sure you won't be surprised, but it usually means saying "please can you help me", then being prepared to listen carefully, writing down what you are told.

Generally people will respond if you go about it in the right manner — not forgetting to thank them for their help.

There is a lot of skill in being able to "ferret out" information and then record it correctly, putting it down logically and in the right order.

You will have had to carry out many projects during your education, and this is when you start to use that skill to its full, finding out for yourself and making use of all available information.

Having brought together the information the skill is then required to be able to present it in such a way that others can easily understand it.

This skill is worthwhile practising whenever you can, the reason being that if you have to make decisions that can have serious consequence for you, then treat the problem as a project.

The more you practice the more useful you will find it, even if it is only to help making the decision to buy a new music centre or buying a new bike.

DECISION MAKING

The way to go about it is to make separate lists using four sheets of paper.

On the first sheet list all the strengths about the idea, all the good points, The costs and the estimated time it will take to achieve it.

On the second sheet list all the problems that might be encountered, the weaknesses about the idea.

On the third sheet list all the benefits it will bring or opportunities it will open up.

On the fourth sheet list all the disasters/problems that it could bring, anything that will be a threat to you in any way.

Having done this go through each sheet and number the items starting with the most important point as number one, the second most important as number two etc.

It is always said that you can 'act in haste and repent at leisure', so now is the time that you have to exercise a great amount of self discipline and take time out to seriously consider the findings.

Time out to think for a while is no bad thing, to take stock of exactly where you are at present, where you are going in the future, look carefully at the style of life around you. Is it what you want?, have you made the right decisions in the past?, have those decisions been based upon the right thoughts?, think about it until you are clear in your mind that you have weighed up all the consequences to be able to make the right decision.

Now comes the crunch — **decision time**

Weigh up the strengths and weaknesses, consider the opportunities and the threats and make a judgement based on the facts that you have put together.

Should you want to discuss it with anyone, then at least you will be able to present it in such a way for them to understand the decision you are about to make, lets hope you always make the best ones.

ACHIEVEMENTS.

It is always advisable to keep records of events, happenings, progress made with the dates, as you will often require to have such information throughout your life.

All that you record in your Pocket Book will only be a part of your achievements as the space available will soon be used up, but it will get you started and if sensible you will always carefully record your

achievements and career details with the dates and
places etc., for future reference.

YOUR ROLE IN LIFE. WHERE ARE YOU GOING ?

What are your "goals", what would you like to do, what
would you like to achieve in the next three, five or ten years?.
It is not a bit of good sitting on your "butt" and winging
about all of those others with nothing to do.
When you have the "guts" to make up your mind to
achieve certain goals no matter how small they appear,
in a fixed time, then you will do it.
List what has to be done and by when to attain those
goals, then set about doing it in earnest.
Parents and other will try to influence you, be a good
listener, make sure you learn from their mistakes, and
draw your own conclusions.

INTERESTS and HOBBIES

Throughout your life it is important to develop interests
and hobbies. Some become more than just a hobby and
turn into a job or a full time occupation.
Many people find great satisfaction in having a deep
interest in a hobby, especially when going through a
difficult period in their lives, such as when loosing their
job or being ill for a long period, it is always something
interesting to look forward to and which you enjoy.
Many people who are retired — that may seem a long
way off for you — as a result of having an interesting
hobby throughout their lives, have a very happy and
rewarding retirement.
Many have interests in the community in which they
live, taking on voluntary work helping others by
belonging to local clubs or organisations, not just as a
member, but actively helping to make things happen,
such as serving as a committee member.

YOU AND THE FACTS OF LIFE

COMMUNITY SERVICE

If you have been taking part in the Duke of Edinburgh Award Scheme, you may already be aware of a great many different organisations in the area where you live. You will know that they all can do with a helping hand, from the care of the elderly to those who run the local youth clubs or other organisations, they need so much support and help you should never be bored!

FACTS OF LIFE AND DEATH

Should you be one of the more fortunate people to have good health, then you have a moral responsibility to keep your mind and body in that state of fitness that you have been blessed with.

Not to abuse it through lacking the strength of character to withstand the pressures that the 'modern day society' invites you to take part in.

Drinking excessively, initially getting involved with soft drugs and then into the hard stuff, to ultimately find yourself on the "scrap heap" of life, without friends or family and little chance of survival.

Those of you who do take an interest in the preservation of your own lives will need all the strength you can muster, as, without doubt you are going to see many of your friends and even close relatives die in horrific circumstances through the scourge of the AIDS epidemic.

There is no intention to be 'prophets of doom', but the medical facts as they are today and sound common sense point to the only way you can deal with this crisis, and that is — **prevention**.

It is said that "prevention is always better than a cure". A cure may be eventually found for AIDS.

TB. is now curable, many types of cancer can be overcome, but regretfully, as yet, there is no known cure for AIDS.

YOU AND THE FACTS OF LIFE

You must consider the present disease as a restraining factor. The religious are not using it as a lever to promote a new born surge in believing, but, you have to take heed of some warnings: these warnings have been about all our lives and today you will be aware of the great publicity that the Government and Heath Authorities have given warning of the danger.

Don't be careless about close friends, don't be the cause of spreading the disease - avoid the occasion for picking it up in the first place.

The message is clear, loyalty to your nearest and dearest is possible, loyalty to someone casual is impossible.

Your life and those of your friends and family are entirely in your hands.

Yours and their survival depend upon the personal discipline you have to observe — simple moral standards throughout your life, with a deep and caring respect for the health and future of all those that you associate with.

DON'T YOU DIE THROUGH IGNORANCE.

FITNESS, HEALTH & HYGIENE

Healthy mind and healthy body - fitness, to be really fit, fit enough to take part and finish a marathon needs a lot of guts and hard training. The hard part is to finish, for some it is easy to take part and finish, but for others such as those who are physically handicapped the effort and self discipline to take part are an example to all of us.

PARTICIPATION

It is important to take part in sporting activities of as many different kinds as possible, especially team games or activities where the joint efforts of all taking part achieve results.

The fun and excitement that you experience no matter what level of ability you attain are part of your quality of life.

If as a result of this you also become fit it is a bonus, as so few people experience the joy of being really fit, you and your team may get an added bonus by winning something.

As a young person you should be taking part in some form of sporting activity, if not - why not.

You are probably better than you think you are - put it to the test, don't just stand on the touch line watching others, do it, be one of them.

Should you be a sports enthusiast a great amount of time and effort for practice will be required to reach any 'club standard', it is not easy to maintain the peak performance for top class levels in many sports.

While you remain an amateur, you may find yourself spending too much time training and practising as a result of which your work or other interests and social activities may suffer. Unless you are a professional sports person, you have to get the balance right, sufficient to keep fit without it taking over all your spare time.

SPORT FOR PEOPLE WITH DISABILITIES

We must not forget that many people have a deep interest and expert knowledge in a great many sporting activities, but may not be able to take an active part in them through illness or some form of disability, yet through their expert knowledge make a considerable contribution to the world of sport.

Some of them take up refereeing and umpiring or are involved in their club by helping to run the activities or giving their services as officials, secretaries or committee members. Many are active members of the supporter club involved in raising funds or helping to train and encourage the younger players.

They get their satisfaction and pleasure by helping to promote the sport rather than playing it.

YOU AND THE FACTS OF LIFE

A HELPING HAND

There is always something you can do to help if you are sufficiently interested and take the trouble to find out. Membership of your local sports club will also involve you in the social events that most clubs have as a part of their normal activities.

This is an added responsibility that you have towards the club, to support the committee who plan and organise events for the entertainment of the members and their friends.

Membership of any club or organisation must have a commitment from their members to give full support for it to be successful, but like many things in life you will only get out of it what effort you are prepared to put into it.

Many life long friendships are forged through membership of clubs and associations. People will encourage you to find out about your own abilities, everyone has hidden talents that given the chance can lead to many new opportunities to different things in life, meet new people, improve your ability to mix with others and widen your circle of friends.

PERSONAL DISCIPLINES

The benefit of having a sporting activity no doubt helps to keep you fit, this alone is not the answer to fitness. You must consider carefully the needs of your body functions and control them totally, if you don't you will suffer for it all your days — and nights.

The type of food you eat, the regular times at which you eat, the correct amount and type of fluid which your body requires to function correctly each day. The right amount of sleep you need to replace the energy used during the day.

Your personal appearance is very important, especially

when meeting someone for the first time, as the "first impression" your appearance creates with them can mean a disaster or a developing acquaintance.

If you choose "way-out" clothes or haircut in order to be unique or stand out in a crowd — YOU have to carry your character with which you have lumbered yourself. Look around for your real friends, those who will honestly tell you how you look, those who will be seen with you.

Remember — more often than not your real friends will judge you by characters of the people you associate with. You may agree that this is all common sense, if you ignore it there is nothing more certain — you will regret it.

METHOD OF INSTRUCTION

INTRODUCTION

This section on Methods of Instruction (MOI) is as used by the Army, it is easy to understand and use, provided you apply the well tried and practiced framework called a **Lesson Plan**.

Instructing becomes interesting and very much simplified, but if you fail to use a Lesson Plan and ignore taking sufficient time for preparation, neither you nor those you are instructing will gain anything.

As an NCO, it will add to your skills and improve your confidence and performance.

Provided you learn how to apply this system of MOI while a cadet, it will remain as a skill for you to call on in a variety of situations throughout your career

You may have the use of an Overhead Projector or even a Video Camera and Computer, but even so you will still have to plan and prepare your presentation in a logical and professional manner, don't get side tracked by the technology!

QUALITIES REQUIRED

The main qualities you need as an instructor are enthusiasm, self confidence and to know your subject.

Good Planning and Preparation breed self-confidence and makes those under instruction feel confident in your ability.

Your enthusiasm will stimulate interest for the class to listen and learn.

Your Manner and Bearing is important.

Look up when you speak, your voice will travel further.

Vary the pitch of your voice to stress a particular point.

Avoid distracting mannerisms, such as saying "OK or RIGHT" after each statement or tapping with a pen on

the table, scratching your ear or nose!!
Watch other instructors or teachers for their mannerisms,
and as a result don't fall into any habits yourself.
Your appearance/turnout is very important, if you are
well turned out and "look the part" you will command
respect and attention.

YOUR ATTITUDE

Your attitude must be right to command attention and
make the class want to listen..
Avoid sarcasm and favouritism, getting a cheap laugh by
making a fool of someone is not good, have a joke by all
means and try to win over the confidence of the class.
Avoid passing remarks that can offend or have a double
meaning at someone else's expence.
Encourage them to join in by being friendly and fair, but
firmness at all times is always advisable.
**Instruct : clearly, completely, patiently, giving
information at a suitable pace, one stage at a time.**
YOUR SQUAD MUST ENJOY BEING INSTRUCTED.

CHECK YOUR OWN PERFORMANCE

Be observant - apply yourself to the task, pay attention to
detail - don't cut corners, never be satisfied with
standards, always look for ways and means of improving
your own performance, the training aids you use, and the
questions you ask.
Carry out a rehearsal of any difficult parts.

BASIC POINTS ON SUCCESSFUL INSTRUCTION
REMEMBER THE SIX P's:-
 PRIOR PREPARATION & PRACTICE PREVENTS POOR PERFORMANCE

PREPARE and PLAN

1. What is the objective?
2. Which is the best method ? (lecture, lesson, discussion,
    exercise, demonstration)

METHOD OF INSTRUCTION

3. Where is the instruction to take place ?
4. What is the size of the class?
5. What time is available.
6. What equipment or aids are available?
7. Are the aids suitable, simple, large enough or even necessary ?
8. What handout notes do I need to produce.
9. What is the present standard of the classes knowledge.
10. Prepare your list of questions and answers for this lesson and have your questions and answers ready from the previous lesson.

QUESTIONING TECHNIQUE

When instructing a squad you will at times need to ask questions.

There is a simple technique to adopt. It is important that all members of the squad are 'kept on their toes', you must therefore **first ask the question to the whole squad,** wait or pause for a few moments for them **ALL** to think of the answer, then **select or nominate one of them** to give it.

REMEMBER:- ASK - PAUSE - NOMINATE.

LESSON PLAN

1. Prepare a Lesson Plan.
2. Use logical stages.
3. Use correct question techniques ASK - PAUSE - NOMINATE who is to answer.

METHOD OF INSTRUCTION

Skills Lessons - for example - Drill, Skill at Arms, remember and use the sequence:

**EXPLANATION — DEMONSTRATION —
IMITATION — PRACTICE.**

METHOD OF INSTRUCTION

A SIMPLE LESSON PLAN

The framework of a lesson plan is set out over page with headings and information for you to follow.
Set it out on a large sheet of paper adding the lesson details to the 'skeleton' for the lesson you are taking.
The plan is divided into three stages:-

STAGE 1 - BEGINNING

Subject ...... Class/Squad ...... Time ..... Location .....
Dress .... Stores required and Training Aids
.... Time allowed .....
Prelims: Safety Precautions: Roll Call: Class formation, seating plan.   Comfort of the class. Lighting levels. Standard of Visual Aids.
Revision: Check their knowledge/skills in the subject previously taught — cadets soon forget.
Introduction: Make sure class know your name.
Objective: It must be clearly stated and understood, definite, limited and attainable in the time allowed.
The reason why: A realistic reason. Incentive to achieve results: Benefits to be gained from the lesson.

STAGE 2 - THE MIDDLE

The main instruction to be taught. Time allowed .....
Divide the subject into several STAGES, select from each stage the "KEY POINTS" that you must bring out in your instruction - such as SAFETY, to ensure a complete understanding of the lesson.
Rule up sheets of paper as the sample on the next page setting out the STAGES or BLOCKS of information as headings on the subject, and the KEY POINTS which are the important points to be made, such as safety, particular information such as figures, codes, references and the correct training aid to use at this particular point, use it for yourself as a pompt, drawing as many lines and spacing them out as you require.

METHOD OF INSTRUCTION

Don't forget to write large enough and clearly, as you may be using this when standing up — not held in your hand reading from it!.

SUBJECT or TOPIC to INSTRUCT/TALK ABOUT

STAGE	KEY POINT
BREAK DOWN THE LESSON TO AS MANY STAGES AS YOU LIKE	IMPORTANT POINTS NOT TO BE MISSED
1	STRESS SAFETY, ANYTHING THAT CAN CAUSE DAMAGE
2	"MEMORY TICKLER" FOR SIZES, MEASUREMENTS REFERENCES, COLOURS ETC
3	

4

CHECK YOUR TRAINING AIDS

Make sure you have all your training aids, maps, compasses, spare bulb if using an OHP, etc.

At the end of each STAGE of instruction, confirm that the key points have been understood, by using good Question Technique.

Correct any errors as they occur ASK THE QUESTION - PAUSE - NOMINATE who is to answer.

STAGE 3 - THE END

Invite questions from the class - if you are asked a question and do not know the answer, do not try to 'bluff' your way out of it. Admit you do not know, but find out and let them know - **AND MAKE SURE YOU DO**.

Ask your PREPARED questions to the class - using the right technique - confirm that they have learned by your instruction, by oral tests, written tests or by practical performance tests.

METHOD OF INSTRUCTION

NOTE: PREPARED questions means preparing them in advance **WITH THE ANSWERS.**
YOU DON'T HAVE TIME TO THINK CORRECTLY ON YOUR FEET
Summary - bring out and stress the achievement of the objective. Look forward - state when is the next lesson/subject.

**ONCE YOU HAVE SPENT TIME ON WRITING
A LESSON PLAN AND REHEARSED IT
— STICK TO IT - YOU WON'T MAKE MISTAKES
AND IT'S SO MUCH EASIER**

**KEEP ALL YOUR LESSON PLANS AND CAREFULLY FILE
THEM FOR EASY REFERENCE.
THE NEXT TIME YOU TAKE THAT LESSON — HALF
YOUR WORK IS ALREADY PREPARED**

QUESTIONS

1. What is the "Framework" used or good instruction.
2. When preparing a lesson what do you have to take to do it correctly.
3. What are the qualities required of a good instructor.
4. What should you do about habits.
5. Look up when you speak, — why.
6. What do you understand by "looking the part".
7. Complete the following sentence; "Instruct, Clearly, completely, _ _ _ _ _ _ _, _ _ _ _ _.
8. As an instructor how can you check your own performance.
9. What are the six "Basic Points of Instruction.
10. Name six of the ten things to do before you Prepare and Plan a lesson.

11. How do you use the "Questioning Technique".
12. If instructing a SKILL, what is the "Sequence of Instruction".
13. What do you understand by a. "A STAGE. b. "A KEY POINT".
14. A COMPLETE lesson is broken into how many parts or stages, what is the name of each one.
15. What are you doing if you are carrying out the "PRELIMS".
16. What do you do about Training Aids before a lesson.
17. If asked a valid question and you don't know the answer, what do you do about it.
18. Name three methods to confirm that all your class members have learned the lesson given.
19. Why and how should you keep the lesson plan that you have just used.
20. What is the last thing you tell a class before finishing.
21. If the lesson is on any Skill at Arms subject, (including Shooting), what is the FIRST and most important action to carry out and who takes part in it.

TRAINING AIDS.

WITH IMAGINATION AND INITIATIVE GOOD INSTRUCTORS MAKE UP THEIR OWN SET OF TRAINING AIDS:-

ITEMS TO SET OUT A CLOTH MODEL OR SAND TABLE TO DEMONSTRATE FIELDCRAFT TACTIC'S, BATTLE DRILLS, PLANNING PATROL EXERCISES.

MODELS OF "GROUND" TO TEACH PHYSICAL FEATURES, CONTOURS ETC.

MADE UP REALISTIC "WOUNDS" FOR FIRST AID COMPETITIONS AND PRACTICE.

SHOOTING IN THE CADET FORCE

INTRODUCTION

Should you live in a town or city it is most likely that your first experience of shooting was at a Shooting Gallery at a fair or in an amusement arcade. If you were very lucky you might have walked away with a useless prize, such as a plastic duck or a bag of marbles! Your ability to shoot accurately had very little to do with your skill. The weapons used in these places are not meant to be too accurate as they would have to give away too many prizes and as a result - not make any profit.!!

SHOOTING IN THE COUNTRYSIDE

Those of you who are fortunate enough to live in the country or who are able to 'get out' into our beautiful countryside, may have the opportunity to use a shot gun or rifle in the pursuit of sport. Some of you will live in parts of the country where the wildlife in large areas of the countryside is preserved and carefully looked after by Game Keepers. Many of their working days are spent with either a shot gun or rifle in their hands. The 'prizes' they win for their shooting could be the fox that kill some of their Pheasants who were sitting on eggs.

CONSERVATION and PRESERVATION

The shepherd on the hills and in the dales has to be a good shot with a rifle to protect his sheep from predators, such as stray dogs who are not kept under control by their owners or again the hungry fox who fancies a bit of lamb for it's dinner. The opportunity to spend time with people in the countryside whose living depends on using a gun, should not be missed. You may not like the idea of seeing some of our wildlife being shot and killed in the pursuit of sport or in the course of controlling vermin, but if you leave that aspect to one side and look at the skills required to be a good shot, and the fact that if you were a gamekeeper or shepherd and NOT a good shot, a great deal of unnecessary suffering by wounding an animal and it escaping to die a lingering death would be caused.

A LIFE-LONG HOBBY

You are very fortunate as a cadet to become involved in shooting right from the start of your cadet career and could, if you so wished, continue to enjoy it throughout the whole of your life. The Cadet Forces all have shooting as one of the subjects that cadets are trained in and therefore put a lot of time and effort into providing ranges, weapons, ammunition and targets for you to have the best possible chances of becoming a good shot.

DUKE OF EDINBURGH'S AWARD SCHEME

Shooting is one of the pursuits recognised for participation in the Duke of Edinburgh Award Scheme and therefore your time and effort spent in becoming a good shot can be rewarded through the scheme. Target Shooting is one of the very few sports that you are able to keep up throughout your life. After your time in the Cadet Force there are many Rifle Clubs throughout the country of which you could join. On the other hand we hope that you would always consider staying in the Cadet Force and passing on your skills in shooting to succeeding generations of cadets.

BE AN ACHIEVER

It must be remembered that the success of anything we do, be it a job, a chore, a sport, invariably goes to those who are both keen and determined to do what ever it is to the best of their ability - to succeed. This especially applies to shooting, where the amount of care and practice you have is direct related to the results you achieve. However keen you are to get a place in the first rugby team, unless you have the physical ability and a natural gift of the skills required, you will have no chance of a place. Not so with shooting. No special skills are required, just keenness, practice and perseverance will bring you the rewards.

JOIN THE TEAM

In some County's they are very keen on shooting and have regular annual rifle meetings at which there is a great competitive spirit, and out of these events many of their teams for Bisley are selected for special training. This is where you have the opportunity to come to the notice of your County Shooting Officer, that is when you are a good enough, consistent shot, showing all the signs of being able to apply that ability, also having the right temperament, interest, application etc., to warrant further training as a member of your County or School 'Shooting Team'. You must bear in mind all that we have said about your ability not only to consistently shoot well, but to work as a valued member of a team. Safety is very important at all times especially when carrying out Skill at Arms Training, but firing live ammunition on a Rifle Range gives SAFETY a more immediate importance. There are strict Range Safety Rules that should be read to you every time you go on the Range.

TYPES OF SHOOTING ACTIVITY.

When you consider the shooting we do within the Cadet Forces it takes on a different meaning to that of the Armed Services.

The reason does not need explaining other than the role of the services and their needs in terms of Skill at Arms using small calibre weapons are more complicated than ours, and of course serve a totally different purpose. You must also remember that a soldiers pay and promotion prospects are linked to his skills, efficiency and fitness. Within the Armed Services there are essentially two distinct "Shooting Activities" which can be split into Shooting as a Sport or Competition Shooting and Qualification/Operational Firing.

We must say at the outset that it is very difficult to try and treat them separately when you get into the serious business of shooting.

The reason being that many of the shooting principles generally apply equally to both Shooting as a Sport and Qualification /Operational Firing, because of this you may sometimes feel that they are both mixed up together, the reason being that the skills required are very much the same, but applied for a different purpose.

COMPETITIVE SHOOTING

Shooting in the Cadet Forces comes under the umbrella of Competitive Shooting. This not only applies to the Shooting Practices for your proficiency qualifications, but also for many District and National competitions, having a variety of conditions that make them interesting and challenging to both the individual and team competitors. Details of these competitions are to be found at the end of this Shooting section. Get your unit OC to enter a team for some of the events, you will all enjoy it, particularly if you are fit and have stamina.

Every year there is the Cadet Rifle Meeting at Bisley. Many hundreds of cadets from the UK and Commonwealth Cadet Forces take part in the various competitions. You could be one of those competitors and/or a member of your county shooting team. It is a great experience to be there and see how keen the competitive spirit is between those taking part.

CADET SHOOTING

SKILL AT ARMS and SHOOTING

We must also consider Skill at Arms and Shooting in relation to the current syllabus of training for the Army Cadet Force and the Army Section of the Combined Cadet Force.

There is a need to understand of the role of Operational Firing and most certainly many of the subjects related to it Vis,. Training Tests, Fire Control Orders, Types of Fire, Section Leading, Patrols etc., but, it must be stressed that this does not actually involve Operational Firing.

MARKSMAN WITH EVERY WEAPON

Like the Armed Services, we do not have an unlimited supply of ammunition, therefore it is important at this stage to point out that it is just as much credit for you to be a Marksman with an Air Rifle, or a .22 Rifle as it is with the GP Rifle, the L81 Target Rifle or an LMG.

You are likely to have the opportunity to spend far more time firing an Air Rifle as the ranges are more readily available and the 'ammunition' (pellets) not so expensive. Provided Air Rifles are properly cared for they can be very accurate, but you will still need to put in a lot of practice to become a Marksman.

There is something rather special about learning how to use a weapon safely and correctly, to take care of it and learn how to fire it producing good results. Don't think for one moment that it's one of those "MACHIO" activities that seems to be the 'in-thing' to have a go at. It is a challenge to you as a cadet, to have the ability, stamina and patience to develop the required skills. In due course you may become a Marksman with one of the types of weapon you fire, if you try hard enough you should master all of them and be awarded your marksman badges.

CADET SHOOTING

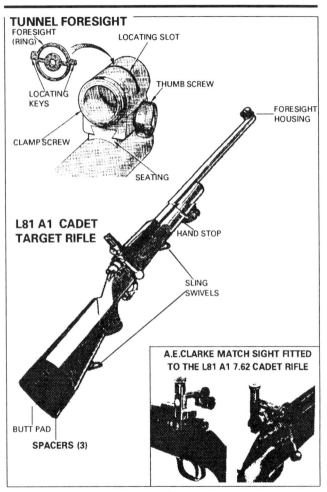

TUNNEL FORESIGHT

FORESIGHT (RING)

LOCATING SLOT

LOCATING KEYS

THUMB SCREW

CLAMP SCREW

SEATING

FORESIGHT HOUSING

L81 A1 CADET TARGET RIFLE

HAND STOP

SLING SWIVELS

BUTT PAD

SPACERS (3)

A.E.CLARKE MATCH SIGHT FITTED TO THE L81 A1 7.62 CADET RIFLE

GO SHOOTING REGULARILY

What is important is for everyone to make good use of what range allocations and ammunition we have made available to us, and for as many as possible to have the chance to take part in shooting on a regular basis.

It follows that when your OC has arranged for a shooting practice he will expect you to be there, not just to shoot, but to help run the range and coach others to encourage them to do better.

Skill at Arms Training will introduce you to the weapons fired in the Cadet Force. The Skill at Arms sections in your Pocket Book will help you towards the knowledge and skills required, but there is nothing like practice to make perfect.

SHOOTING WITH THE TA

Your cadet unit/school should have close liaison with the local TA units and through this contact a great deal of shooting practice can be arranged. Not that you would expect to fire ALL the weapons they use nor the practices they run, but it is another opportunity for you to practice and also makes good competition for both you and the TA soldier. Your contribution to time on the open ranges with the TA will no doubt be to help them run the range by assisting in the Butts, signaling and marking up targets. You may get lucky and use an Electric Target Range (ETR), when there is no marking to be done. Perhaps the greatest difference between 'Shooting as a Sport' and 'Qualifying/Operational Firing' is that a soldier has to be very fit to carry out 'Qualifying/Operational firing' practices, as many of them involve practices running down the range or tactical firing on ETR ranges or Close Quarter Battle Ranges (CQBR).

PRACTICE MAKES PERFECT

If you are already keen on shooting in particular, you
must take advantage of every opportunity to spend time
firing on the range.

There is always room for improvement, nothing easily
attained will be held to be of much value by you. You
must strive to improve your performance, knowing that
the enjoyment will be a just reward by being a good shot.
As a Cadet Recruit - a word of warning - do not be put-off
if at first you don't get a reasonable result, just remember
if at first you don't succeed -try, try again. You must stick
at it, as it is more than ever necessary in shooting. The
reason being that your score suffers directly by the errors
you make, there is no second chance, the mistake you
make you pay for right away. If you make less mistakes
than the others - you will win.

BUILD YOUR CONFIDENCE

Have confidence in yourself and your own ability, for what
others can do you also can do better - if you try hard enough.
Why not have a shot at it. Hopefully, this Skill at Arms
section dealing with shooting will help you to:-
1. Think more seriously about your own training and
   what you could do to improve it.
2. Give you information and ideas that you are able to
   use in your own training.
3. Improve your results and give you more confidence in
   your ability.
4. Arouse your interest and dedication in pursuit of better
   results.
5. Give you an opportunity to pass on your skills to
   others who may be just starting to shoot.
6. Consider the time, patience and interest that your
   Officers and Instructors have to put into your training
   and their expectations of you in return.

Once you start to improve - nothing will hold you back - only you can make the choice. Don't miss a chance to have a practice shoot, no matter what type of weapon or range.

PERSONAL QUALITIES

It is within the ability of almost anyone to become a good shot, provided they are 'mentally' and 'physically' fit. Mental Fitness - because it is to a great extent the 'mental control'.that is required once you have learned the skills needed.

The determination and keenness to succeed relies on Mental Fitness.

You will know that the determination of the Girl Cadets of the Cadet Forces, have in a very short time, been rewarded for their shooting prowess by winning competitions against very experienced competitors.

We will no doubt see many more of the Girl Cadets taking prizes in the future.

Physical Fitness in this context, is the need to have those parts of the body working sufficiently well to hold, sight and fire the weapon accurately, and to re-load - if it's not a self loading weapon!

Many firers on the range find out - for the first time - that their eyesight is not as good as they imagined it was - even as young as you are - have your eyesight checked at regular intervals.

On the plus side, shooting is a great sport and gives you a lot of fun and satisfaction. It does repay you for all the time and effort you have gone through to arrive at producing good results.

PRODUCING A GOOD 'GROUP'

You will read and be constantly told that "your ability to shoot well depends entirely upon being able to GROUP TIGHTLY" or " you must have a good GROUPING capacity".

CADET SHOOTING

To explain this, if you imagine that perhaps the ideal method of holding and firing a weapon would be to have it clamped firmly in some device on the firing point - so as it cannot move, load and fire it at a target 100 metres away.

You may not belive it, but a weapon fired under these 'ideal' conditions would not put all the shots through the same hole in the target, it would produce shots spread out in a "GROUP".

It is not suggested that you can hold it as firmly as some device, but to start off with, to be a good shot it is essential to learn to shoot when in the prone or lying position.

In this position the greater part of your body area is in contact with the ground, giving you a stable or firm base from which you can master the techniques and skills that you will be taught.

SAFE and SKILLED

Lessons will have been taught by your instructors for you to handle the weapons SAFELY and to master the basic skills. Once you are qualified in these basic skills, then you will start to be given the training in some depth by coaching you for marksmanship during live firing practices. Your 'coach' will modify the basic techniques to suit your individual needs.

GOING ON THE RANGE

Having arrived on the Range and moved to the area of the firing Point in preparation for your shooting, the most important action that must be carried out are the Range Safety Drills.

These and other Range Standing Orders will be explained to you by the Range Officer, who is responsible for Range Discipline and the safety of those on or in the vicinity of the Range.

CADET SHOOTING

PERSONAL SAFETY/HEALTH

You are at all times responsible for your own safety, not to do anything that will constitute a danger to yourself or others. The noise of weapons being fired can damage your ear drums - UNLESS YOU TAKE PRECAUTIONS by wearing some form of protection.

You must wear EAR DEFENDERS at all times when firing a weapon. Do not take part in shooting practices without them, the only exception being when firing an Air Gun.

PERSONAL INSPECTION

You will be inspected - your pockets and all personal equipment, webbing etc, will be checked to make sure that no DRILL ROUNDS are brought onto the Range. When you have finished on the range and just before you leave, you will be inspected again, this time for any live rounds of ammunition or empty cases. It is very easy to have missed a loose round in the bottom of your webbing equipment, but now is the time that you must be sure that you have none.

Should you find any, don't try and hide them, give them to the Range Officer or the Instructor when they inspect you as below.

YOUR PERSONAL DECLARATION

At the actual time of your inspection by the Range Officer or Instructor you will make a declaration (tell them) as they come to you by saying:-

"I HAVE NO LIVE ROUNDS OR EMPTY
CASES IN MY POSSESSION, - SIR"

These and other Range Rules apply equally to all personnel on the Range, you will see your instructors and officers inspect each other in your presence.

CADET SHOOTING

MARKSMANSHIP PRINCIPLES

The Definition of a Good Shot - What is Essential?
"To fire a shot without it disturbing your aim".
To achieve this:-

1. Your FIRING POSITION and the HOLD must be FIRM ENOUGH to SUPPORT the weapon.
2. The weapon must point naturally in the direction of the target, without any undue physical effort.
3. The alignment of your sights and aiming must be correct.
4. You control the rhythm of your breathing and operate the trigger correctly.
5. The shot will be fired and 'followed through' without undue movement disturbing your aim."

You must learn these Marksmanship Principles, until they become firmly established in your mind.
The application of them demands great concentration on your part, this combined with the determination to be a Marksman will ensure success.

LYING POSITION and HOLDING

You must develop the control you have over HOLDING the weapon, to keep it steady. This is the foundation upon which to carry out the other activities, Vis BREATHING, AIMING, TRIGGER OPERATION, FOLLOW THROUGH.
Only when you have mastered the correct HOLDING will you start to improve upon your results.

GET THE BASIC'S RIGHT - FIRST.

THE LYING POSITION.

The lying position is the basic shooting position as it gives the firer the best support for the weapon, it is least tiring and presents the smallest image as a target to the enemy.
To maintain steadiness and be able to achieve a perfect

hold, the first essential is that you are comfortable and feel that your weapon is a part of you. The importance of this cannot be over emphasised.

POSITION ON GROUND

The position to be adopted on the ground, is with your body slightly oblique to the line of fire from which you are able to achieve the CORRECT AIM in the shortest time.

When getting on the ground hold the PISTOL GRIP with the Right hand, lie down, breaking your fall with the LEFT hand, keep the weapon parallel to the ground, make sure that no dirt gets into the MUZZLE.

When you are down on the ground, tilt the weapon to the right, and support it by placing your LEFT hand under the HAND GUARD across the palm of your hand and hold with your fingers together.

The grip should be no more than a stable platform for the weapon.

NO attempt should be made to grip the HAND GUARD tightly or pull it backwards into the shoulder.

The position should be one of support.

The LEFT elbow is positioned as close as possible - in a comfortable position - to a point directly below the weapon.

This position is intended to support the weight of the weapon on the bone of the arm, rather than using your muscular effort to support and hold the weapon, which could not be sustained for very long.

The BUTT should be in a position against the muscle between the shoulder joint and the lower edge of your collar bone - it should not come into contact with the bone itself.

Your RIGHT hand is the controlling hand and is the most important factor in good shooting. It should be high up on the PISTOL GRIP, with the web of the skin between thumb and forefinger positioned at the back of the PISTOL GRIP.

The grip must be firm, pulling back into the shoulder, but take care NOT to twist the weapon causing the SIGHTS not to be upright.

The first joint of your forefinger should be naturally on the TRIGGER. The position of the RIGHT ELBOW is determined after taking the correct grip with your hand on the PISTOL GRIP.

Your elbow also helps to keep your right shoulder in the correct position all the time.

Your body should be slightly at a angle to the 'line of fire', and your muscles in a relaxed state.

As you may not be accustomed to regular visits to the range, you may find it difficult to relax as there is always a certain amount of excitement in shooting. However in spite of this it is a part of the Self Discipline that you will need to master every time you get down to fire, REMEMBER: BE — COOL — CALM, and COLLECT your THOUGHTS.

GET COMFORTABLE

Your LEFT leg should be in line with your body, your RIGHT leg is positioned to form a continuation of the line of fire.

Relax your leg muscles and turn your toes outwards with your heels on the ground. This position gives you the maximum amount of contact between your body and the ground, affording you the most comfortable position.

This position often, and quite naturally puts extra pressure on your chest in contact with the ground. This can affect your breathing rhythm and you may feel that it restricts your breathing.

If this is so, bend your right knee and bring your leg up slightly. This will raise the right side of your body just enough to make your breathing easier.

Keep your head in an upright position, this is it's natural position and therefore the instinct to maintain your sense of balance and to correctly position your eyes immediately behind the sights.

Don't press your cheek hard against the CHEEK PIECE of the BUTT. Rest it lightly in a position that is comfortable and that you can keep for the time you are firing a practice.

Don't get your eye too near to the BACK SIGHT. The distance should never be LESS than 25mm away.

AUTOMATIC ALIGNMENT WITH THE TARGET

The Marksmanship Principle -

"that requires the rifle to point naturally at the target" needs little explanation as you will know how to adopt the correct firing position, but, if you are in a position that you have to strain even the smallest muscle to achieve the CORRECT AIM PICTURE it can affect your results.

At the moment you fire your weapon it will move against or be affected by that 'small muscle strain'.

This strain is in force at the very moment you fire, in fact before the round leaves the MUZZLE of the weapon, the weapon will move against this strain and as a result your correct aim will be "off" and your results affected.

On firing it cannot be helped that your weapon will move, but natural alignment will go a long way to ensure that the movement is kept to a minimum. Once you have had some experience of firing it will become easier for you to get into a correctly aligned position each time you fire. Until that time arrives you will have to practice 'testing and adjusting' until you find the most 'comfortable position'.

A useful tip to help find a 'comfortable position' is to shut your eyes and come up into the aim. As your eyes are shut you will instinctively adopt the most comfortable stance. On opening your eyes, the AIM PICTURE should be on or very near the POINT OF AIM you had.

If not your position should be altered.

ADJUSTING YOUR POSITION - OTHER WAYS

Other ways to adjust your position are as follows:-
Aim at the target and then relax your hold. You should not notice any great change in your aim.

If there is, then it is an indication that you need to adjust your position.

If you need to correct lateral - LEFT to RIGHT errors. Keep your left elbow still, move your body slightly to the LEFT or RIGHT as required.

To correct VERTICAL errors, keep both your elbows still, and lift your body slightly forward or backwards as you require. Keep your BUTT in the same position in your shoulder.

The more you practice, it will become second nature to automatically adopt the correct position without adjustment.

SIGHT ALIGNMENT - AIMING

The CORRECT AIM PICTURE requires several different actions to be carefully co-ordinated at the same time, not just once, but time after time using exactly the same formula on each occasion. It is a lot to ask of our human make up to perform this, that is why you have to practice and have the patience to develop the skill.

To achieve this CORRECT AIM PICTURE you have to align:-

1. Your EYE.
2. The CENTRE of the BACK SIGHT.
3. The CENTRAL POINT of the TIP of the FORESIGHT.
4. Place the sights - so aligned on the point of aim on the target. See the diagram below.

CADET SHOOTING

CORRECT SIGHT ALIGNMENT (MILITARY SHOOTING)

POINT OF AIM

The correct focusing of your eyesight is essential to carry out the aiming. It is important to understand that you are asking your eyes to focus on two objects at different distances both at the same time. The objects are the TARGET, OR the TIP of the FORESIGHT.

The critical part of SIGHT ALIGNMENT is the connection between the BACK SIGHT APERTURE and the FORESIGHT.

Any errors you make are multiplied in proportion to the range of the target, so it is most important to make sure that the FORESIGHT is in clear focus at the moment of 'SHOT RELEASE'.

The tendency is to focus on the target and in so doing draw your attention away from the connection there should be between the FORESIGHT and the APERTURE BACK SIGHT.

With sufficient practice and experience your eye will automatically line up the centre of the APERTURE in the BACK SIGHT, BUT, don't get carried away by thinking this does not need regular practice and concentration - it does!.

FATIGUE AWARENESS

Should you be involved in a long period of firing there is no doubt that some form of fatigue will become apparent.

Usually you will notice that it is your eyes that become

tired, especially if you are inclined to remain in the aim too long.

As your eye gets tired its power of clear vision rapidly reduces. It can become upsetting if your results become erratic.

To do this there has to be an instantaneous movement of your trigger. (This is not to be confused with a common fault of a nervous firer who -ignoring all that has been taught - may be inclined to close their eyes and 'snatch' the trigger.) This instantaneous movement should not change the grip you have with your right hand and therefore the immediate action of your trigger finger will not alter your CORRECT AIM.

It is out of the question to take your time over the actual 'operation of the trigger' to actually fire the weapon - YOU DON'T HAVE TIME.

TAKE YOUR TIME

This is when it is important for you to strictly control the amount of time that you allow yourself for firing the number of rounds in each practice.

It is better to take a more leisurely approach, come down off the aim and start again.

While out of the aim, relax and give your eyes a rest. It is always said that to look at the grass near to you on the range is good for the eyes, green being a restful colour. Don't look down the range or at distant objects as your eyes have been accustomed to being focused on near objects such as your sights, therefore look at objects close by.

Once you are in the aim - discipline yourself to get off your shots in say, the space of SIX seconds - dependent upon your individual skills, preference and the conditions of the practice.

Just give it some careful thought for a moment, consider

that no matter how strong and steady your hold may be with your weapon, you cannot physically hold it in that EXACT POSITION for more than a few seconds. Not forgetting that your eyes will get tired quickly.

It is the co-ordination of all activities, that when your eye says "CORRECT AIM" the weapon MUST fire. NOT before, or AFTER, it MUST GO ON THE DOT.

CONTROL OF BREATHING

We all breath naturally at a steady rate with very little change in the rate of the number of breaths we take per minute, it has a natural rhythm - that is UNLESS we do something to upset it and it takes very little to do just that. Operational Shooting Practices invariably involve running down the range. You will experience that when you are out of breath - no matter how fit you are - that it is more difficult to concentrate on what you are doing. When you come up into the aim, your sights are not in focus, in fact may be blurred. You are far from being steady - never mind getting the right AIM PICTURE. The reason for this is a lack of oxygen in the blood stream. It must be rapidly replaced by CORRECT BREATHING, which in turn reduces the tension and strain, allowing you to get back to the normal rhythm of breathing in the shortest possible time. You will now appreciate that it is very important to keep your breathing under control when you are shooting.

The need to be "cool - calm - and collected" especially when leading up to the point at which you actually make the decision to fire the shot.

To assist you in this refer to the diagram below and the notes. Practice the timing for "Breathing for Firing" as shown in the illustration over the page until it becomes second nature, then apply it when you are shooting.

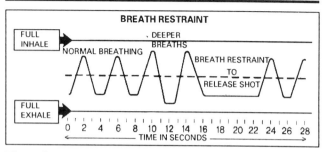

Three Stages

There are three stages in the normal breathing cycle that are important to consider when shooting.

a. During normal breathing your lungs are neither completely filled nor emptied.

b. When breathing out there is a natural pause.

c. The time for the whole "cycle" takes about SIX seconds. It is plain to see that the ideal time to fire a shot will be when your body is having a natural pause in the breathing cycle. The idea is to slightly extend that pause by a couple of seconds, to EIGHT seconds.

BREATHING FOR FIRING

1. Take several SLOW, DEEP BREATHS, giving the oxygen time to be absorbed into your blood stream.

2. Don't empty your lungs, take a slightly larger breath and hold it for about six seconds - see diagram above — "Breath Restraint to Release Shot".

3. During those critical six seconds, you will find the CORRECT AIM and operate the TRIGGER, afterwards, continue to breath normally.

If for some reason you decide not to fire, relax and start again. REMEMBER: This can only be achieved by the independent movement of the TRIGGER FINGER whilst the remainder of your body is perfectly still.

Eventually co-ordinated control of your breathing and release of the shot will become a reflex action.

TRIGGER CONTROL & OPERATION

In the early stages of shooting a beginner has to consciously direct their finger to pull the trigger, but with training, this becomes a conditioned reflex action. Errors in trigger control can loose a firer many points, especially at short range.

TRIGGERS

There are two basic types of trigger you may come across in shooting, a TWO STAGE (normally found in military rifles) and a SINGLE STAGE usually fitted on small-bore rifles, but in recent time more are now being fitted to full-bore rifles.

It is important that the grip of the RIGHT hand (LEFT hand for left handed firers) does not interfere with the trigger operation.

The only part of the trigger finger that should be in contact with the rifle should be part which is ON THE TRIGGER. The trigger should operate in the same way each time and go at the same pressure.

With the two stage trigger, the first pressure is taken up while settling into position.

When ready as soon as a clear sight picture is seen, the second pressure is operated, smoothly and quickly in one movement.

With a single stage trigger the operation is the same as for the second stage of a two stage trigger.

THE FOLLOW THROUGH

It is possible that you may respond to TRIGGER action or other influences at the very moment the weapon is fired and the BULLET is still in the BARREL.

This can cause a shot to be misplaced, even so, it is

essential that the shot is "followed through" to the target. It requires you to concentrate during the period of TRIGGER operation and SHOT RELEASE.

CALLING THE SHOT

It is essential that the firer should be able to "CALL THE SHOT", in other words, be able to predict if a shot has been misplaced and where it may go.

On the FOLLOW THROUGH as above if the rifle does not come to rest where expected, the position where it does come to rest can indicate where the shot will have gone. If it comes to rest at a different point each time , the GROUP is likely to be large and other factors will need to be examined e.g. Position, Sling or Hold.

CHARACTERISTICS OF THE WEAPON

Particularly in Competitive shooting, the ability to fire your weapon and for it to produce a "GROUP" of shots within a certain specified maximum area, is the essential requirement for you and your weapon to achieve. You have to have complete confidence, not only in your own capability, but also your weapons ability to achieve this goal. Once this confidence is achieved the weapon becomes an extension of your body.

TESTING YOUR INDIVIDUAL WEAPON

A short range is better to test weapons, 30 or 100 metres - they are not affected by errors due to the wind. Check that the weapon you are about to use is in fact 'your weapon'. Ensure that the Barrel and CHAMBER are dry cleaned for firing.

Check that the weapon is functioning correctly, and if appropriate, that the magazine is correctly filled.

A Grouping Practice of five or more rounds should then be fired at any type of target having an easily defined Aiming Mark.

CADET SHOOTING

Should you make a faulty shot, this should be declared to your coach. Weapons of the same type often have slight variations when fired, also the weather conditions, wind etc. may have to be taken into consideration as it can effect how your weapon fires.

With practice under a variety of conditions, you will get to know how your weapon performs and become accustomed to its own characteristics.

This aspect of shooting is especially important when taking part in your early training, but just as important in competitive shooting.

When firing your practices on the range you should have an experienced shot with you as a "Coach", who will be down by your side on the firing point.

The SLING - AN AID TO GOOD SHOOTING

Many of the 'Top Shots' in the world who shoot at Bisley use a sling as a shooting aid. The purpose of using the sling is to give extra support and stability to the weapon you are holding, and to reduce some of the strain or fatigue in supporting the weapon. There are two types of sling.

The first one is known as a SINGLE POINT SLING, in that it is secured only at the forend of the rifle and forms a loop that you put your arm through, it passes over your wrist, with the wide band of the sling well above your left elbow on your upper arm (see diagram - Single Point Sling - on next page). This helps to keep the LEFT arm vertical under the weapon and does not exert any sideways pressure. The second - a TWO POINT SLING is secured at the forend and on the BUTT as normal. This is used in a similar manner to the Single Point Sling, with the sling wound over your wrist and round your arm, again with it above your elbow on your upper arm.

ALWAYS CHECK THAT IT IS THE CORRECT RIFLE YOU ARE ABOUT TO SHOOT WITH

CADET SHOOTING

THE SINGLE POINT SLING

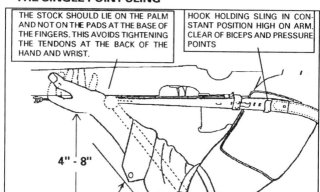

THE STOCK SHOULD LIE ON THE PALM AND NOT ON THE PADS AT THE BASE OF THE FINGERS. THIS AVOIDS TIGHTENING THE TENDONS AT THE BACK OF THE HAND AND WRIST.

HOOK HOLDING SLING IN CONSTANT POSITION HIGH ON ARM. CLEAR OF BICEPS AND PRESSURE POINTS

4" - 8"

30 Degrees

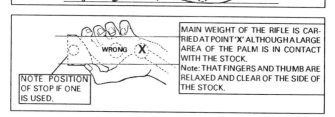

WRONG X

NOTE POSITION OF STOP IF ONE IS USED.

MAIN WEIGHT OF THE RIFLE IS CARRIED AT POINT 'X' ALTHOUGH A LARGE AREA OF THE PALM IS IN CONTACT WITH THE STOCK.
Note: THAT FINGERS AND THUMB ARE RELAXED AND CLEAR OF THE SIDE OF THE STOCK.

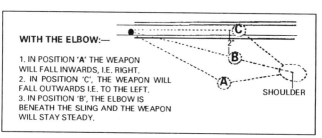

WITH THE ELBOW:—

1. IN POSITION 'A' THE WEAPON WILL FALL INWARDS, I.E. RIGHT.
2. IN POSITION 'C', THE WEAPON WILL FALL OUTWARDS I.E. TO THE LEFT.
3. IN POSITION 'B', THE ELBOW IS BENEATH THE SLING AND THE WEAPON WILL STAY STEADY.

C
2"
B
A
SHOULDER

CADET SHOOTING

SINGLE POINT SLING

The illustration on the previous page gives a very clear picture of how a SINGLE POINT SLING is used in TARGET SHOOTING.

A Single Point sling is not usually used in military shooting as the firer uses the sling and fitments which are part of the weapon.

In the end it is a matter of personal choice which one you use. Most shooting teams buy leather slings that are softer material to handle and also wider, as a result of which they are more comfortable.

Points to remember if you are using a sling:-

Unless you have your own sling, you must mark the exact position of the buckles on the sling you use, this will ensure that you are consistent in the way you use it. The position of the sling on the upper arm must always be as far up the arm as is possible/comfortable.

CARE and CLEANING

This subject has already been dealt with in some detail, but it must be emphasised that your CARE and CLEANING when you are involved in competitive shooting must be meticulous. This extra care of your weapon may reveal something that could put you out of the competition - if you had not found it. It will pay dividends to be extra careful with all aspects of Care and Cleaning. Proper cleaning will extend the barrel life, careless cleaning can cause damage.

Before the Shoot

1. Clean out the barrel using full length rod, rod guide , jag and flannelette. NEVER poull a dirty patch back up the barrel.
2. Polish the barrel by repeating as above.
3. Dry all metal surfaces, especially the bolt and inside the action

CADET SHOOTING

TARGETS

The illustrations and information on targets in the
following pages are a sample of the many different
targets you will come across if you develop a keen
interest in shooting.

Please be aware that they are **NOT** to scale and are
reproduced to give you a representation of how they
appear.

In addition to the table of Target Sizes given below, the
actual sizes of the cards they are produced on is given by
each target.

4ft TARGETS

SCORING AREAS	CIRCLE DIMENTIONS		
	TYPE 'A' 500m	TYPE 'B' 300m	TYPE 'C' 200m
BULL	15"	9"	6"
INNER	30"	18"	12"
MAGPIE	48"	30"	30"
OUTER		48"	48"

FIGURE TARGETS

FIG 11.	Height = 45"	Width = 18"
FIG 12.	Height = 22 1/2"	Width = 18"

SHOOTING RECORDS

We have included Shooting Records with the Targets, as
in competition shooting the type of records you have are
a replica of your target and the information is compiled
on the firing point by one of your team members or a
coach.

There are so many different types of record it would be
impossible to illustrate all of them.

The Shooting Record Sheet shown are to give you an
idea as to how it is set out and the information that is
recorded.

310

CADET SHOOTING

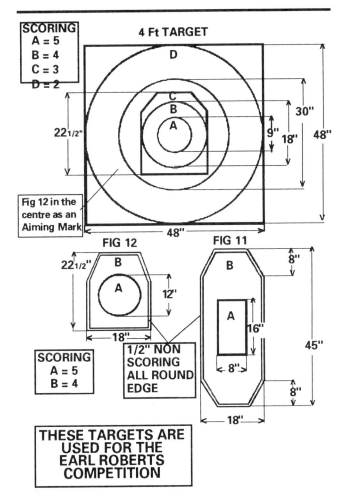

4 Ft TARGET

SCORING
A = 5
B = 4
C = 3
D = 2

D
C
B
A

30"
48"
22 1/2"
9"
18"

48"

Fig 12 in the centre as an Aiming Mark

FIG 12

22 1/2"
B
A
12'
18"

FIG 11

B
A
16"
8"
45"
8"
8"
18"

SCORING
A = 5
B = 4

1/2" NON SCORING ALL ROUND EDGE

THESE TARGETS ARE USED FOR THE EARL ROBERTS COMPETITION

311

CADET SHOOTING

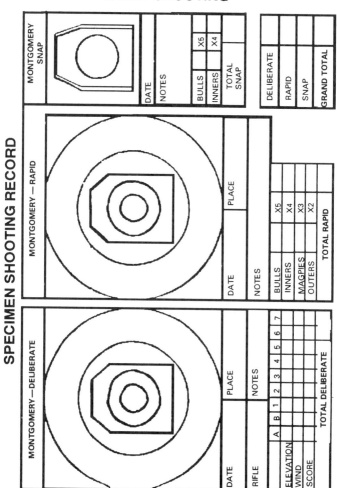

SPECIMEN SHOOTING RECORD

MONTGOMERY — DELIBERATE

DATE
PLACE
RIFLE
NOTES

	A	B	1	2	3	4	5	6	7
ELEVATION									
WIND									
SCORE									

TOTAL DELIBERATE

MONTGOMERY — RAPID

DATE
PLACE
NOTES

BULLS	X5
INNERS	X4
MAGPIES	X3
OUTERS	X2

TOTAL RAPID

MONTGOMERY SNAP

DATE
NOTES

BULLS	X5
INNERS	X4

TOTAL SNAP

DELIBERATE	
RAPID	
SNAP	
GRAND TOTAL	

312

CADET SHOOTING

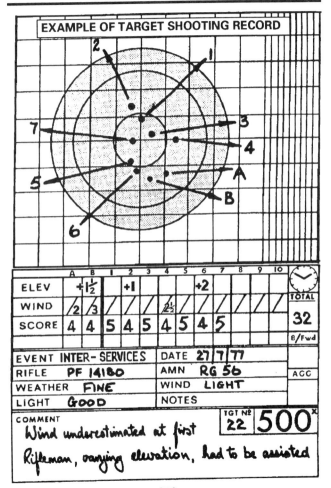

EXAMPLE OF TARGET SHOOTING RECORD

	A	B	1	2	3	4	5	6	7	8	9	10		TOTAL
ELEV	+1½		+1			+2								
WIND	2	3				2½								32
SCORE	4	4	5	4	5	4	5	4	5					B/Fwd

EVENT	INTER-SERVICES	DATE	27/7/77	
RIFLE	PF 14180	AMN	RG 56	AGG
WEATHER	FINE	WIND	LIGHT	
LIGHT	GOOD	NOTES		

COMMENT   TGT № 22 500ˣ

Wind underestimated at first

Rifleman, varying elevation, had to be assisted

313

CADET SHOOTING

TARGETS

National Small Bore Rifle Association 25 yds Cadets and Schools Card Size 300mm x 200mm

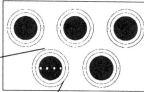

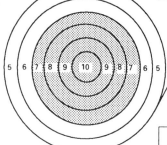

ILLUSTRATION ON LEFT SHOWS DETAILS OF **SIX** SCORING CIRCLES 10 POINTS IN THE BULL, DOWN TO 5 POINTS.

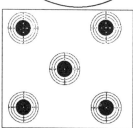

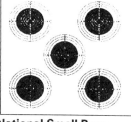

National Small Bore Rifle Association 6 yard (5.5 metres) Air Rifle Target Size 170mm square. This target has SIX Scoring rings, NINE points in the Bull down to 4.

National Small Bore Rifle Association 10 Metre Air Rifle Target Size: 170mm square. This target has NINE Scoring rings, 9 points in the Bull down to 1.

CADET SHOOTING

ARMY CADET FORCE ASSOCIATION
L98A1 GP RIFLE GROUPING / ZEROING TARGET 25 m

| RANK..... | NAME.................. | DATE......... | PRACTICE No.... |

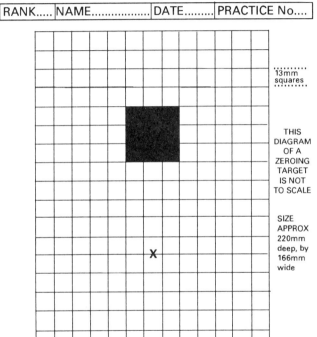

13mm squares

THIS DIAGRAM OF A ZEROING TARGET IS NOT TO SCALE

SIZE APPROX 220mm deep, by 166mm wide

Note:
a. When using the bottom of the black sqaure as the POA (Point Of Aim) the CZP (Correct Zeroing Position) is at X.
b. Each square is equivalent to one graduation in either elevation or direction.

315

COMPETITIVE SHOOTING IN
THE CADET FORCES

COUNCIL FOR CADET RIFLE SHOOTING (CCRS)

The CCRS was formed in 1969 to bring together several other associations who up to that time were involved in the promotion of shooting in the Cadet Forces and schools. These associations were The Imperial Cadet Association, The Public Schools Rifle Matches Association and a committee who organised the Inter Services Cadet Rifle Meeting (ISCRM).

BACKING GIVEN

The Ministry of Defence and the Territorial Army Association both give financial and administrative help in support of the work carried out by the CCRS. This is provided through all the Cadet Forces - Sea Cadet Corps, Army Cadet Force, Combined Cadet Force and the Air Training Corps. In addition the Army gives direct assistance at the main shooting event of the year - the Inter Services Cadet Rifle Meeting - at Bisley.

CENTRAL AUTHORITY

The aim of the CCRS is to act as a central organisation who can speak with some authority and give advice on shooting matters in general. It has the authority - approved by the MOD (Ministry of Defence) to keep in contact with other shooting authorities and units of the

Cadet Forces to give assistance and information affecting cadets.

COMPETITION ADMINISTRATION

The CCRS arranges and administers many postal shooting competitions, coaching courses and other shooting events for cadets at schools and units not only in the UK, but throughout the Commonwealth.

The Council also provides the administration support for teams of cadets who are selected to represent Britain in National and International Shooting Matches, both at home and overseas.

The HQ of the CCRS is at Derby Lodge, Bisley, Surrey, where it provides a base for information and administration throughout the year, as well as canteen and recreational facilities for all cadets attending National Meetings at Bisley.

YOUR SUPPORT

You will appreciate that to take care of shooting across the whole of the Cadet Forces including many of those in the Commonwealth is not an easy task.

In spite of this nothing gives those who spend their time looking after you and your shooting, more satisfaction than when results come in for the Postal Competitions and then seeing all those who arrive with their County Shooting Teams at Bisley to take part in the ISCRM.

We must remember that we all rely on the support that you as a cadet give to Competitive Shooting in your unit. This interest and support provides the demand for the organisation and all the related costs for running the Ranges and other facilities for competitions on a national basis.

In the following pages you will find the various **Postal Shooting Competitions** and their conditions available for you in your unit.

COMPETITION SHOOTING

Following the Postal Competitions are the competitions and conditions that are laid down when taking part in the Inter Services Cadet Rifle Meeting (ISCRM) currently held each year at Bisley.

If your cadet detachment is not entering these competitions, then ask your officers and instructors to do something about it, it is great fun and creates competition between you and other detachments in your area. You never know your detachment might walk away with the top score!.

MAJOR POSTAL SHOOTING COMPETITIONS FOR THE ARMY CADET FORCE AND THE COMBINED CADET FORCE

THE COMMONWEALTH TARGET RIFLE COMPETITION

A team event of 4 firers.
Firing with the Cadet L81 A1 Target Rifle as issued.
Two Classes: Class A Teams using Match Sights.
Class B Teams using sights as issued.
Conditions: A DELIBERATE shoot at 300x and at 500x.
TWO "sighters" and SEVEN rounds to count at each distance.
May be fired on any ONE DAY from 1st April to 31st March the following year.
Entry Fees: As stated on your entry form.

THE EARL ROBERTS COMPETITION

A team event of 4 firers using the Cadet L98 GP Rifle as issued.
Conditions: Four practices:-
1. Deliberate at 300x.
2. Fire with movement 300x to 100x.
3. Rapid fire at 200x.
4. Snap shooting at 200x.

COMPETITION SHOOTING

May be fired on any ONE DAY from 1st April to 31st March the following year.
Entry Fees: As stated on your entry form.

THE MONTGOMERY OF ALAMEIN
NOTE: COMPETITION FOR OPEN CADET UNITS ONLY
A team event of 4 firers using the Cadet L98 GP Rifle as issued.
Conditions: Three Practices. All fired from 200x.
    1. Deliberate.   2. Rapid.   3. Snap.
May be fired on any ONE DAY between 1st September and 7th June the following year.
The FINAL COMPETITION is fired "shoulder to shoulder" at Bisley in July, during the ISCRM (Inter Services Cadet Rifle Meeting), between the TOP FIVE TEAMS.
Entry Fees: As stated on your entry form.

THE COUNTRY LIFE COMPETITION
A team event for teams using the No 8 Rifle.
Conditions: TWO Classes:
Class A Teams of 9 (8 to fire and a Team Leader)
Rifles equipped with Match Sights.
Class B Teams of 5 (4 to fire and a Team Leader)
Rifles with sights as issued.
Four Practices:
1. Grouping - 5 Rounds.   2. Rapid - 10 Rounds.
3. Snap - 5 Rounds. 4. Landscape - 3 Rounds per firer.
May be fired on any ONE DAY between 1st February and 15th March.
NO ENTRY FEES.

THE FFENNELL COMPETITION
 A team event of 8 firers.
Conditions: TWO Classes:
Class A Teams using ANY .22 Target Rifle.

NOT WITH TELESCOPIC SIGHTS.

Fired on NSRA British Match (1966) 10 Bull Cards.

Class B Teams using the No 8 Rifle as issued.

Fired on NSRA 5 Bull Decimal Targets: (Cadets & Schools) or NSRA Tin Hat Cards.

TWO cards per competitor. TEN rounds to count on each card.

May be fired any time between 1st April and 31st March the following year.

The whole team NEED NOT fire on the same day.

Entry Fees: As stated on your entry form.

THE CADET HUNDRED (Army Cadet Force only) SMALL BORE COMPETITION.

This is an INDIVIDUAL competition.

Conditions: Firers using any .22 Rifle.

NOT WITH TELESCOPIC SIGHTS.

Fired on NSRA 5 Bull Decimal Target (Cadets & Schools).

TWO cards per competitor.

TEN Rounds to count on each card.

This competition is fired in TWO stages, between September and February the following year.

The TOP 200 firers in Stage 1 go on to Stage 2.

The top forty individuals are selected to represent the Army Cadet Force against the Air and Navy Cadets in the **WHISTLER TROPHY**.

THE .22 RIFLE ACF TEAM COMPETITION

This is for teams of FOUR firers who are firing in the Cadet Hundred competition at Stage 1.

NO ENTRY FEES.

COMPETITION SHOOTING

THE "STAINIFORTH CHALLENGE CUP

NOTE: This is for CCF Schools/Colleges only.
A Team Event of 8 firers, using the No 8 Rifle. Match sights permitted.
Fired on NSRA 5 Bull Cadet/Schools (1971) Targets, one card per competitor.
TEN rounds to count.
This competition is fired in TWO STAGES, between September and December.
The top 10 teams go forward to the second stage.
Entry fee: £4 per team.

THE 6 YARD - AIR RIFLE - COMPETITION

A team event of 8 firers using any commercially available .177 calibre Air Rifle.
NOT FITTED WITH TELESCOPIC SIGHTS.
Conditions: Four NSRA cards per firer.
FIVE rounds per card to count.
May be fired on any ONE DAY between 1st April and 31st March in the following year.
Entry Fees: As stated on your entry form.

THE 10 METRE - AIR RIFLE - COMPETITION - three position.

A team event, **for teams of 8 firers**, using any commercially available .177 calibre Air Rifle.
NOT FITTED WITH TELESCOPIC SIGHTS.
Conditions: Four NSRA cards per firer, fired in the positions as below:-
1. ONE card fired in the PRONE position.
2. TWO cards fired in the STANDING position.
3. ONE card fired in the KNEELING position.
ALL cards to be fired in the order as above.
May be fired on any one day between 1st April and 31st March in the following year.
Entry Fees: As stated on your entry form.

COMPETITION SHOOTING

INTER-SERVICES CADET RIFLE MEETING COMPETITIONS

These are the competitions arranged annually by the Council for Cadet Rifle Shooting and take place at the "home" of competitive shooting - Bisley, near Brookwood, Surrey.

Bisley has a long history in the promotion of competitive shooting.

If you are fortunate enough to go there you will come under the spell of the atmosphere of competitive shooting.

Over the years many civilian rifle clubs have established their Shooting Lodges or their headquarters within 'Bisley Camp'. Some of them have very attractive buildings, with one theme in common, that is, the walls and in some cases the ceilings of their principal rooms are covered with the names of competitions and those who have won prizes.

You are able to trace the history of shooting not only through the "Rolls of Honour", but the many photographs of those who have been foremost in keeping their club at the top of competition charts.

If you would really like to go to Bisley it is not so difficult. All that you required is to consistently be a good shot and get into your County or School Team - its up to you.

CONDITIONS AND RULES
WEAPONS

All competitions in the ISCRM are fired using the 7.62mm L81A1, Cadet Target Rifle. The AE Clarke special Match Sight sight may be used to replace the issued back sight, (see illustration on page 290)

The illustration on the next page is the principal type of

COMPETITION SHOOTING

target that you will be shooting at in the CCRS Competitions. You will notice that these targets are different from the normal military type targets.

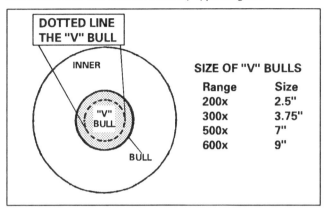

SIZE OF "V" BULLS

Range	Size
200x	2.5"
300x	3.75"
500x	7"
600x	9"

NRA Bisley Targets
White with Circular Black Aiming Mark

Divisons	Diameter in inches				Scoring
	600x	500x	300x	200x	
Aiming Mark	36	36	21	14	—
Bull	13.5	10.5	5.5	3.5	5
Inner	27	27	13.5	9	4
Magpie	36	36	21	14	3
Outer	Rest of target 5' 10" wide x 5' high		36	24	2

WHAT SHOOTING COMPETITIONS DO YOU TAKE PART IN — ASK YOUR OFFICER TO APPLY TO ENTER A TEAM FROM YOUR UNIT

COMPETITION SHOOTING

COMPETITION. MATCH A - INDIVIDUAL

Open to any Cadet competitor attending the meeting.
Prizes: 1st Challenge Cup and Silver Medal.
2nd Bronze Medal (For both distances fired)
3rd Bronze Medal
TIES - All Cadets scoring 33 or over will fire three extra tie shots at the end of their shoot.
These MUST BE RECORDED on the Score Card.
If still a tie for first place at each distance a tie shoot will be shot.
CONDITIONS
a. Distance: 300 and 600 yards.
b. No of Shots: 2 sighting shots and 7 to count at each distance.
c. Targets: One per team. Details as table above.
d. Timing: 50 minutes at each distance.
e. Scoring: As shown in table above
f. HPS: At each distance 35.
Total HPS: 70

COMPETITION MATCH B - PATRIOTIC SHIELD

Open to any Cadet competitor attending the meeting.
Prizes: 1st Patriotic Shield and Silver Medal.
2nd Bronze Medal
3rd Bronze Medal (For both distances fired)
TIES: All Cadets scoring 33 or over will fire three extra shots at the end of their shoot.
These MUST BE RECORDED on the Score Card.
If still a tie for first place at each distance a tie shoot will be shot.
CONDITIONS
a. Distance: 300 and 500 yards.
b. No of Shots: 2 sighting shots and 7 to count at each distance.
c. Targets: 1 per team. Details as table above.

d. Timing: 50 minutes at each distance.
e. Scoring: As shown in table on previous pages.
f. HPS: Per distance shot 35.
Match HPS: 70.

MATCH C - FRANKFORT TROPHY

Open to : Teams of four Cadets from any Cadet Unit attending the meeting.
 Prizes: 1st Challenge Shield and four Silver Medals.
2nd Four Bronze Medals
3rd Four Bronze Medals
Special Prize - The Sheerness Trophy to the top scoring Sea Cadet Team.
TIES: CCRS rules apply in all practices.

CONDITIONS

a. Distance: 300 and 500
b. No of Shots: 2 sighting shots and 7 to count at each distance.
c. Targets: 1 per team. Details as in table.
d. Timing: 50 minutes at each distance.
e. Scoring: As shown in table.
f. HPS: Per distance shot 35.
Match HPS: 70.

FRANKFORT TROPHY - MISCELLANEOUS CASH PRIZES

Teams may elect, on payment of a separate entry fee, to qualify for special cash prizes.
These will be awarded to the first FIVE teams, as well as three teams who entered the previous year and who have shown the greatest improvement, in places gained above their previous year's position.

COMPETITION MATCH D - THE WATTS BOWL

Open to: Teams of four Cadets from any Cadet Unit attending the meeting.
Prizes: 1st Challenge Bowl and four Silver Medals.
2nd Four Bronze Medals.

3rd Four Bronze Medals.

TIES: CCRS rules apply in all practices.

CONDITIONS

a. Distance: 500 yards.

b. No of Shots: 2 sighting shots and 10 to count.

c. Targets: 1 per team. Details as above table.

d. Timing: 70 minutes per team.

e. Scoring: As shown in table.

f. HPS: 200 points.

WATTS BOWL MISCELLANEOUS - CASH PRIZES

Teams may elect, on payment of a separate entry fee, to qualify for special cash prizes.

These will be awarded to the first FIVE teams, as well as three teams who entered the previous year and who have shown the greatest improvement, in places gained above their previous year's position.

COMPETITION MATCH E - BOSSOM CUP (GRAND AGGREGATE)

Open to: Any individual Cadet who has fired in each of Matches A, B, C, and D. The Individual.

The Patriotic Shield. The Frankfort Trophy and the Watts Bowl Competition. Prizes:

1st Challenge Cup and Silver Medal.

2nd Bronze Medal.

3rd Bronze Medal.

The RMRA Medal — Presented to top Sea/Marine Cadet.

The Squire Trophy — Presented to the top Sea Cadet.

The Campbell Trophy - Presented to the top ATC Cadet.

The Gill Trophy — Presented to the topATC Team with the highest aggregate score.

The Centenary Trophy - Presented to the top ACF team with the highest aggregate score.

The ACF Medal — Presented to the top ACF Cadet.

TIES: A tie for first place will be shot off at 600 yards

following the completion of Match L, the Inter Cadet Force Final.

CONDITIONS

a. The Cadet scoring the highest aggregate in matches A, B, C and D.

b.HPS: 260

NOTE:

THE FOLLOWING COMPETITIONS — MATCH **F, G, H, I,** AND **J,** ARE BASED ON SCORES ATTAINED AND TAKEN FROM THE PREVIOUS COMPETITIONS.

THEY ARE NOT SHOT FOR IN THE NORMAL WAY, BUT SHOULD A TIE OCCUR IT IS DEALT WITH AS SHOWN IN THE CONDITIONS.

COMPETITION MATCH F - NAVY LEAGUE CUP

Open to: Any Sea or Marine Cadet who has fired in Matches A and B. Prizes:

The Medals are presented by the Sea Cadet Corps.

1st Challenge Cup and Medal.

2nd Medal.

3rd Medal.

CONDITIONS

a. Sea or Marine Cadet placed highest in Match J.

b. HPS: 140 points.

COMPETITION MATCH G - RIFLE BRIGADE CUP.

Open to: Any Army Cadet who has fired in Matches A and B.

Prizes: 1st Challenge Cup and Silver Medal.

2nd Bronze Medal.

3rd Bronze Medal.

CONDITIONS:

a. Cadets with the highest scores in Match J - The Cadet Hundred.

b. HPS: 140 points.

COMPETITION SHOOTING

COMPETITION MATCH H - THE BOULTER CUP

Open to: Any Air Training Corps Cadet who has fired in Matches A and B.
Prizes: Medals presented by the Air Training Corps.
1st Challenge Cup and Silver Medal.
2nd Bronze Medal.
3rd Bronze Medal.
 CONDITIONS
a. The ATC Cadets placed highest in Match J - The Cadet Hundred.
b. HPS: 140 points.

COMPETITION MATCH I - THE CANADA TROPHY.

Open to: One team from Army Cadet Force Counties.
Prizes: Challenge Trophy and four Medals. Medals presented by ACFA.

CONDITIONS:

a. The team with the highest aggregate score in Match B.
b. HPS: 280 points.

COMPETITION MATCH J - THE CADET HUNDRED.

Open to: Any Cadet who has fired in Matches A, B and C.
Prizes: 1st Lady Gwendolin Guinness Challenge Cup and Silver Medal.
2nd Bronze Medal. 3rd Bronze Medal.
A National Rifle Association Cadet 100 Badge to each competitor.
TIES: Will be broken by counting out in accordance with NRA Rules entirely on the Match A 600 yards score.
A tie for first place will be shot off at 600 yards following Match L - The Inter-Cadet Force Final.
TIES: Will be dealt with under the CCRS rules.
CONDITIONS
a. Top 100 Cadets making highest aggregate scores in

Matches A, B and C.
b. HPS: 210 points.

COMPETITION MATCH K - THE SOMERSET CUP.

Open to: Forty Eight Cadets as selected for Match L -
The Inter-Cadet Force Final.
Prizes: 1st Challenge Cup and Council for Cadet Rifle
Shooting Gilt Medal.
2nd Council for Cadet Rifle Shooting Silver Medal.
3rd Council for Cadet Rifle Shooting Bronze Medal.
CONDITIONS
a. Distance: 600 yards.
b. No of Shots: 2 sighting and 10 to count.
c. Targets: 2 Cadets squadded per target.
d. Timing: 15 minutes for each Cadet.
TIES: Ties for first place will be shot off on the spot.
Cadets with scores of 47 or over are to remain on the
Firing Point. CCRS rules apply in all practices.

COMPETITION MATCH L - THE INTER-CADET FORCE FINAL.

Open to: A maximum of TWO TEAMS of EIGHT firers
from each of the Cadet Forces.
Prize: 1st Challenge Cup and eight Silver NRA Medals to
winning team.
CONDITIONS
a. Distance: 600 yards.
b. No of Shots: 2 sighting and 10 to count.
c. Targets: 2 Cadets squadded per target.
d. Timing: 15 minutes for each Cadet.

COMPETITION MATCH M - THE MONTGOMERY OF ALAMEIN CUP.

Open to: The FIVE teams of four cadets taking highest
place in Postal Match fired during the current season.

COMPETITION SHOOTING

This match is fired with the Cadet GP Rifle L98A1.
Prizes: 1st Challenge Cup and four CCRS Gilt Medals.
2nd Challenge Cup and four CCRS Silver Medals.
3rd Challenge Cup and four CCRS Bronze Medals.
CONDITIONS:
There are three Practices: **Deliberate. Rapid. Snap**

PRACTICE 1. DELIBERATE.

a. Distance: 200 yards.
b. No of shots: 2 sighting shots and 7 to count. Another round will be allowed for a misfire.
c. Targets: Army 4ft targets.
d. Timing: 15 minutes.

PRACTICE 2. RAPID.

a. Distance: 200 yards.
b. No of Shots: 5.
c. Target Army 4ft targets.
d. Timing: 30 seconds.
e. **Procedure:**
1. 5 shots per cadet in 30 seconds starting with rifles loaded an on aim.
2. No allowance for misfires or jams.

PRACTICE 3. SNAPSHOOTING.

a. Distance: 200 yards.
b. No of shots: 5
c. Targets: Large Snapshooting Fig 12 (59) with a 305mm (12 inch diameter circle).
d. Timing: 5 exposures each of 5 seconds with intervals of approximately 10 seconds between exposures.
e. Scoring: 5 and 4 points. Shots outside the 13mm (1/2 inch border do not count).
f. **Procedure**
1. Before rifles are loaded, one 'Dummy Exposure' of the

target will be made. If a shot is fired at this exposure it will not count for any purpose and will be a lost round to the firer.

2. Rifles loaded and on aim. One shot only to be fired at each exposure.

3. No allowance for misfire or jams.

COMPETITION POOL BULL - CASH PRIZE.

Open to: Any Cadet attending the meeting.
Prizes: Cash - depending on the number of entries.
Entrance fees:
Fees are notified on the meeting notice board.
Targets: usually have an aiming mark, the winners are those that get their shots inside the aiming mark and at the end of the meeting share out the money collected between them.

SHOOTING TERMS

WASHOUT - None of your shots have hit the scoring area of the target.
SIGHTERS - Shots fire at the start of shooting to assist you to centralise your group.
TIES - Where the total number of points scored by firers are equal.
AGGREGATE - The total scores of an individual(s) or team(s) added together.

COMPETITION SHOOTING

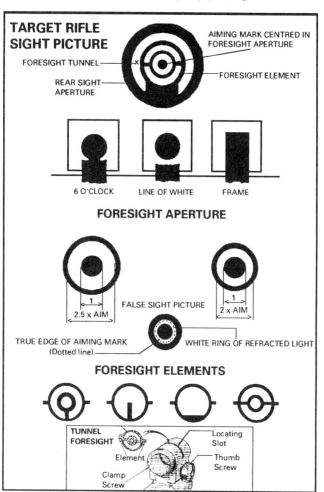

TARGET RIFLE SIGHT PICTURE

AIMING MARK CENTRED IN FORESIGHT APERTURE

FORESIGHT TUNNEL

FORESIGHT ELEMENT

REAR SIGHT APERTURE

6 O'CLOCK

LINE OF WHITE

FRAME

FORESIGHT APERTURE

1
2.5 x AIM

1
2 x AIM

FALSE SIGHT PICTURE

TRUE EDGE OF AIMING MARK (Dotted line)

WHITE RING OF REFRACTED LIGHT

FORESIGHT ELEMENTS

TUNNEL FORESIGHT

Locating Slot

Element

Thumb Screw

Clamp Screw

KNOTS AND THEIR USES

A lot depends on knowing how to tie just the right knot or hitch for a particular job.

While learning to tie knots it is no use using a thin string or twine made up of loose strands. You need a piece of rope or cord not less than a quarter of an inch thick and several feet long.

An important point to remember is that it is not a good idea to ever cut a rope just to shorten it, as you will find that no sooner had you cut it, than you needed a longer rope for some other purpose.

As mentioned in the Expedition Training, it is always useful to have a length of string or rope with you, but there is not much point in having a rope if you don't know how to tie a useful knot in it.

Like most skills it is only through practice that you will become proficient, this is especially so with knots.

The occasion you need to use a knot will more than likely be in an emergency situation, you must realise that this will mean instant re-action with no time to think of what to do. This is when your ability to tie the — "right knot at the right time" — could prevent a disaster.

A ROPE

The main part of a rope is called the "standing part" - see illustration.

When the end is bent back toward the standing part, the loop formed is called a "bight", regardless of whether it crosses the rope or only lies parallel with it.

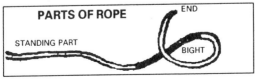

PARTS OF ROPE

END

STANDING PART

BIGHT

KNOTS AND THEIR USES.

THUMB KNOT and FIGURE OF EIGHT KNOT

Both used to make a 'stop' on a rope: to prevent a rope from fraying at the end.

REEF KNOT. For joining two dry ropes of the same size. The most generally useful knot. Always used in First Aid

SINGLE SHEET BEND.
For joining two ropes of different size.

DOUBLE SHEET BEND.
For joining two wet ropes of different size.

HAWSER BEND.
For joining larger ropes or cables.

DRAW HITCH.
For fastening a 'head rope' (e.g., a boat's painter) so that it can be quickly released.

334

KNOTS AND THEIR USES

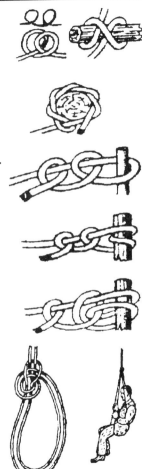

CLOVE HITCH This is the most useful knot that you will ever learn. It can be made under strain, will not slip on itself nor along a pole, and can easily be cast loose.

TIMBER HITCH is useful for hauling, the more it is pulled the firmer it holds.

TWO HALF HITCHES. Two turns of a rope, which, when drawn together, holds securely. It is the quickest and simplest way to make a rope fast to a post.

ROUND TURN and TWO HALF HITCHES. The quickest way to make a rope fast under strain. One of the most useful and easily made knots .

FISHERMANS BEND. For fastening ends of ropes to spars, poles, etc., or to other ropes.

BOWLINE ON THE BIGHT
To form a loop that will not slip. One loop is made larger than the other.
This is the sling for lowering a person from a building. It enables the person to be supported, with the longer loop under the knees and the short loop under the armpits.

335

THE SPANISH WINDLASS

This not a knot, but is closely related to them. You may come across a situation where knowing how to use a Spanish Windlass could be helpful.

The windlass as you will see from the diagram, gives you great pulling power on a rope, by means of a lever using it to wind the rope round a post or stake, one end of which is in the ground.

The rope is wound round the post and a bar or piece of wood with the rope hitched over it.

The power given could be used to haul a boat out of the river or to move a vehicle, one end of the rope is fastened to the object to be moved, and the other is made fast on to a tree or some other suitable anchor. The stake or post must be strong and sound, likewise the material used for the lever as there is considerable pressure on both when in use. Check your rope for any damage and be sure it is strong enough for the job.

Arrange your rope as in the diagram, pulling the lever round the stake.

The stake needs to be held firmly by driving it into the ground making the hole big enough for it to turn. It may be necessary to "overhaul" your windlass as too much rope may be wound round it, it will depend upon the size of the stake used for the windlass and the distance you have to haul the object.

Warning - it can be dangerous if you do not use strong enough material, or if it snaps or if you let go of the lever. Check your rope and Windlass frequently, secure the load you are pulling with other rope to prevent it running away in the event of an accident.

SIGNALS TRAINING.

INTRODUCTION

Signals equipment issued for your use costs the Ministry of Defence a considerable amount of money to buy and maintain, therefore it is important that it is cared for and used correctly, at the same time you must learn how to operate efficiently, using procedures the same as the Army and TA. If you don't, then you will be a menace if taking part in exercises or visiting units.

Communications for a modern army are as important as ammunition and petrol, as without good communications things can very quickly go wrong, supplies will not get through, casualties not evacuated etc.

The following notes are intended to help you with some basic background information which you need to know. The important thing is to become disciplined in the procedures and practices to such an extent that it becomes second nature when YOU GO "ON THE AIR".

SECURITY

You must realise that if you transmit a message on a radio then it will be heard by both friendly and opposing forces.

It follows that you must become security minded "on the air". In addition the opposition may have a Direction Finding capability, which means if you send long messages they will find out where you are, with the obvious consequences, so, you will discipline yourself to automatically obey the following rules.

1. Keep your message as short as possible.
2. Speak clearly without over emphasis
3. If possible make a note or rehearse what you are going to say, don't think 'on net'.
4. If it is a long message split it into parts.
5. Encode those parts of the message which might give

337

SIGNALS

valuable information such as grid references and
timings.
6. If you cannot get through to other stations, move, and
try a different position for your antenna before
increasing power.

CODES

The usual method of ensuring that the opposition does
not find out what you are up to is through the use of
codes.

The most secure of these is what is known as a one time
code, that is, a code which is used only once and then
discarded.

The British army now uses a code of this type called
BATCO, short for Battalion Code. It is easy to use for
simple Grid References or long messages. You may be
able to learn more of this should you go on exercises
with your own TA Unit or have a signals troop/section in
your ACF area.

APPOINTMENT TITLES

Appointment titles used to be used for all key personnel,
they have now been replaced by call signs except for the
appointment title SUNRAY who is any Commander. e.g.
Bde, Regt, Bn, Coy, Pl, Tp or Section.

In addition the second in command is known as
SUNRAY-MINOR.

This is useful since you and the person you are talking to
will know who you are talking about, but others will not.

CALL SIGNS

All radio stations on a military net have a call sign. This
identifies the user to other users without the need to give
away unit names. Always find out which call sign you are
before you use a radio.

SIMPLE VOICE PROCEDURE (VP)

THE REASON WHY VP

1. Because every word spoken on a transmission can be listened to by everyone.
2. Because no matter how smart your equipment is, communications can suffer from interference and your message may not be understood.
3. Because if everyone spoke at the same time it would be chaos.

ABBREVIATIONS and AIDS for ACCURACY

To assist in accurate reception of messages, figures, orders etc. and in addition to the use of the PHONETIC ALPHABET, specially selected words are used in transmissions.

These words are called '**PRO WORDS**'. Each word has a special meaning used within your transmission information.

This enables signallers to keep 'chat' on the radio to a minimum since all messages take the same form this is done with the use of PRO WORDS

PHONETIC ALPHABET

Because letters and figures form the greater part of most transmissions, it is important that all users have a standard method of pronunciation, this is especially important if communications are difficult.

For this reason the PHONETIC ALPHABET has been adopted.

You may need to spell out a message, in this case you would use the phonetic alphabet, you will often find that it is useful on a telephone to be certain that detail being given is correctly received.

Always precede the spelling with the words " I SPELL " to give the signaller at the other end warning that he will need to be prepared to write down the letters.

The Phonetic Alphabet

A — Alpha	B — Bravo	C — Charlie
D — Delta	E — Echo	F — Foxtrot
G — Golf	H — Hotel	I — India
J — Juliett	K — Kilo	L — Lima
M — Mike	N — November	O — Oscar
P — Papa	Q — Quebec	R — Romeo
S — Sierra	T — Tango	U — Uniform
V — Victor	W — Whiskey	X — X-Ray
Y — Yankee	Z — Zulu	

e.g. The town name "York" would be sent as
   " I spell Yankee Oscar Romeo Kilo.
Numbers/Figures can also be sent digit by digit in bad conditions.
e.g.. "Twenty three fifty nine hours " would be sent as
   "FIGURES two three five nine hours"

PRO WORDS

Those PRO WORDS in common use are set out below.
"I SPELL" - I'm going to spell out a word, letter by letter.
e.g. YORK - "I spell Yankee Oscar Romeo Kilo"
"FIGURES" - I'm going to send a number, figure by figure.

   e.g. FIGURES - "Three Six Eight Five Eight Two"
   (368582)
You can combine PRO WORDS if it is required:
   e.g.. "FIGURES One Nine. I SPELL Alpha Golf.
   FIGURES Six Six" (19AG66)

"HELLO" - Is used to introduce an initial call.

"MESSAGE" - Indicates a message you must write down.

SIGNALS

"**SEND**" - go ahead with your transmission.
"**OVER**" - This is the end of my transmission, I want a reply, go ahead and send it.
"**OUT**" - This is the END of my transmission. No reply is expected.
"**WAIT OUT**" - Your transmission has been received, further transmission on the same matter will follow later.
"**ROGER - SO FAR - OVER**" - Have received/sent message more to follow on this transmission.
"**ROGER**" - Message received OK, or I have received your last transmission OK.
"**WRONG**" - What has been sent is wrong, the correct version is ....

EXAMPLES USING PRO WORDS:-

1. ALL messages start in the following manner.
"HELLO" - followed by the CALL SIGN of the station you wish to talk to.
> *e.g.. "HELLO A23 THIS IS A11"*
2. If the message is short it would immediately follow this.
> *e.g.. "HELLO A23 THIS IS A11 send rations now"*
3. If you do not require an answer end the message with "OUT".
> *e.g.. "HELLO A23 THIS IS A11 send rations now OUT"*
4. If the message is long send it in parts, each part ending with
> *' ROGER SO FAR OVER'.*

This indicates that there is more to follow.
The other station will answer with
> *'ROGER SO FAR OVER'*

to confirm he has received it and is ready for the next part.
After you have sent the last part say 'OUT' to end message.

5. Remember - "OVER" - means I have finished and am ready/waiting for your reply.
   "OUT" - means I have finished and need no reply.
   This means that you should **NEVER SAY**, as they do in the Movie's :--**"OVER and OUT"**.

6. You must also learn **NEVER** to ever say **"REPEAT"** on the radio if you cannot hear or have missed a part of the message, always use **"SAY AGAIN"**.
   The word "REPEAT" is used by mortars and artillery **only** to mean FIRE at the same target again, not that you as a cadet will be in such a situation, but it could become a habit if using it.
   This might be very upsetting for someone if used wrongly and at the wrong time.

7. If you are looking after a radio, and receive a message asking for information which you do not have readily available or for someone who is not present, use the PRO WORD - **"WAIT OUT"**, make a note of the CALL SIGN, then get the information or fetch the person concerned.

CONTROL OF YOUR VOICE WHEN TRANSMITTING

The manner in which your voice is transmitted can make all the difference to the quality of the signal received at the other end. Practice and remember the following :--
RHYTHM - keep a natural rhythm by dividing the message into suitable phrases.
SPEED - slightly slower than normal conversation - it has to be written down.
VOLUME - as normal volume, there is no need to shout.
PITCH - a higher pitch transmits clearer, but not to feel 'uncomfortable'.

USE OF ABBREVIATIONS

When used can save time in talking and writing down a message. Many abbreviations are used in our conversation every day, so it is quite natural to use some of them 'on the air'. e.g., NCO, ACF, CO, MT.

IF WORKING IN GOOD CONDITIONS

Common abbreviations are spoken as in normal conversation:-

NCO as NCO instead of November Charlie Oscar.

ACF as ACF instead of Alpha Charlie Foxtrot.

CO as CO instead of Charlie Oscar

ETA as ETA. ETD as ETD etc.,

IF WORKING IN BAD CONDITIONS

Abbreviations should only be used if they are going to save valuable time, it would be better to use correct full words.

Headquarters - is shorter than
"I SPELL Hotel Quebec"

Reconnaissance - is shorter than
"I SPELL Romeo Echo Charlie Charlie Echo".

DISCIPLINE

The Operator at the **CONTROL** no matter what his rank, is in charge of the NET and is responsible for it's efficient operation.

 As already said chaos will reign if more than one station speaks at a time so to prevent confusion there are strict rules to follow as below:-

1. LISTEN OUT to make sure the frequency is clear before speaking. Don't try to cut-in to other transmissions.

2. Make a SHORT PAUSE at the end of a phrase or part of your message, remember the person receiving will be writing it down.

3. ANSWER all calls immediately and in the correct order.

ORGANISATION - A RADIO NET

The term NET is the abbreviation of NETWORK, meaning where several transmitting stations are grouped together

for the purpose of talking to each other.
There are TWO types of STATION:

1. The CONTROL. 2. The SUB-STATION.

A10 In the diagram below the CONTROL STATION has a
CALL SIGN - 0
The SUB-STATION "CALL SIGNS" are A10, B10, B20, and
B30.

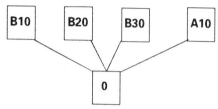

The CALL SIGNS are a combination of LETTERS and
FIGURES, which enables them to be identified as a
communications station, an organisation or an individual
on the radio net.

SEQUENCE OF ANSWERING CALLS.

An important discipline in answering calls is that they
must be answered in ALPHABETICAL ORDER FIRST, then
in their NUMBER ORDER throughout the NET.
CONTROL ALWAYS ANSWERS FIRST - if it is included in
the call.
TYPES OF CALL Types of CALLS can be grouped under
FOUR headings as follows:-
1. **SINGLE CALL** - from one Station to another:
   e.g., "HELLO B10 this is B20" or "HELLO A10 this is 0"
2. **A MULTIPLE CALL** - from one STATION to TWO or
MORE STATIONS, BUT NOT the whole NET:
   e.g., "HELLO 0, B10 and A10 this is B20" or
   "HELLO 0, A10 and B10 this is B20"
3. An **ALL STATIONS CALL** - from ONE STATION to ALL

STATIONS:
> *"HELLO all STATIONS this is 0 "or*
> *"HELLO ALL STATIONS this is B10"*

4. **COLLECTIVE CALL** - a CALL to TWO or more STATIONS on the NET who have a pre-arranged call designated to them: e.g.,
> *"HELLO CHARLIE, CHARLIE 1 this is 0"*

AN OFFER

An **OFFER** - this is like a 'warning order', a SHORT transmission to warn STATION(S) that a message follows.

1. An OFFER is made when the SENDER has reason to believe that the RECEIVER may be involved for some reason that they might NOT receive the message at all.

In this example the STATION CALL sign B10 has a message for CALL sign B20 which does not have to be written down, but is not sure that they are in a position to receive it - in fact they are able to:
> *"HELLO B20 this is B10 over"."B20 send over"*
> *"B10 move when ready, over/out".*
> *"B20 ROGER out"*

2. When the RECEIVER has to take notes it will depend upon the length and content of the message, but the SENDER must use his common sense as to when the OFFER should be made. e.g.,
> "HELLO 0 and B20 this is B10 message over"
> "0 send over" "B20 send over" "B10 no MT at grid 6STWTDAZ or grid AGSVRT or grid HJKBTR DR now returned - over"
> "0 roger out" "B20 roger out"

CORRECTING MISTAKES AND REPETITION OF MESSAGES

When SENDING you may make a mistake during the TRANSMISSION and will have to correct it.

This is done by using the PRO WORD "WRONG" and going back to the last correct word transmitted as in the example below:

> *"HELLO A10 this is 0 rations at grid 342467 WRONG" "rations at grid 342476 over"*
> *"A10 roger out""*

There may be some occasion that you have to emphasize a particular point in a message. This is done by using the PRO WORD "I SAY AGAIN". As this takes up valuable time it should not be used very often. e.g.,

> *"HELLO A10 this is 0 no cheese with the rations"*
> *"I SAY AGAIN no cheese with the rations*
> *"0 roger out"*

If you wanted to emphasize the whole message, you would say "I SAY AGAIN" at the end of the message and send the whole message again

When receiving a message, you may for many reasons miss a part of it. It would be a waste of time to have all the message sent again and there is a method used in this instance.

You obtain the parts that are missing by referring to a part already received, these parts are known as 'catch words' or 'catch phrases' and you will indicate what you need repeating by using the following PRO WORDS:-

**SAY AGAIN,   WORD BEFORE,   WORD AFTER,
ALL BEFORE,   ALL AFTER,   FROM ..... TO ...**

If you needed the whole of the message you would use "SAY AGAIN". e.g.,

> *"HELLO B20 this is A10 send transport before 1800 hrs over" "B20 say again" "A10 send transport before 1800 hrs over" "B20 roger out"*

NOTES.

Stations are dealt with individually, using the correct sequence of answering, until "ROGER" is obtained.

The SENDING STATION does not use "I SAY AGAIN" in reply to a request for a REPETITION.

CATCH WORDS or CATCH PHRASES must be easy to identify, it is wrong to use a word that appears in the message more than once as it causes confusion.

The PRO WORD "OUT" should be used whenever possible in GOOD working conditions.

On SINGLE CALLS, the CALL SIGN may be dropped after the initial exchange.

LIMITED RESPONSE

When it is established that all CALLED STATIONS are in communication, you should make use of LIMITED RESPONSE in order to improve security since the CALL SIGN responding to CHARLIE CHARLIE (Collective Call) and ALL STATIONS calls are of value to anyone listening in.

The procedure is to nominate one or two STATIONS ONLY to acknowledge as shown in the following examples:

1. "HELLO ALL STATIONS this is 0, Text A10 ACKNOWLEDGE over" "A10 roger out"
2. "HELLO CHARLIE CHARLIE 3 this is 0, text, A10 and B30 ACKNOWLEDGE over" "A10 roger out" "B30 roger out"

IN YOUR OWN INTEREST

The impression that signals training is rather technical may have been overcome now that you have read this section.

Apart from being a very interesting cadet activity, your ability to operate a wireless transmitter correctly is not only a valuable skill, but also very desirable one, take

every opportunity offered to you for signals training.
Once you have become a proficient signaller there will
be many opportunities for you to use that skill.
On attachments to the Army or on exercises with the TA
you will become more involved and appreciate how
useful it is to be a skilled operator.
The disciplines and procedures are used today by a great
many organisations in industry, commerce, and the
emergency services.
You never know when in an emergency, you might be
called upon to use these skills, don't be found wanting if
the situation presented itself.
You can practice by using the procedures and applying
the disciplines and principles every day in many
situation.

QUESTIONS

1. What are the six rules for "Security on the air".
2. Why use codes.
3. Who is a SUNRAY and a SUNRAY MINOR.
4. What identifies the user to another user.
5. Give the three reasons for having Voice Procedure.
6. Say the Phonetic Alaphabet.
7. What is a Pro Word used for and why.
8. If you are to spell out a word, how do you start.
9. If sending numbers, how do you send them.
10. How do you introduce an initial call.
11. How do you know if you must write down a message.
12. How do you know when to send a transmission.
13. What do you say at the end of a transmission.
14. What do you say at the end of your message if you
    want a reply.
15. Having sent part of a message with more to send,
    how do you tell the receiver there is more coming.
16. What does ROGER mean.
17. How do you tell a receiver when you have sent

incorrect information in your transmission.

18. Why should you NEVER say "Over and Out"
19. Who uses the message "REPEAT"
20. If you cannot hear or miss a word, how to you ask for it to be repeated.
21. In the middle of a message you need to stop, how do you tell the sender.
22. What do RHYTHM, SPEED and PITCH refer to, explain what each of them mean.
23. Common abbreviations are used when.
24. How do you give common abbreviations when working in bad conditions.
25. Which operator is in charge of the NET.
26. What is sequence of answering calls.
27. Name the different types of call , explain the difference between them.
28. What do you understand by an "OFFER".
29. What is a "Catch Word" or a "Catch Phrase".
30. Why use a LIMITED RESPONSE call.

OPPORTUNITIES FOR THE 2 STAR + CADET

INTRODUCTION

This section has been written to ensure that you are made aware of all the opportunities that there are open to you as a cadet once you have achieved 2Star. If you don't ask - then perhaps you won't get to know, but it does rather depend upon your officers and instructors making you aware of the dates of events and activities, **so ask "what's on".**

A cadet with APC 2 Star has "one foot on a lower rung of the ladder", giving access to a whole variety of exciting and challenging opportunities.

APC training at times will be difficult and demanding, it will be hard work, but great fun and very rewarding, especially now that it is directly linked to the Duke of Edinburgh Award Scheme.

This offers you greater opportunities than many other national youth organisations to earn your DofE Award at all levels, read carefully the DofE section in this book.

OPPORTUNITIES CHART — see page 363.

The CHART on page 363 shows you the different `routes' you might take on your `cadet career path'.

You will notice that some of the `boxes' on the chart have a message in them; for instance - **"READ NOTE A"**.

The **"NOTES"** referred to are set out below and it is important that you read them in conjunction with the chart. With reference to the MOD attachments, you must read the conditions required of you before applying.

CONDITIONS CHART NOTE "A" — see page 363

It is a requirement to have successfully completed the 4 STAR to become eligible for subsequent appointment as an Under Officer.

OPPORTUNITIES FOR THE 2 STAR + CADET

This is **NOT AUTOMATIC**, you will have to prove over a period of time that by performance and aptitude as a responsible senior cadet you have the qualities that are considered essential for further progress. A good report on the **MASTER CADETS COURSE** will help.

Your dedication to the cadets in your unit, your manners and behaviour on and off parade, your reputation within the County and the recommendation of your officers, will all be taken into consideration before you are recommended as a potential Under Officer. You will have to attend selection interviews within your County Cadet Force.

CONDITIONS CHART NOTE "B" — see page 363

Having been recommended by your officers and instructor to be appointed as an Adult Sergeant Instructor, and approved by the County Cadet Commandant, you will become a member of the Warrant Officers and Sergeants Mess.

Your Regimental Sergeant Major will without doubt, take a special interest in you as a member of his Mess. He will expect you to observe the rules of the Mess, be a supportive member of all Mess activities and become a member of the County team of senior ranks.

Your progress will also be watched by your officers who will expect you to set high standard in all you do as an example to your cadets.

Further opportunities for promotion will be made available to you through the senior NCO ranks as your service and experience progresses.

As a part of your training and development you will be required to attend courses at the Cadet Training Centre. Promotion is not automatic, but provided your performance and qualities as an adult leader are recognised, you may then subsequently be recommended.

OPPORTUNITIES FOR THE 2 STAR + CADET

CONDITIONS CHART NOTE "C" — see page 363

If it becomes apparent that your interest in the ACF and your performance as an adult member of the County is outstanding in every respect, then you may be considered as a potential officer.

If this is the case you will be involved in the selection process, which will be fully explained to you in every respect. If you are appointed to a commission it will be for a probationary period of two years, during which time you will be expected to fulfil certain training obligations. They are as follows:-

1. During your first year you will complete your Initial Training Course which is usually within your own County.

2. During your second year you will be expected to attend the Cadet Training Centre, Frimley Park to do your Instructors Course. It will also be expected of you to attend at least one Annual Camp during the two years.

On completion of this period, and having carried out the obligations required, earned a satisfactory report on your performance and suitability as an officer, your commission may be confirmed - subject to your Cadet Commandant's recommendation.

Promotion is NOT automatic in the Army Cadet Force, all officers attend the Cadet Training Centre for courses to qualify for promotion to Captain, Major and Lt Colonel/Colonel onwards.

Each County Cadet Force has an `establishment' of officers and instructors.

This sets out and controls the number of officer or instructors in each rank that may be held at any time, therefore promotion is often subject to a vacancy being available in a particular rank.

SPECIAL TO ARM COURSES

It is important that you understand what these courses are about. They are arranged each year by the Ministry of Defence for the more senior cadets, who are training at 3 Star level and above.

They are a bonus for you as a cadet, introducing you to the practical and technical skills and trades within the Army, all of which have similar skills/trades in civilian industry and commerce, with recognised qualifications. It must be appreciated that all courses are subject to change and the information given is purely as a guide and for your interest, to encourage you to apply for vacancies. They are usually run during the Easter and Summer holiday periods and depend entirely upon the availability of Army personnel and facilities.

You must ask your officers/instructors about them, to check out the current type and dates of courses that are available and then apply for a vacancy in good time. Courses have a limited number of places on them and dates by which all `bids' or applications have to be made. The Army puts a great deal of time and resources into the planning and organising of these **Special To Arm** courses. The best way we can show our appreciation is to make sure that all places are taken up, and by this we mean that if you do get a place — THEN YOU DO TAKE IT UP, otherwise you deprive another cadet of the opportunity and get the Cadet Force a bad name.

When attending courses, you will most likely be asked to pay a Daily Ration Fee, similar to Annual Camp messing fees as a contribution to the cost of rations.

OPPORTUNITIES FOR THE 2 STAR + CADET

Special To Arm Courses all take place at Army establishments, therefore, it will be expected that your appearance, turnout and behaviour will be first class at all times.

All the Army requires from you is to be keen, interested and learn all you can and enjoy your attachment with them.

The paragraphs below set out examples of the type of courses, where they are held, the qualifications you require, the duration and the objectives of the course.

We need to remind you that these are subject to change, new courses established and others withdrawn, so check with your officers/instructors.

We hope many of you will take advantage of these opportunities, they are great courses.

NOTE: As with all training that will involve physical activity, if you suffer with any physical or other condition that could be affected by strenuous exercise or other physical activity, you must declare this to your officer/instructor, who will advise you as to your suitability to apply for course vacancies.

THE ROYAL ARTILLERY

Courses are held at The Royal School of Artillery for a five day period.

Qualifications: for cadets who are badged to the Royal Artillery, there are no places available for girl cadets.

Object of the course: To introduce you to Field Gunnery.

ROYAL SIGNALS

Classified Signallers Course Courses are held at the School of Signals for a five day period for boy and girl cadets.

Qualifications: You must have a thorough knowledge of

OPPORTUNITIES FOR THE 2 STAR + CADET

Voice and Operating Procedures and must have passed your Cadet Signals Classification Test.

Object of the course: As a classified signaller to give you an insight into Army Signalling.

To demonstrate and give practice in handling signalling equipment used within the Infantry Battalion.

ADVANCED SIGNALLERS COURSE

Courses are held at the School of Signals for a five day period for boy and girl cadets.

Qualifications: Passed GCSE Maths and Physics Grade A, B or C, or if not actually passed should be reading these subjects at this level in the year you are nominated to go on the course.

You must have a thorough knowledge of Voice and Operating Procedures and have passed your Cadet Signal Classification Test.

The aim of the course: The Advanced Signalling course is one form of post classification training for the senior cadet.

The object of the course is: to train selected cadets in more advanced signalling and to widen your technical interest in the Royal Signals.

ROYAL ELECTRICAL & MECHANICAL ENGINEERS

Mechanical and Automotive Engineering Course Courses are held at the School of Electrical and Mechanical Engineering for a period of twelve days and are available for boy cadets only.

Qualifications: Required to have APC 3 Star or above, be 16 years of age or over and should if possible be serving a recognised apprenticeship at a trade associated with Automotive Engineering.

Object of the course: To give you an elementary knowledge of general engineering, including bench fitting, welding and automotive engineering which will assist you either in the Services or in industry.

Electronics Appreciation Course Courses: are held at the School of Electronic Engineering REME for a period of four days and are available to boy cadets only.

Qualifications: Required to have APC 3 Star or above, be 16 years of age or over, have GCSE Maths and Physics or if not actually passed GCSE Maths/Physics should be reading these subjects at this level in the year of nomination.

Object of the course: is to introduce you to Electronics and electronic equipment currently in use in the Army.

ARMY CATERING CORPS

Introduction to Basic Cookery Course Courses are held at the Army Catering Corps Training Centre for a period of five days and are available for boy and girl cadets.

Qualifications: You are required to have your APC 2 Star or above, have a particular interest in cookery/catering.

Object of the course: is to introduce you to methods of catering used in the Army, the efficient use of rations and the planning and preparation of menus.

ARMY PHYSICAL TRAINING CORPS

Physical Training Cadet PT Leaders Course.

Courses are held at the Army School of Physical Training or at the UKLF School of Physical Training for a period of five days and are available for boy and girl cadets.

Qualifications: You are required to have your APC 2 Star or above and be physically fit, with an interest in Physical Training.

Object of the course : is to teach you the basic principles of Physical and Recreational Training.

Physical Training Cadet PT Instructors Course

OPPORTUNITIES FOR THE 2 STAR + CADET

Courses are held at the UKLF School of Physical and Recreational Training for a period of five days and are available for **boys only**.

Qualifications: You are required to have your APC 2 Star or above and be 16 years of age or over.

Object of the course: is to teach you the principles and organisation of Physical and Recreational Training as required by the APC syllabus.

OUTWARD BOUND COURSE

Personal Development Courses are held at the Joint Services Mountain Training Centre for a period of fourteen days and are available for boy and girl cadets.

Qualifications: You must be between the age of sixteen and a half and nineteen years old, be physically fit and able to carry a 40lb pack on a 3 day mountain expedition. It is essential to have had practical experience in and a good knowledge of map and compass - passed 3 Star in Map and Compass.

Object of the course: is to offer you the opportunity to develop your leadership skills through taking part in mountain expeditions, rock climbing, canoeing etc.

THE LORD LIEUTENANT'S CADET

In every County throughout the UK The Lord Lieutenant is appointed by Her Majesty the Queen.

It is an honorary appointment whose role is to act as the personal representative of Her Majesty the Queen.

In recognition of the appointment, the Lord Lieutenant is treated with due respect and courtesy by all people in the County.

Many duties are performed by the Lord Lieutenant on behalf of Her Majesty, from attending events such as the annual Remembrance Day Parade, to carrying out the opening of new Public Buildings, Hospitals and supporting large scale public celebrations.

The Lord Lieutenant is held in high esteem by the Services The Territorial Army in particular is always aware of their presence, as they often attend parades and military functions.

INTEREST IN THE CADET FORCES

As a mark of the Lord Lieutenants interest in the Cadet movement, many County Cadet Forces, (Sea, Army and Air Cadets) are required to appoint a Lord Lieutenants Cadet on an annual basis.

In the majority of Counties the Lord Lieutenants keep their cadets very busy, accompanying them on many of their official engagements, acting as an escort and carrying out minor duties on their behalf.

TOP JOB

This is a job for the `Top Cadet' in the County.

To be seen in public at the side of the Queens Representative requires an individual with special qualities, which can be attained by being a good cadet.

You will appreciate that is a particular honour to be selected as the **Lord Lieutenants Cadet** and carries with it a the responsibility of representing all the members of the ACF in the County.

SELECTION

Most Counties during their Annual Camp have a selection Board to choose THE CADET as their nomination. They will most likely have passed their 3 Star, be 16 years old, of particularly smart appearance, keen and at ease when talking to their seniors.

They will require an out-going personality and will probably have achieved the rank of cadet sergeant and may be taking part in the Duke of Edinburgh Award Scheme.

In some Counties they may have different requirements of the cadets being selected, but if you ask your officers/ instructors they should know, as the `rules' are usually published by the Cadet Commandant.

There is great competition to be selected as the Lord Lieutenants Cadet. If you are fortunate enough to be in a County where this appointment is open to competition every year, and your progress has brought you to the notice of your officers/instructors as an outstanding cadet, then you will be considered as a candidate to join the selection process.

It is something worth trying for, you will have to work at it to become recognised. If you make **Top Cadet** and are appointed as your County representative as the Lord Lieutenants Cadet it will remain the most unforgettable `milestone' in your cadet career.

UKLF CADET LEADERSHIP COURSE

The aim of this course: is to develop the more senior cadets ability as a leader.

Duration: 8/9 days.

Qualifications: You must have applied to your Cadet Commandant, who in turn will have to recommend you to take part in the course.

You must be over sixteen years and under seventeen and a half on the 1st of April.

Have passed 3 Star, or be considered sufficiently knowledgeable to manage the instruction given.

Be a Cadet NCO, physically fit, capable of marching 12

miles in boots.

Able to take part in obstacle and confidence courses.

Rations:

You will be expected to pay ration cost similar to Annual Camp messing fees.

Equipment: Instructions will be issued regarding the kit you should take.

At the end of the course you will be given your Grading and Certificate of Attendance.

> **NOTE:** You will be required to have a certificate from your Parent/Guardian stating their permission for you to fly in service aircraft, whether you can swim, and consent for you to undergo surgery in an emergency. This certificate will be issued to you for completion.

CADET TRAINING CENTRE LEADERSHIP COURSE.

The aim of this course: is to develop your initiative and self reliance. You will carry out exercises involving problems of practical leadership. Duration: The course is one week.

Qualifications: It is open to both boy and girl cadets of the CCF (all three service sections), the Air Training Corps, The Sea Cadets and Army Cadets.

Those nominated to attend should be cadet NCO's who have obtained APC (CCF) Advanced or APC (ACF) 3 Star or hold an equivalent qualification in the case of the Sea Cadet Corps or Air Training Corps.

You are expected to have at least one year or more to serve in the cadet force.

You must be very fit, at least 16 years of age and not over 18 at the time of attending the course.

CANADIAN ARMY CADET LEADERSHIP and CHALLENGE COURSE

The aim of this course: is to teach advanced leadership and adventure training skills.

Qualifications: It is open to those who are already 4 Star cadets and who arè 16 years of age.

You need to be very fit as strict fitness requirements are laid down as set out below.

Run 1.5 mile
(Male) 11.15 min. (Female) 13.45 min.
Sit Ups
(Male) 42 in min. (Female) 36 in min.
Push Ups
(Male) 29 in min. (Female) 25 in min.
Chin Ups
(Male) 5. (Female) 3.

You must be able to hike a distance of 20km.

You must be able to hike on flat terrain a distance of 15km carrying 15kg pack within 240 minutes.

The duration of the course is six weeks.

Location: is Banff in western Canada.

BAOR VISITS

The aim is: to give you an opportunity to be attached to a Field Force unit of the Army serving in BAOR to gain some experience of the Regular Army at work, and to gain from the Social experience of visiting a foreign country.

Qualifications: You must have your 1 Star or above at the time of your visit and must be 15 years of age or have had a minimum of 18 months service in the ACF.

If you have shown a keen interest in the Army and are strongly recommended by your OC , it will help you to get a place on a visit.

OPPORTUNITIES FOR THE 2 STAR + CADET

These condition are strictly adhered to, as younger
cadets do not benefit from this visit.
Duration: One week.
Costs: Each year the cost of the visit is made known to
every County ACF. These cost are towards travelling to
Germany and rations while on your attachment to the
host unit.

TAKE ADVANTAGE OF ALL COURSE AND
VISIT OPPORTUNITIES AVAILABLE TO YOU.
ASK YOUR OFFICERS AND INSTRUCTORS
TO FIND OUT THE EXACT DATES — THEN
GET YOURSELF ORGANISED TO GO
"DON'T DELAY - DO IT TODAY"

OPPORTUNITIES FOR THE 2 STAR + CADET

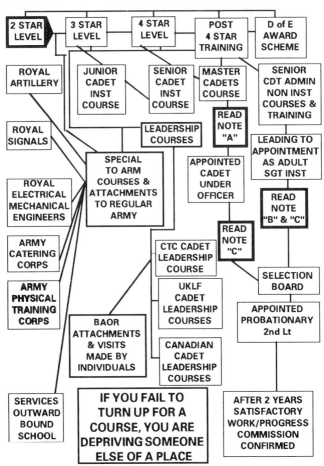

SEE PAGES 350 to 352 — REFERENCE CHART NOTES A", "B" AND "C"

THE WORLD OF WORK

You may still be at school or have recently left, you may already be employed in a job or are at the stage of considering your options.

The advice you may have received from your careers teachers or the local careers office has been useful in trying to decide on what job you might do or even put you on a career path that interests you.

Dependant upon the state of the job market for young people, in other words are there any vacancies or is unemployment and living on the dole the current situation, you will know best in your part of the country. Job opportunities vary in different parts of the country and you would always be well advised to find out where the vacancies are.

How being a Cadet helps.

Membership of the Cadet Force gives you many opportunities to develop both as a member of a team, as an individual and as a full member of your family and the community in which you live.

As a cadet you will naturally have an interest in the Armed Services, although it does not automatically follow that you are to join one of them as a career, but should you do so.

There are a great many different career paths available, gaining recognised qualifications along the way.

Many technically skilled jobs carried out in the services have recognised equivalent civilian qualifications. This means that on completion of a service career, you will still be comparatively young.

TECHNICAL SKILLS AND TRAINING

It must be remembered that the "Teeth Arms" of the services have many highly skilled jobs carried out by their soldiers, who all need as may recognised qualifications as their opposite numbers in the "Technical Arms". As an example; the infantry driver or the driver of a tank need similar knowledge and skills as much as the REME Vehicle Mechanic, often carrying out their job under anything but ideal conditions. At a young age it is difficult to consider or understand the importance of thinking about your future in the terms of a "career path".

YOUR SECOND CAREER

What we can point out, is that having completed your time in the services your will still be a comparatively young person, and be in an ideal position to set out on a "second career". Ask yourself, what better start could I possibly have, having completed a career in the services, with a fist full of qualifications and many years of experience, operating up to date systems and equipment, having had the benefit of some of the best methods of training and practising man management skill.
You should also remember, that coupled with this is the knowledge, that the majority of employers are always keen to take on people who have acquired skills and knowledge in the services.
They appreciate the great value of the training you will have received, the standards of performance that will have been expected, and your personal commitment to do the job correctly. Have no doubts about it, they know that you will be an valuable asset to them.

KNOWLEDGE and COMPETITION

Today you must recognise that the `world of work' is more competitive and there is constantly growing need for new technical skills, new jobs are being created, new challenges and opportunities are arising.

challenges and opportunities are arising.

In both leisure and at work you will have to make up your mind what you can do to the best at, so that it can be seen as your personal best or strongest point, and that you get the most satisfaction from doing it. It is important to make the right choice at each stage of your career.

There are many different types of employer, who in turn will subject you to a variety of attitudes and working conditions. No choice you make will have been a disaster, as with each change of job you will have gained more experience of life and getting on with people, developed new interests and skills, increasing your value as a person, adding to your own capabilities to hold down a more interesting and rewarding job.

JOB SATISFACTION

Very often a rewarding job is thought to be one with more money, but many people find it acceptable to do a job with little prospects of advancement, without an above average wage packet, yet are very happy doing it, rather than having more money and being unhappy at work.

When you are young this seldom last for long as boy/girlfriends come along, or you want to buy a new bike or a video etc., and then you are prepared to "put up with" the longer hours at work and travel further to get there - to earn more, to spend it - the choice is yours.

Don't let yourself be influenced too much by what other people think you should do, but, at the same time, do listen to their suggestions.

Talk to as many different people as you can who are in jobs you think could interest you, use all the facilities available to seek out information and select the parts of special interest to you.

JOB CHANGES

You will not have to be afraid to change jobs, as the greater the variety of work you do within your chosen career, the more experienced and valuable you become to a potential employer, thus giving you not only the opportunity for advancement, but a more interesting and fulfilled career.

The purpose of many government training schemes for young people, is to enable you to sample different jobs, gaining experience of the world of work.

Many of the initial skills you will learn are those needed in most jobs; for instance, how to work with and get on with other people, learning basic office skills, learning how to run your personal budget etc.

THE COST OF EXPERIENCE

Experience is expensive, as it takes a long time to get it, what is important is to make the best possible use of both time and experience while you can.

To sum up - you need to:-

1. Know clearly what job you would like to do and how to achieve it.
2. Know exactly the qualifications you need to have in order to carry out that job - education and training.
3. Discover what prospects there are in your chosen job.
4. Be aware of what barriers and new opportunities exist to hinder and help you.

DECISION MAKING

Having found out all the information you can, then comes the task of making the decision. Think carefully and consider your options, read the questions posed below and write down your thoughts or answers.

1. What alternative courses are open to me.
2. Which appears to suit me best.
3. Is the risk worth the reward I might gain.

4. Can I make the decision or should I get other advice?
5. Will it affect me alone or others as well?

OPPORTUNITIES OR QUALIFICATIONS.

What will you be tinker, tailor, soldier, sailor, depends on what your talents are and what sort of person you are. The task you have is to match your ability and interests to a job. The Careers service and others are not there to find you a job, but to advise and help you decide what kind of job will best suit your talents and skills.

It is important that you know the kind of job you would like to do, even if you have to do something different for a period of time until a vacancy occurs.

No matter what career path you follow you will find that to "hold down" many jobs you will need to have some qualifications at a variety of levels and ability. These obviously depend upon the type of work you do.

As a guide you can follow four basic levels of jobs - operatives, craftsmen, technicians or technologists. We set out below an explanation of them with the qualifications/training required.

OPERATIVES - Need little skill, short training, jobs such as small machine operators, milkman, labourer, shop assistant, cleaner and many others, GCSE's are seldom required, however other important qualities are essential, such as getting on with people, being a caring person, manual skills and strength, reliable, honest and often working on their own.

CRAFTSMEN - These are people who will have had several years training - including perhaps a three or four year formal apprenticeship. Good GCSE grades in two or three subjects may be required to get the job.

Continued training or education at college will often be required - either on day release or evening classes.

The qualifications aimed for are often:-

**BTEC National Certificates (2/3 GCSE's) or
BTEC National Diploma (3/4 GCSE's)**

Many employers initially take on their trainee craftsmen on training schemes, and then select those who "show willing" to train on for better, more responsible jobs. Craft jobs are for example vehicle mechanic, printer or joiner, etc.

TECHNICIANS - Require high levels of technical or scientific knowledge.

After three or four years of further education, often combined with long and intensive training within their employment they will be fully qualified -unless they go on to advanced work, when further training will be necessary. Entry requirements are often four or five very good GCSE grades and the minimal training qualification would be the BTEC National Certificate/Diploma. Examples would be tool makers, draughtsmen, health inspectors, estate agents, computer programmers, etc.

TECHNOLOGISTS - Highly skilled professional persons often requiring several years at a Polytechnic or University or other professional training which can be several more years of education plus practical experience before finally qualifying. `A' levels are required as an entry qualification. Jobs include, doctor, dentist, lawyer, optician, accountants etc.

APPLYING FOR A JOB - WRITING A LETTER.

Many employers will advertise for staff asking applicants to "apply in writing". One of the main reasons for this is that it will give them a good idea of how you write, the care you take in preparation and the way you present yourself to them.

Your letter must be set out correctly as shown in the example shown on the next page:-

THE WORLD OF WORK

SPECIMEN LETTER

Mr J.M.Jones (Initials & name of the person)   Your home
The job Title. Director. Manager. Partner etc.   address
The Name of the Firm.   here Number &
Name of Street,   on right.
Name of Town/City.   Telephone No
County & Post Code.   to contact you
                                            Day/Date/Month/Year

Dear Sir/Madam or the persons surname Mr/Mrs if   you
already know them.

The first sentence saying what job it is you are applying for.
Details of your age, school attended, say what subjects you
have studied and to what standard.

Any part-time jobs you have had, training schemes taken
part in. A paragraph about yourself, school duties, clubs or
organisations you belong to and any responsibilities you
have had.

Your hobbies or interests, sports activities or involvement
in the ACF, Duke of Edinburgh Award or any other
achievements that would be of interest to a potential
employer.

Tell them that you would like to work for them and that you
would like to be considered for an interview.

A sentence at the end saying when you would be available
to attend for an interview if you were chosen as a potential
employee.

You finish it off
Yours faithfully,

Sign your name.- then under it
PRINT YOUR NAME IN BLOCK CAPITAL LETTERS.

THE WORLD OF WORK

SELL YOURSELF TO THEM

Your letter of application must tell the person reading it a lot about you. It has to interest them sufficiently to want to send you an application form asking you to attend for an interview for the job that they have on offer.

Your letter must "sell YOU to them", it follows that you must take a lot a care in putting it together.

Write it in pencil as a rough copy to start with so as you can easily change it at will, when you have finished the letter keep your original copy for future reference.

For a large company you should address it to the "Personnel Officer" or "Training Manager".

For a small firm address it to the Managing Director or Manager/Manageress.

LETTER PRESENTATION

The care you take to layout your letter, the way you set it out on paper, with a space at the beginning and end of each line, correct punctuation and spelling, clearly written in your own handwriting, on good quality paper using a matching envelope, will all help to impress the person receiving it to ask you to attend for an interview.

A NOTE OF WARNING: Regretfully, many employers who receive letters of application for jobs, even if it is in answer to their advertisement, do not have the manners or the courtesy to reply to you. Therefore do not be disappointed if you write many letters without results, just keep on trying.

JOB APPLICATION FORMS.

When you receive an application form, remember it is the only one you get, so have a photo copy made of it and use the copy to fill in the details in pencil.

371

Read it very carefully, if asked for block letters (CAPITAL LETTERS) be sure you use them.

Some forms are complicated and it take time to fill in, but like your letter of application, the way you go about it and the care you take, will tell those who read it a lot about you. Check it for accuracy of detail, especially dates and spelling. Ask someone to double check it before transferring the information to the original form - then get it checked it again, make a photocopy of it before sending.

PERSONAL REFERENCES and TESTIMONIALS

You may be asked for a testimonial or the names of people who would give you references. In this case,- having asked them first if they would be prepared to give you a reference - you would give the names of people who have known you well, such as your head teacher, the vicar/priest at your church, your ACF Company or Area Commander or any other responsible persons, who are not members of your family.

A testimonial is a letter written on your behalf by one or more of the people who have been asked to give you a reference.

Should you be asked for documents to be sent i.e., birth certificate, school report, etc. or when taking documents to an interview, always use photocopies, keeping the originals safe at home.

PERSONAL HISTORY - YOUR CV

Early in your career, naturally you will not have had a great deal of experience in terms of different jobs over a period of years, but as time goes on your personal history will grow into quite a complicated story.

It is important that you keep records of your whole life story in note form of every job, with dates of promotion, qualification you gain.

THE WORLD OF WORK

The term may not be familiar to you, but this "life story" is referred to as a "CV", which is a Latin abbreviation of Curriculum Vitae - an old-fashioned Latin term meaning 'the course of your life'.

You will often be asked for your "CV", the reason being that it provides a prospective employer with a complete, accurate and factual record of your achievements in date order, showing the progress you have made as a person and how your life style and interests have developed.

CORRECT INFORMATION

In no way is your CV an extension of your imagination, it must be factual and you will have to be prepared to back up anything you put into it.

Should you be foolish enough to state untrue information you could find yourself in serious trouble, apart from losing your job.

To assist you in building your CV the following broad headings with brief explanations will give you some guidance on how to compile your life history as your own CV, do remember, it is only as accurate as it is up to date - so up-date it regularly, you never know when you might need it.

Always start with dates of the most recent events under the headings below, the latest events in your career are usually the of the most interest.

PERSONAL DETAILS - This is the CV of.... First Names followed by your Surname. Your current address. Telephone number. Date of Birth.

EDUCATION - Names and places of schools attended, the levels attained, and in what subjects. Details of Further Education, College or University. What you have done or are doing to improve your education.

EMPLOYMENT - The people you have worked for or schemes enrolled in, the dates and places. Part time or full time, paid or voluntary. The training you have had, what level/use it was put to. Any special skills or knowledge you have.

GENERAL HEALTH - Any serious illness, allergies or physical disabilities that could affect your ability to carry out a job more or less effectively.

HOBBIES, INTERESTS and ACTIVITIES - to indicate your involvement as an individual or as a team person. This would include your Cadet Force sports clubs or teams etc. How you have applied yourself to these, the time and effort you devote to them and what standards you have attained, such as your cadet rank and proficiency levels gained, also include details of any courses you have attended.

QUALIFICATIONS - mention your Senior Cadet Training as an instructor, your responsibilities. First Aid is important to all employers, Duke of Edinburgh Award Certificates, Life Saving, etc.

Some employers will ask for more searching information, the reasons are not to pry into your personal life, but to ensure that they match the person as near as possible to the job to be done.

It is not normal for you to state the wages or salary you are being paid on a CV that you send to a prospective employer, but for your own records always keep this information on your own copy CV.

PUT ALL THE INFORMATION DOWN NEATLY AND IN LOGICAL ORDER, DON'T CRAM IT ALL INTO ONE PAGE

MEDICAL EXAMINATION

Be prepared to be told that you will be required to undergo a strict medical examinations and tests as a part of the selection process, especially if you choose a service career and depending upon the type and needs of the business your prospective employer is running.

THE WORLD OF WORK

BEFORE - GOING FOR AN INTERVIEW

So your letter and CV had the desired effect, you have
hopefully received an application form, filled it in so well
that it has impressed the prospective employer
sufficiently to want to see you and talk to you. It would be
a bad move having got so far not to properly prepare
yourself for the final stage - **the interview**
Before we go on, you will remember earlier we said not
to be disappointed if you do not get a reply to your letters
of application, this is very often the case that many firms
do not have a proper selection and interviewing system,
so again, many will not have 'application forms' or skills
in interviewing.
Later in your career you may have to employ people,
hopefully, by then, you will have been trained in the
techniques of selection and interviewing and make a
better job of it.

THE AIM OF AN INTERVIEW

The aim of the interview is for the employer or the person
who is responsible for staff recruitment to meet you and
for you also to meet them.
They will have spent time looking at the information that
you will have sent, and as a result formed some opinions
about you.
They will want to check you out, to get further
explanation of what you have said, to see if it meets up
with their expectations of you.
You must remember that at a young age new employees
are not exactly an asset to the firm. You will be costly to
recruit, a costly non-productive, untrained, unskilled
liability until such time that you start to be good at your
job, and can be left to get on with it.
This applies to any occupation that you go into,
therefore from the employers point of view they are

taking a calculated risk in employing you, hoping that before they have not spent too much on your wages and training, that you have responded by showing signs of becoming proficient in your job.

WHAT ARE THEY LIKE TO WORK FOR

Once you have decided that "this is the job/firm that I would like to work at/for", then you have a lot of work to do before going for the interview.

You have to spend time finding out all you can about the firm. Many of the questions are obvious, if you cannot find the answers, they can be some of the questions you can ask at your interview.

Important things to know are as follows:-

1. What are they like to work for, are they "top of the charts" or do they have a poor reputation as a local employer.

2. Do all their staff have contracts of employment. A copy should be sent to you if or when you are offered a job.

3. What sort of training do they give you, is there a formal training scheme, will you be included on it. Will it be part of your contract of employment.

4. Do they allow time off for Block Release or Further Education as part of your training, do they encourage you to attend.

5. How do they promote people, is it from within the firm, or do they take people from outside. Do they promote themselves as an equal opportunities employer.

6. Do people stay with the firm for a long time, or is there a lot of "hiring and firing".

7. What business are they in. What do they make or do. Are they a growing firm in modern buildings.

8. What are the working conditions like, do they provide

protective clothing, what is their safety record like. Get to know someone who works there and talk to them.

9. What outside activities are organised, do they have sports facilities for the staff, do they have any social activities or a social club, first aid team, fishing club etc.

10. How easy/difficult is it to get and from work/home - do the journey to check it out, how long does it take, how much does it cost.

11. If you are a member of the TA or ACF will they grant you special leave for annual camp or courses.

All the above points are important to check out.

The best way is to find out from someone who works there, it really is worth your while to take the time and trouble.

You will no doubt think of other questions which will only be to the good, as there is nothing worse than coming away from an interview only to remember something that you should have ask -like - what is to be my starting wage?.

THE INTERVIEW.

On the day of an interview, be properly prepared, be on time - early, not late. Take some time and trouble over your personal appearance, be neatly dressed, smart and clean, in sensible clothes.

Small things like, clean shoes, clean hand and finger nails, tidy hair.

Remember first impressions are more often than not, lasting impressions.

Don't forget to take with you any documents or records that may be of importance, your ACF training records, DofE Award certificates, First Aid etc. - all photo copies if possible.

THE WORLD OF WORK

This Pocket Book will also be a useful record of your "Cadet Career" with all the records of your attainments and activities.

YOUR IMAGE

If you want the job you have got to make an impression on the person(s) interviewing you, firstly your appearance, then your manners, sitting half on a chair with one foot on the table will not create the right impression !.

Sit up, look at the person asking you the question, think about it and then try to explain your answer rather than saying "yes" or "no".

It is best to `speak up and then shut up', don't `woffle'.

If you don't understand the question - say so - (see the samples of "likely questions" an employer may ask you at the end of this section)

QUESTION TIME

No doubt you will be asked if you have any questions. If anything has come to mind during the interview deal with that first, after which you can ask the questions that you will have not found the important answers too before the interview.

Do not be shy or afraid to produce your notes from which you can then ask your questions, as this will show the interviewer that you are really interested in the job and have put a lot of effort into your preparation.

At an interview you will be expected by the interviewer to do most of the talking, watch the professional TV chat shows to check this out, make sure you go prepared to say all you should say - no more, and you will create the right impression to get the job, good luck at your interviews.

REMEMBER — "YOU NEVER GET A SECOND CHANCE TO MAKE A FIRST IMPRESSION".

THE WORLD OF WORK

SAMPLE QUESTIONS YOU MAY BE ASKED AT AN INTERVIEW.

There are many questions that you might be asked at an interview, it is better to think what you might say, talk to your friends about them before an interview.

Probable questions include:

Tell me about yourself. Why do you want this particular job. What makes you think you would be good at the job. What do you do in your spare time. What qualities do you think you have to offer. What is your ultimate career ambition. What kind of books or newspapers do you read at home. Did you enjoy school. What grades did you do well/badly in. What do you know about this firm. Have you had any work experience before. Why did you leave your last job. Why do you think you would like to work here. Would you be interested in attending training courses. Would you be prepared to go to night school. Would working overtime present any difficulties. Would you like to move around between departments. How do you get on with people in authority. Do you like working with other people or by yourself. Can you get on with other people. Have you ever been in any trouble with the Police. If you had a choice would you prefer work or the afternoon off. Would you be prepared to spend a short period away from home. What sports do you play and who for. What other hobbies or interests do you have. Would you like to ask any questions.

You will no doubt think of many others, add them to the list, practice "GOING FOR AN INTERVIEW" with your friends, and be better prepared for those questions and put over the right attitude to a prospective employer.

THE WORLD OF WORK

NOW AT WORK

The first day at work or the first day in a new job will be a "milestone" in your life that you will never forget, many events will always remain in your memory when you make a change of direction, resulting in a new experience of life.

No one owes you a living, nor has to give you a job. It is your responsibility to "hold it down" and make it work, not just for you, but for those who work with you as a member of a team, no matter how small that team may be.

THE RIGHT ATTITUDE

Your attitude towards other people at work especially those older than you will affect how they regard you and treat you, how much they will be prepared to tell you or teach you. You will have to take instructions, direct orders and be disciplined by people from whom you will find it hard to accept. Your options are few, two in fact, like it or lump it !!.

We all go through this experience when young, it is not uncommon as we tend to think that we know best at times and it is not until some time afterwards that we can look back and reflect on the experience and the lessons learned.

The day will come much sooner than you think when you will have the job of looking after a new youngster and 'dishing out the orders', when that happens you will have to try and get them to do their best for you

WORKING PRACTICES

Working to set standards is always difficult until it becomes a way of life, like being at work on time - five minutes before, not five minutes late - presents some people with a problem.

Keeping a place clean and tidy, wearing the correct

protective clothing, having to observe strict security procedures and many other situations gets very irksome, yet it is all part of the job - discipline at work.

The sooner you are able to come to terms with all that is required of you, the sooner you will be noticed and make a good impression upon those who supervise you. Opportunities for advancement will only be given to those who are likely to respond to the trust given them - make sure you are capable of taking advantage of any opportunity offered to you.

VALUE OF BEING A CADET

If you have carefully read and thought about this section on Careers and The World of Work, you will be aware, that provided you become a 'full member' of your cadet unit, supporting your officers and instructors, you, as individual will have a great many of the personal values required to become a good proposition as an employee, the Cadet Force is giving you that opportunity, don't waste it, use it - the choice is yours.

WELBECK COLLEGE

You would not be a cadet if you did not have an interest in the Army and you will know that many cadets do take up the Army as a career. It is important that we tell you of opportunities open to you as one of your options for a career.

Welbeck College is the Army's own residential college for 150 science sixth formers of both sexes, who would like to become officers, mainly in one of the technical Corps. A majority of Welbexians are ex-members of the Cadet Forces so this is of particular interest to you as a cadet.

IN THE COUNTRYSIDE

The College is the old Welbeck Abbey, once the country seat of the Duke of Portland. The splendid stately home and beautiful grounds are set amid the 3000 acre Welbeck Estate in Sherwood Forest area of North Nottinghamshire.

The parkland, has many lakes and extensive playing fields as well as providing space for cross-country running, sailing and CCF activities.

All students at the College are members of the Combined Cadet Force.

EDUCATIONAL QUALIFICATIONS

Maths and Physics are the main "A" Levels studied and are compulsory. All students have a third "A" Level option which can be selected from other scientific or technological subjects or from a range of 'arts' subjects including languages. Everyone, whether taking an 'arts' "A" level or not, is required to do some English, history, German and economics and to take the General Studies "A" level exam.

This is to ensure a broadly-based education although with emphasis on the sciences.

Welbeck is not aiming to produce "boffins" but rounded personalities who will eventually become leaders.

To this end the students, who are civilians although intending eventually to become Army Officers, are given every opportunity to develop their leadership potential. They also attend lectures on the life and role of young officers in the various Corps and have a chance of visiting Army units to help them decide which they want to join.

COLLEGE ACTIVITIES

The large range of sporting activities, societies and extra-mural outings are organised by students themselves under only the general guidance of the college staff. Theatre and music are favourite pastimes and everyone joins in the major sports of rugby, hockey, cricket and athletics, although there is a wide choice of minor sports and adventurous training activities.

Matches are played against major schools in the area where Welbeck has a fine sporting record.

Students are admitted in 2 intakes a year, January and September when they are between the ages if fifteen and nine months and seventeen and a half.

Special arrangements are made for the January entrants so that they can take their 'A' levels in November, i.e. after the full two year course.

Selection is controlled by the Ministry of Defence to whom prospective candidates send their applications.

WHAT IT COSTS

The education at Welbeck is free, but a contribution towards boarding costs is paid depending upon their parents/guardians income.

Those who complete the course and are recommended as suitable by the College Principal are admitted to the Royal Military Academy, Sandhurst for their Officer training.

A large proportion of students do sufficiently well at their "A" levels to qualify for university degree courses. Some go to civil universities either before or after they have been commissioned.

Others attend the Royal Military College of Science at Shrivenham, which is run by the Cranfield Institute of Technology, where they study engineering or applied science for their BSc.

If you are interested to find out more about Welbeck College, get in contact with your School Liaison Officer through the Army Recruiting Office in your area.

They will be able to offer more information and advice on conditions of entry, selection procedures and application deadlines.

BANDS IN THE ARMY CADET FORCE

INTRODUCTION

In recent times the whole question of Bands in the Army Cadet Force has taken a giant step forward.
In the past if you joined a Cadet Band you soon found out that you would have to carry out your band practice and at the same time be expected to keep up with ALL the training for the APC Syllabus.

BAND UNITS

There are now some units where ALL the cadets are in fact members of the Band. This makes good sense for all concerned to be interested in military music and come together to play and form a Band. This does not mean that it is to the exclusion of other training. You will have to pass your One Star Training first. The syllabus then changes from Two Star onwards, and is directly related to your improving standards and ability with the instrument(s) that you have chosen to play.

DRUM and BUGLE BANDS

However, BAND UNITS don't make up all the Bands in the ACF, as many cadet detachments have their own bands, the majority of which are **Drum and Bugle** bands. Although they may be small in the number of cadets who actually play, many of them join together for practices and parades especially when at annual camp.
Depending upon the music instruction you may be able to have at school or within the ACF, it will decide on your musical qualifications, but it must be appreciated that you will have to put in a great deal of effort to become sufficiently skilled to earn recognised qualifications.

BANDS IN THE ARMY CADET FORCE

It does make it difficult if you are keen to learn to play in a band and there is not one in your immediate area. However, with the help of parents and friends it is surprising what you can do if you put your mind to it. Being able to play a musical instrument of one sort or another is a much envied and rewarding talent, and the majority of parents will be very proud of you and supportive when they see you doing something worthwhile with your time.

You will appreciate that most cadets have to buy their own instruments, they are very expensive, yet will last you a lifetime - provided they are taken care of.

Second hand instruments are often advertised in the press or specialist music magazines, so if you are interested, look around for a bargain, you never know, ask your uncle Fred, he may have a trumpet hidden away in his loft!

FINANCE and SUPPORT

While talking about the cost of instruments and running a Band, you may not know this, but Bands in the Cadet Force are NOT supported financially by the Ministry of Defence or issued with instruments, uniforms or other equipment. This also means that the use transport to fetch and carry instruments etc., is restricted and makes it very difficult. Bandmasters, Band Sergeants, adult helpers etc, often use their own cars to 'round-up' their cadets, this again is expensive for them, however, they and YOU will all be involved in helping to raise funds to "run the Band".

No matter which type of Band you might play in, you will be helping to raise funds - assuming those you play for at band engagements give the Band generous donations for your performances.

BANDS IN THE ARMY CADET FORCE

RECOGNITION OF EFFORT

Those of you who are NOT members of a Band, will have to bear in mind that a Cadet who is also a Bandsman is most likely to be putting far more time and effort into his CADET WORK than you are.

In view of this we should all be grateful in the first place, that there are Adults who have the interest, skills and sufficient time to 'take on' the training and work involved in running a Band.

BAND PRACTICE

Many hours are spent on the care and maintenance of the Band Instruments and equipment - not to mention the

cleaning! Secondly we should recognise the efforts made by the cadets themselves in the bands, who are prepared to accept the challenge of being trained, often turning out several times in a week for a special band practice. Their example is much to be admired.

QUALIFICATIONS

Those of you who have the opportunity to play in a Full Military Band and to be trained in the Woodwind, Brass or Percussion sections of the Band will be tested as laid down in the Full Military Band Syllabus for your particular instrument(s).

The standards for the tests are set by either the Associated Board of the Royal School of Music or the Grade Examinations for Trinity College of Music of London.

BANDS IN THE ARMY CADET FORCE

To attain this grade of proficiency could be very useful, especially if you wish to become a professional musician or join the Army as a Bandsman.
The grades achieved for passes in each of your APC levels are as set out over page.

BAND — APC QUALIFICATIONS

2 STAR
Pass Grade 3 in Associated Board or Trinity College practical exam.
3 STAR
Pass Grade 4 in Associated Board or Trinity College practical exam.
4 STAR
Pass Grade 5 in Associated Board or Trinity College practical exam.

DRUM and PIPE BANDS

No doubt if you are a Scots Cadet you may have a special interest in Pipe Music, although we must say that there are many Drum and Pipe Bands south of the border; in which case there is a syllabus of training for Corps of Drums and Pipe Bands.
The testing of Cadets in their performance in Corps of Drums and Pipe Bands is carried out by the Adults of their respective units.
Having passed ONE STAR APC, you then will be able to continue your Band Training and through improved performance at each level, attain your APC at TWO, THREE and FOUR STAR as a member of a Full Military Band, Corps of Drums or/and a Pipe Band.

DUKE OF EDINBURGH AWARD

The qualifications you attain at each stage of your training will of course go towards achieving your Duke of

BANDS IN THE ARMY CADET FORCE

Edinburgh Award at Bronze, Silver and Gold. It would be to your advantage to talk to your County D of E Award Officer to find out about it and enroll in the scheme at your earliest opportunity.

OTHER SKILLS REQUIRED

It must not be forgotten that as a Bandsmen you have to be very efficient at Foot Drill and your Turnout has to be immaculate at all times.

The reason for these high standards are that you will spend a lot of time playing in engagements on a Band Stand or Beating Retreat in the City Square — always in the 'eye of the public'.

What is seen of you - your turnout, how you play and march will make an impression on the public, improving the reputation and image of the Army Cadet Force in your area. This can only be attained by regular practice and training.

TEAM EFFORT

If you join a Cadet Band you will be expected to be regularly ON PARADE for training, and in so doing support your Band Instructors to produce good music, which in turn will enable you to attend those special events, demonstrating to the public how hard you have worked by the way you all play and march.

Like being the member of any good team, it's a great feeling to be part of a good Band, many cadets have followed a musical career through starting to play in their Cadet Band. If you have an opportunity and are interested in Military Music - have a go at it.

APC SYLLABUS
LEVELS OF QUALIFICATION and PERSONAL TRAINING RECORDS

INTRODUCTION.

Set out in the following pages you will find the Syllabus of Training, for Army Proficiency Certificate (APC).

This covers each grade of training from Recruit through to 4Star, broken down by subject and Section (lesson). The pages following the syllabus, are **Training Record** pages relating to **each** of the APC grades.

Each row of "boxes" across the page represents a subject, each "box" has a small number within it. This number matches up with the Chapter and Section Reference numbers of the syllabus, and relates to the syllabus on the previous pages.

This is for **you** to record **your** training, it is very simple to use.

Having been taught a particular lesson, and are happy that you have learned and fully understood what it is all about, then, **IF your instructor is of the same opinion**, ask him to initial and date the relevant "box" for you.

Providing you have the good sense and self discipline to record your training in this way, it will help you to know when you are ready to be tested in a particular subject. At the same time, indicate the subjects/lessons on which you still require instruction .

This will help to improve your training and also other cadets in your unit. You will no doubt find many other advantages, for instance; to prevent you being taught the same thing again!.

Make good use of these records throughout your cadet career, but remember, like all records and information, it will only be useful - **if it** is kept up to date on a regular basis.

APC SYLLABUS

RECRUIT SYLLABUS

DRILL
Training Manual Reference Vol 1 Ch 1, Sections:-
1 The Aim and Purpose of Drill
2 Position of Attention, Stand at Ease, Stand Easy.
3 Turnings at the Halt
4 Compliments (Saluting) The Reason why, origin and
information
5 Saluting to the Front
6 Introduction to Marching
7 Marching and Halting in Quick time (on the March)

TURNOUT
Training Manual Reference Ch 2, Sections:-
1 How to wear uniform. Jersey or Shirt Sleeve Order with
Brassard.
2 Cleanliness, Appearance and Dress - including hair.
3 Care and Cleaning of Uniform
4 Demonstration and Practice - How to wear and care for Uniform
(Jersey and/or Shirt Sleeve Order with Brassard)

MILITARY KNOWLEDGE
Training Manual Reference Ch 3, Sections:-
1 Ranks and Badges of Rank
5 The History of the ACF up to the present day
6 Instruction and explanation of the Enrolment Ceremony

SKILL AT ARMS
Training Manual Reference Ch 4, Sections:-
2 Talk on Safety.
3 Rules for handling and firing the Air Rifle
4 No 8 (.22) Rifle
5 Cadet GP Rifle Demonstration on the fire effect of an Air Rifle
and the No 8 Rifle to show their penetrating ability

EXPEDITION TRAINING
Training Manual Reference Ch 7, Sections:-
1-2 Introduction and the Country Code

APC SYLLABUS

ONE STAR SYLLABUS

DRILL — Foot Drill.
Training Manual Reference Ch 1, Sections:-
8 Forming Up in Three Ranks
9 Open and Close Order March
10 Falling Out and Dismissing from a Parade
11 Wheeling on the March in Quick Time
12 Changing Step on the March in Quick Time
13 About Turn on the March in Quick Time
15 Saluting on the March. Eyes Right and left
Rifle Drill
18 Position of Attention, Stand at Ease, Stand Easy
19 Change Arms from the shoulder
20 Slope Arms from the Shoulder. Shoulder Arms from the Slope
21 Ground Arms from Slope. Take Up Arms from the Ground Arms
Training Manual Reference Vol 1, Ch 2, Sections:-
1-4 Demonstration and Practice - How to wear Webbing
    Equipment
Training Manual Reference Vol 1 Ch 3, Section:-
7 ACF Organisation to County Level
8 The Cadets Progress

SKILL AT ARMS
Training Manual Reference Ch4, Sections
3 The Air Rifle - Safety, Loading and Unloading
4 The No 8 (.22) Rifle - Safety Precautions, Care & Cleaning, Sight
    Setting, Loading, Unloading and Ammunition and
    Safeguards
5 The Cadet GP Rifle: General Description, Safety and the Sight
    System
6 Stripping, Assembling and Cleaning
7 Magazine Filling, Sight Setting, Load, Unload, Make Safe and
    Safe Handling and Handling practice.
8 Holding and Aiming in the Lying Position and practice.
9 Firing in the Lying Position
10 Firing Drills and Firing Drills practice.
11 Mechanism of the Weapon, Immediate Action and Possible
    Stoppages

APC SYLLABUS

SHOOTING
Manual Reference APC (ACF) Syllabus Pages 43-44.
To fire the Air Rifle Grouping Test at a distance of 5.5 metres.
PASS CLASSIFICATION: HPS = 100 points
Scoring: **1"** = 25. **2"** = 20.   **3"** = 15.   **4"** = 10.
OR the No 8 (.22) Rifle Grouping Test at a distance of 25 metres.
Scoring: as the above.
PASS QUALIFICATION (for both of the above) 2nd Class 75. Pass 60.

USE OF MAP AND COMPASS
Training Manual Reference Ch 5, Sections:-
1 Care of Maps, Reliability and Marginal Information
2 The Grid System
3 Conventional Signs
4 Map Scales
5 Introduction to the Light Weight Compass
6 North Points and Bearings
7 Setting a Map by Landmarks and Compass

FIELDCRAFT
Training Manual Reference Ch 6, Sections:-
2 Personal Camouflage and Concealment
3 Personal Camouflage and Concealment - Practice
4 Moving with and without a Rifle
5 Movement and Observation Practice
6 Elementary Obstacle Crossing
7 Crossing obstacles - Practice
8 Introduction to Night Work
9 Elementary Night Movement (Sections 10 to 12 are 2 Star
    Syllabus).
13 Duties of a Sentry and Practice Subject:

EXPEDITION TRAINING
Training Manual Reference Ch 7, Section:-
3 Campcraft to include improvised shelters. Camping Practice.
    Training and Preparation for a test exercise, to include the
    pitching and striking of tents, cooking and movement across
    country for at least 4 miles.

APC SYLLABUS

FIRST AID - CASUALTY CODE
Training Manual Reference Ch 7, Section:-
4 Priorities
a. Mouth to Mouth Resuscitation. Recovery Position.
b. Stopping Bleeding - direct and indirect pressure and elevation.
  Application of a dressing. Treatment for shock.
  Treatment for cuts and grazes - cleaning affected parts.
c. Recognition of fractures and immediate treatment.
  Immobilisation of fractures of ankle, leg and arm.
d. Treatment of blisters, stings and burns.
  Recognition of injury to joints or muscles.
  Treatment for dislocation and sprains.
  Dealing with foreign bodies in the eye, ear or nose.

THE CADET AND THE COMMUNITY
Training Manual Reference Ch 8, Sections:-
1 Introduction. The value of citizenship, sense of service to the
    Community and an outline of the Cadet and the Community
    syllabus.
2 The Emergency Services, how and when to make an emergency
    call.
3. Responsibility Training. Carry out to a satisfactory standard,
    three simple domestic tasks in Detachment Hut.

TWO STAR SYLLABUS

DRILL
Training Manual Reference Ch 1, Sections
Foot Drill
1-15 Practice Recruit and 1 Star Foot Drill Movements, including
    Left and Right turns on the march
16 Marking Time in Quick Time
17 Parading & inspecting a squad, moving it off & falling it out.

Drill - GP Rifle
22 Present Arms from the Slope. Slope Arms from the Present
23 Saluting at the Halt and on the March (Slope Arms Position)

APC SYLLABUS

Turnout.
Training Manual Reference Ch 2, Sections:-
1-4 Instruction on how to improve standard of turnout and
 bearing in uniform.

Military Knowledge.
Training Manual Reference Ch 3, Section:-
9 Familiarisation of the Cadet with the history of the Regiment or
 Corps to which he is badged.

SKILL AT ARMS - Cadet GP Rifle
Training Manual Reference Ch 4, Sections:-
12 Aiming Off and Miss Drill.
13 Firing from Other Positions.
14 Use of Cover, Carriage of the Weapon and Reaction to
 Effective Enemy Fire and practice.
15 Training Tests: No 8 Rifle. Cadet GP Rifle and on the LMG.
16 Visual Training: Judging Distance - Visibility. Unit of Measure
 and Appearance Methods. Aids to Judging Distance.
17 Elementary Observation.
18 Recognition and Indication of Targets.
19 Fire Control Orders.

SHOOTING
Manual Reference APC (ACF) Syllabus Pages 46 and 48.

Grouping Test
The Cadet GP Rifle fired on a Gallery at 100 metres or 25/30 metre
range. or fired with Air Rifle or No 8 (.22) Rifle.
PASS QUALIFICATION 2nd Class 75. Pass 60. HPS = 100 points.
Rifle Application Course
Fired with the No 8 .22 Rifle at a range of 25 metres.
PASS QUALIFICATION: HPS = 200 points.
      Marksman = 180   1st Class = 170
      2nd Class = 160.   Pass = 140.
Fired with an Air Rifle at a range of 5.5 metres. HPS = 200 points.
      Marksman = 180.   1st Class = 160.
      2nd Class = 140.   Pass = 120.

APC SYLLABUS

USE OF MAP AND COMPASS
Training Manual Reference Ch 5, Sections:-
8 Relief and Vertical Intervals
9 Types of Bearings
10 Measuring Magnetic Bearings with a Lightweight Compass
11 Measuring Grid Bearings with a Lightweight Compass
12 Conversion of a Grid to a Magnetic Bearing
13 Preparation of a Route Card
14 Setting a Compass for Night Marching (including Direction
    Finding Exercises by day)
15 Finding North by the Pole Star

FIELDCRAFT
Training Manual Reference Ch 6, Sections:-
14 Ground and Cover
27 Movement
16 -17 Patrol Formations and Signals to include practice
18 Safety Precautions with Blank Ammunition and at night
10 Elementary Night Movement - (Practical)
11 Observation at Night - (Practical)
12 Identifying sounds at night - (Practical).
Patrolling
19-20 Aims of Patrolling, Types of Patrol. Sequence of action to be
    followed when mounting, carrying out, and debriefing a
    patrol.
Reconnaissance Patrol - Action on objective
28 Ambushes: Organising into groups, communications,
    springing (explanation and demonstration). Action on lights/
    trip flares/meeting the enemy when ambushed
20 Rehearsals; RV Drills. Patrol Debriefing.

EXPEDITION TRAINING
Training Manual Reference Ch 7, Sections:-
4 Training and preparation and participation in a TWO STAR
    expedition. Minimum of 15 miles on foot and one night out.
    (Cadets may qualify for the Duke of Edinburgh Bronze Award
    provided special arrangements are made in advance through
    the County D of E Award Officer).

APC SYLLABUS

FIRST AID
Training Manual Reference Ch 7
Cadets under instruction of their own QUALIFIED First Aid Instructors trained to pass Essentials of First Aid certificate of St Johns or the equivalent certificate of other Voluntary Aid Societies under the Rules/Conditions of that Society

THE CADET AND THE COMMUNITY
Training Manual Reference Ch 8, Section
2 Visit and receive a talk from one of the statutory services in the local area Police, Fire, Ambulance, Coast Guard. Prepare a street plan and mark the location of the emergency services in the locality.
Assist with at least two community functions in the local area as a member of a group during the period of working for 2 STAR.

BAND TRAINING
Manual Reference APC (ACF) Syllabus pages 95 to 99 and APC (ACF) Syllabus Corps of Drums Pipe Bands page 111.
To teach cadets to play a musical instrument to the standards as set out in the APC (ACF) Syllabus, for one of the following types of band:-
Corps of Drums (less Pipe Bands). Corps of Drums - Pipe Bands. Full Military Band

THREE STAR SYLLABUS

SKILL AT ARMS
Training Manual Reference Ch 4, Sections:-
The LMG (Bren)
20 Introduction - Safety Precautions. Stripping, Cleaning and Assembling
21 Magazine Filling, Loading, Sight Setting, Unloading and Making Safe
22 Stripping Practice
23 Aiming, Holding and Firing
24 Immediate Action, Gas Stoppage Drill
25 Firing and Immediate Action Practice
26 Handling

APC SYLLABUS

SHOOTING

Manual Reference APC (ACF) Syllabus pages 49 to 52.

GP Rifle Course

Practices: Grouping. Deliberate. Rapid. Snap.

Fired on Gallery or ET Range at 100 and 220 metres or on a 25 metre range.

PASS QUALIFICATION:	HPS = 70 points.
Marksman = 60.	1st Class = 54
2nd Class = 47.	Pass = 35.

LMG Course

Practices: Grouping. (2) Single Rounds and Bursts.

Application: (2) Single Rounds and Bursts.

Fired on a Gallery Range at 100 and 200 metres.

PASS QUALIFICATION	HPS = 95 points
Marksman = 80.	1st Class Shot = 71.
2nd Class = 62.	Pass = 47.

USE OF MAP AND COMPASS

Training Manual Reference Ch 5, Sections:-

16 Position Finding

17 Back Bearings

18 Plotting your Position

19   Map Reading Exercises

FIELDCRAFT

Training Manual Reference Ch 6, Sections:-

18 Safety Precautions (Rifle and LMG)

21 Section Organisation and Place in the Battalion

22 Section Formations and Field Signals

23 Section Formations and Field Signals - Practical

24-25 Fire and Movement (Explanation - Demonstration - Practical)

26 Gun Group Tasks, Section Battle Drills. Section in Attack - Practice

EXPEDITION TRAINING

Training Manual Reference Ch 7. Section:-

6. Training and preparation for the THREE STAR Expedition.
    Minimum of 20 miles on foot with TWO nights out. Cadets
    who have attained DofE Silver Award Expedition on foot,

qualify for THREE STAR pass in this subject. The THREE STAR EXPEDITION with additional conditions **MAY** qualify a cadet for the DofE Silver Expedition, subject to sufficient notice and the County D of E Award Officers approval of the Expedition/Exploration.

THE CADET AND THE COMMUNITY

Training Manual Reference Ch 8, Section:-

3. Spend 30 hours over six months on local Community activities as an individual member.
   This can be carried out in Cadets own time, but it must be certified that they attended.

OR Successfully take part in a Community Project organised by the Detachment over a period of at least 15 hours, while working for THREE STAR.

JUNIOR CADET INSTRUCTORS CADRE

Training Manual Reference Ch 9, Sections:-

2 Methods of Instruction. To learn how to instruct in the following subjects up and including ONE STAR level:- Drill, Turnout & Military Knowledge. Skill at Arms. Map & Compass. Fieldcraft.

NOTE: Senior Cadets will not be "tested" at this level, no "Pass" or "Fail" will be awarded. However, Senior Cadet will be assessed on their performance and a report will be submitted when they have completed the course.

BAND TRAINING

Manual Reference APC (ACF) Syllabus pages 100 to 104 and APC (ACF) Syllabus Corps of Drums: Pipe Bands page 112 to 113.

To teach cadets to play a musical instrument to the standards as set out in the APC (ACF) Syllabus, for one of the following types of band, Corps of Drums (less Pipe Bands). Corps of Drums/Pipe Bands. Full Military Band ~

CHECK YOUR TRAINING RECORDS AGAINST THE SYLLABUS. KEEP THEM — *"UP TO DATE"* — THEN YOU AND YOUR INSTRUCTORS WILL KNOW EXACTLY WHAT YOU NEXT NEED TO LEARN.

APC SYLLABUS

FOUR STAR SYLLABUS

THE CADET AND THE COMMUNITY
Training Manual Reference Ch 8, Section:-
4. Over three month period assist in planning, organising and
    leading a Community Project. OR, over a six month period
    make a study of the social welfare needs in the local
    community and provide not less than 30 hours service
    spread over a period of three months on the decided project.
Give a lecture to detachment on project, based on a written report
    to be submitted by the cadet

SHOOTING APC (ACF) Syllabus page 52.
To train and take part in shooting competitions with the following
weapons:- No 8 (.22) Rifle or any .22 Rifle. The Cadet GP Rifle L98 A1.
7.62 Target Rifle.
Competitions Smallbore.
Enter ACF Cadet Hundred, qualify for second stage, obtain average
score of 95 on four targets, under conditions laid down by the Council
for Cadet Rifle Shooting (CCRS).

GP RIFLE L98 A1.
Enter "Montgomery of Alamein" or "Earl Roberts" non central
competition. Obtain scores or better as below, under conditions
laid down by the CCRS.
> **Montgomery of Alamein 72 points.**
> **Earl Roberts 170 points.**

7.62 L81 A1 Target Rifle.
Enter "Commonwealth Target Rifle Match" under CCRS
conditions, OR fire at the ISCRM (Inter Services Cadet Rifle
Meeting) at Bisley in the "Frankfort Shield" and MUST obtain a
score of 60 points or better.

SENIOR CADETS INSTRUCTORS' CADRE
Having proved your ability on the Junior Cadet Instructors Cadre,
this course aims to improve your knowledge and technique of
instruction.
You will be expected to have good knowledge of all subjects up to
and including 3 Star.

APC SYLLABUS

You will be taught how to instruct in the following subjects Drill, Turnout and Military Knowledge. Skill at Arms. Use of Map and Compass Fieldcraft. All of the above subjects will be up to and including 2 Star.

BAND TRAINING
Manual Reference APC (ACF) Syllabus pages 105 to 110 and APC (ACF) Syllabus Corps of Drums: Pipe Bands page 114 to 115. To teach cadets to play a musical instrument to the standards as set out in the APC (ACF) Syllabus, for one of the following types of band:- Corps of Drums (less Pipe Bands). Corps of Drums - Pipe Bands. Full Military Band

PHYSICAL ACTIVITY - ONE TO FOUR STAR INCLUSIVE
Manual Reference APC (ACF) Syllabus pages 77 to 80.
AIM: To encourage physical activities by including a wide range of challenging pursuits and sport from which every detachment can choose one or more in which to participate during training from ONE to FOUR STAR levels.
In addition to improve individual cadets strength, agility and endurance by training for the Physical Achievement Tests equivalent to those of the Duke of Edinburgh's Award Scheme.

Detachment Activities.
Cadet detachments **MUST** undertake at least ONE of the activities listed below, or obtain their Cadet Commandant's approval to carry out an alternative.

Physical Activities -
Challenging Pursuits: Canoeing. Hang Gliding. Hill Walking. Life Saving. Parachuting. Paracending. Rock Climbing. Sailing: Dinghy - Offshore - Windsurfing. Skiing: Cross Country - Downhill. Sub-aqua Diving.
Sports: Athletics. Boxing. Circuit Training. Cricket. Cross Country Running. Cycling. Football. Hockey. Judo. Orienteering. Rugby. Swimming.

THE AIM OF ACF TRAINING
THE AIM OF ARMY CADET FORCE TRAINING IS TO PRODUCE A FIT YOUNG PERSON WITH AN UNDERSTANDING OF BASIC MILITARY SUBJECTS, INITIATED INTO THE ART OF LEADERSHIP, AWARE OF THEIR RESPONSIBILITIES AS A CITIZEN AND WITH A WELL DEVELOPED INTEREST IN THE ARMY AND THE COMMUNITY.

RECORD OF TRAINING ACHIEVEMENTS

Recruit

Date started			Date completed						Date Passed Test
Drill	Ch 1.								
	Sec 1.	2	3.	4.	5.	6.	7.		
Turnout	Ch 2.								
	Sec 1.	2.	3.	4.					
Military Knowledge	Ch 3.								
	Sec 1.		5.		6.				
Skill at Arms	Ch 4.								
	Sec 2.	3.	4.	5.					
Expedition Training	Sec 1.		2.						
Notes									

1 Star

RECORD OF TRAINING ACHIEVEMENTS

	Date started	Date completed								Date Passed Test
Drill (Foot Drill)	Ch 1.	9.	10.	11.	12.	13.	15.			
	Sec 8.									
Drill-Rifle. Turnout & Military Knowledge	Ch 1.	19.	20.	21.	Sec 1-4.	Sec 7.	8.			
	Sec 18.				Ch2.	Ch 3.				
Skill at Arms	Ch 4.	5.	6.	7.	8.	9.	10.	11.		
	Sec 3.	4.								
Shooting	Group Size	Air Rifle HPS = 90	Grouping Test	No 8 .22 Rifle HPS = 100						
	Score									
Map and Compass	Ch 5.	2.	3.	4.	5.	6.	7.			
	Sec 1									
Fieldcraft	Ch 5.	3.	4.	5.	6.	7.	8.	9.	13.	
	Sec 2.									
Expedition Training	Ch 7.	Test Exercise: Place.	Date							
	Sec 3.									
First Aid (Casualty Code)	Ch 7.	Priorities - A	B.	C.	D.					
	Sec 4.									
The Cadet & Community	Ch 8	2.	3.							
	Sec 1.									
Physical Activities	Dates									
	Scores									

402

2 Star   RECORD OF TRAINING ACHIEVEMENTS

Date started _____   **Date completed**   **Date Passed Test** _____

Subject	Chapter / Sections	Details
Drill/Turnout Military Knowledge	Ch 1. Revise 1Star Drill — Sections 1 to 15.	Ch 2. Turnout — Sec 1-2, 3-4 / Ch 3. Mil/K — Sec 9.
Skill at Arms	Ch 4. — Sec 12. 13. 14. 16. 17. 22. 23. 17. 18. 19.	Alternative Shoot Air Rifle or No8 .22 Rifle
Shooting Records	GP Rifle Course — Date / Score	Date / Score
Map and Compass	Ch 5. — Sec 8. 9. 10. 11. 12. 13. 14. 15.	
Fieldcraft	Ch 6. — Sec10. 11. 12. 14. 16-17. 18. 19-20. 27. 28. 20.	
Expedition Training	Ch 7. Sec 4.	Dates, Place, Distance etc.
First Aid	Examination taken by	Place / Date
The Cadet & Community	Ch 8. Sec 2.	Visits and Projects Dates and Places
Band Training	Instrument(s) Played	Dates and Qualification(s)
Physical Activities	Dates	Scores

3 Star

RECORD OF TRAINING ACHIEVEMENTS

	Date started	Date completed						Date Passed Test
Skill at Arms	Ch 4. / Sec 20.	21.	22.	23.	24.	25.	26.	
Fieldcraft	Ch 6. / Sec 18.	21.	22.	23.	24.	25.	26.	
Shooting Records	GP Rifle Course: Grouping, Deliberate, Rapid, Snap, Application	LMG Course: Grouping, Rounds, Bursts, Rounds, Bursts		23.	24 & 25.	26.		
Map and Compass	Ch 5. / Sec 16.	17.	18.	19.				
Expedition Training	Ch 7. / Sec 6.	Dates, Place, Distance etc,.						
First Aid	Examination taken by	Place	Date					
Jnr Cadet Ins Cadre	Date From _____ To _____ Place held at	Result						
The Cadet and the Community	Ch 8. / Sec 3.	Activities and Projects						
Band Training	Instrument(s) played.	Dates and Qualification(s)						
Physical Activities	Dates / Scores							

ABBREVIATIONS

ACF	Army Cadet Force	Dets	Detachments
ACFA	Army Cadet Force Assoc	DF	Defensive Fire
AI	Adult Instructor	Dvr	Driver
APC	Army Proficiency Certificate	DOP	Dropping Off Point
ACIO	Army Careers Information Office	DS	Directing Staff
Adj	Adjutant	DP	Drill Purposes
AM	Ante Meridian	DZ	Dropping Zone
ATO	Ammunition Technical Officer	ECC	External Chest Compression
AWOL	Absent Without Leave	ES	Extreme Spread
BAOR	British Army of the Rhine	ESA	Expected Scoring Area
Brig	Brigadier	ETA	Estimated Time of Arrival
BRCS	British Red Cross Society	ETD	Estimated Time of Departure
Capt	Captain	En	Enemy
CCRS	Council for Cadet Rifle Shooting	Engr	Engineer
CP	Command Post	Eqpt	Equipment
CPOA	Corrected Point Of Aim	Fmn	Formation
CTC	Cadet Training Centre	FEBA	Forward Edge of Battle Area
CCF	Combined Cadet Force	Fup	Forming Up Place
CTT	Cadet Training Team	FPF	Final Protective Fire
Cdt	Cadet	FFI	Free From Infection
CEO	Cadet Executive Officer	freq	Frequency
CO	Commanding Officer	FRV	First Rendezvous
C of E	Church of England	Gen	General
Col	Colonel	GN	Grid North
Coy	Company	GMA	Grid Magnetic Angle
Cpl	Corporal	GP	General Purpose
CSM	Company Sergeant Major	GPMG	General Purpose Machine Gun
CQMS	Company Quarter Master Sergeant	HE	High Explosive
CZP	Correct Zeroing Position	HQ	Headquarters

ABBREVIATIONS

IA	Immediate Action	OP	Observation Post
i/c	In Command	OS	Ordnance Survey
ICE	Individual Compass Error	Psn	Position
ISCRM	Inter Services Cadet Rifle Meeting	pm	Post Meridian
JCIC	Junior Cadet Instructors Cadre	POA	Point Of Aim
Km	Kilometre	Ptls	Patrols
Km/h	Kilometres Per Hour	PV	Permissable Variation
L/Cpol	Lance Corporal	QM	Quartermaster
LAW	Light Anti-Tank Weapon	RSM	Regimental Sergeant Major
LMG	Light Machine Gun	RC	Roman Catholic
Lts	Lights	RV	Rendezvous
Lt/Lieut	Lieutenant	SAA	Small Arms Ammunition
Lt Col	Lieutenant Colonel	SCIS	Senior Cadet Instructors Cadre
Maj	Major	Sgt	Sergeant
Mt	Motor Transport	S/Sgt	Staff Sergeant
MTO	Motor Transport Officer	SITREP	Situation Report
MAW	Medium Anti-Tank Weapon	SLO	Schools Liaison Officer
MP	Military Police	SSI	School Staff Instructor
MPI	Mean Point of Impact	TA	Territorial Army
MN	Magnetic Narth	TAVRA	Territorial Army Volunteer
MOD	Ministry Of Defence		Reserves Association
MTM	Mouth To Mouth	TO	Training Officer
NBC	Nuclear Biological Chemical	TEWC	Tactical Exercise Without Cadets
NSP	Normal Safety Precautions	TMH	Trigger Mechanism Housing
NCO	Non Commissioned Officer	Wdr	Withdraw
NRA	Natioinal Rifle Association	WO I	Warrant Officer 1st Class
Ni	Night	WO II	Warrant Officer 2nd Class
OC	Officer Commanding	Wpns	Weapons
OIC	Officer In command	UKLF	United Kingdom Land Forces

ADDRESSES & TEL NUMBERS

NAME _____

ADDRESS _____

_____ POST CODE _____

TEL ___|___|___|___|___|___|___|___|___|___|___|___|

NAME _____

ADDRESS _____

_____ POST CODE _____

TEL ___|___|___|___|___|___|___|___|___|___|___|___|

NAME _____

ADDRESS _____

_____ POST CODE _____

TEL ___|___|___|___|___|___|___|___|___|___|___|___|

NAME _____

ADDRESS _____

_____ POST CODE _____

TEL ___|___|___|___|___|___|___|___|___|___|___|___|

NAME _____

ADDRESS _____

_____ POST CODE _____

TEL ___|___|___|___|___|___|___|___|___|___|___|___|

NAME _____

ADDRESS _____

_____ POST CODE _____

TEL ___|___|___|___|___|___|___|___|___|___|___|___|

ADDRESSES & TEL NUMBERS

NAME _____

ADDRESS _____

_____ POST CODE _____

TEL _|___|___|___|___|___|___|___|___|___|_

NAME _____

ADDRESS _____

_____ POST CODE _____

TEL _|___|___|___|___|___|___|___|___|___|_

NAME _____

ADDRESS _____

_____ POST CODE _____

TEL _|___|___|___|___|___|___|___|___|___|_

NAME _____

ADDRESS _____

_____ POST CODE _____

TEL _|___|___|___|___|___|___|___|___|___|_

NAME _____

ADDRESS _____

_____ POST CODE _____

TEL _|___|___|___|___|___|___|___|___|___|_

NAME _____

ADDRESS _____

_____ POST CODE _____

TEL _|___|___|___|___|___|___|___|___|___|_

ADDRESSES & TEL NUMBERS

NAME _____

ADDRESS _____

_____ POST CODE _____

TEL __|__|__|__|__|__|__|__|__|__|__|__|

NAME _____

ADDRESS _____

_____ POST CODE _____

TEL __|__|__|__|__|__|__|__|__|__|__|__|

NAME _____

ADDRESS _____

_____ POST CODE _____

TEL __|__|__|__|__|__|__|__|__|__|__|__|

NAME _____

ADDRESS _____

_____ POST CODE _____

TEL __|__|__|__|__|__|__|__|__|__|__|__|

NAME _____

ADDRESS _____

_____ POST CODE _____

TEL __|__|__|__|__|__|__|__|__|__|__|__|

NAME _____

ADDRESS _____

_____ POST CODE _____

TEL __|__|__|__|__|__|__|__|__|__|__|__|

FORWARD DATES

Date	Event